# The Rain
## on My Face

# The Rain on My Face

Quentin Quatermain

Illustrated by
Chloe Flavelle

AVICENNA PRESS (1969)
London

First published in England in 2004 by
Avicenna Press (1969),
11 Brownlow Road, London, NW10 9QN.

Printed by Kyodo Printing Co, Singapore
Typeset by Surface, stephen.jb@ntlworld.com

To B and to all the publishers and agents
who did me a great favour by rejecting this book;
too many to mention individually,
but in irony – an English quality.

# Prologue

Take a successful businessman around the world. He builds a factory.
It does well. He builds another factory. That one does well, too.
He sets up an export network. He undercuts his competitors, opens
subsidiaries, works 20 hours a day and owns a fleet of Mercedes cars.
He goes on expanding. And that's what most businessmen do.
But an English businessman?
He buys a factory. It does well.
Then he sells it, buys a place in the country and settles there.

\*      \*      \*

This is a story that could only have happened in England
and, perhaps, only in North Norfolk
where an Englishman turned his back on Europe,
bought a place in the country and settled there,
at home among his roots.
So this book speaks for England.

# Winter

The couple are up from London to buy a house in North Norfolk. They huddle together at a flint beach on its coast. Nearby, three fishermen have their lines out. It is near sunset early in January. A gale is getting up. And on the beach it is already cold.

The north wind begins to rip in from the Arctic. It cuts through their clothes like a knife. The sea is bursting with white horses heading straight for the shore. They've been on the way for weeks and thousands of miles and now they're crashing on the beach with a snarl the way a dog snarls when it tears the throat out of a rabbit. The water drags itself back in a death rattle over the shingle. The beach is empty for miles.

The man shivers, tightens his coat and turns to the woman.

1

"There's nothing between us and the North Pole," he says. "This beach is prehistoric. It must have been like this for twenty thousand years."

"Or fifty," says the woman. And keeps her head down.

A few hundred yards out to sea and low in the water is an old black-hulled schooner. It's heading west and it's struggling to claw its way off shore.

The fishing lines are lost in the exploding spray. One of the fishermen picks up his rod, reels the line in, dashes forward and hurls it out again.

The air fills with the sound of crashing waves. The man and the woman watch the line streak into the sea's foam-ripped belly. They stand on the beach under the bloodied sky. They see the ship's black hull in the ocean's well. They blink at the lash of the rough-tongued wind and at the high-flung thick salt spume. And they feel the rain on their faces. They turn and look at each other.

Yes! This is how they want to live.

*       *       *

The couple's two sons had recently left home to travel the world. One had a university place waiting, the other a job in Australia. A year out was very popular. Their parents had given them money and a mobile phone. Eve, petite, dark-haired, bright-eyed and quick of movement, had wept a little when they left and said:

"Please ring us when you can."

And after they had gone, the 25-year itch – the generation itch – had come upon their parents. They had reached their fifties and realised that their own time was running out. Lawrence, tall, optimistic but thoughtful, with spectacles and untidy hair, pointed out the watershed they faced and asked her: "So what are we going to do about it?"

But they already knew. For years they had been dreaming of settling in the English countryside. Now, free at last, they decided to live their dream. And they put their London home up for sale.

The estate agent told them the market was very strong. It was the winter of 1989 and they were in one of Britain's biggest property booms.

"You'll sell your property in no time," he had said.

And he seemed right – for within a few days someone had made an offer. It wasn't too good but it wasn't too bad either. A month later the market collapsed into one of its biggest slumps and they never saw agent or buyer again. But they didn't know that when they went house hunting, hunting for their English dream.

And for their search? They turned their backs on the West Country. People usually settled there when they left London, they reminded each other. And they didn't want to live with Londoners. So they went east and drove around East Anglia for a day or two. And then something had drawn them up to North Norfolk. Years before they had spent weekends on its coast and had met a few people living and working in that open landscape. Now they thought it could be the one place in all England that was still wild, that was least like a theme park.

"But that doesn't mean much," said Lawrence. "The whole country seems to be one nowadays. When it's not being a car park."

Leaving the sea to the fishermen and the schooner, they headed back to the coast road. Their path inland lay through the salt marshes that separated the sea from fields and hills. Lawrence turned and gazed back at the beach for a moment. A flock of geese wheeled high above him and headed out to sea.

"You remember how once I lived in Kenya? Years and years ago, long before we met? When I was working there, writing those books?"

"Yes, I remember." Eve turned to him and smiled. "And you've been looking for it ever since, haven't you, darling?"

"Yes, but in England," he said. "I had to come home. We all come home. But its empty landscape, the animals, the direct way I lived, on the earth and living on the edge – you know? It had all been irresistible. Now I want it in England. But can there be anywhere in England that has it, too?"

Somehow he knew that if he was ever to have the feeling again, of living on the edge and merging with the seasons, it would be up on the North Norfolk coast.

\*     \*     \*

They had begun their search the day before – in a drizzle. They started in Cromer, a Victorian watering hole jammed by a pier into Norfolk's top right corner. In those days it had been fashionable. Having faded with Britain's empire, it was now a neglected backwater. But the sands still stretched each side of the pier. They were still wide enough for a game of cricket – and the lifeboat station was still at square leg. The pier theatre still put on two shows a day. Above the pier a few alleys still wound themselves around the church. And they still hid dark pubs gleaming with flashes of brass and sheltering solitary drinkers. But now the church was a cornered stag besieged by a supermarket, a cinema, a post office and an ironmongers, not to mention a secular fifth column – a community centre by the font.

Cliff-top lanes still led eastward to isolated cottages. Bestowed among them lay the tenuous and romantic allure of Poppyland. To those who remembered, memories of crumbling churches and a miller's beautiful daughter still lingered there like the morning mist between the trees behind the cliffs.

But Eve and Lawrence turned west. They passed herds of cliff-top caravans, they drove through candyfloss seaside Sheringham and they climbed wooded hills before descending to sea level. Here a no-man's-land of marsh and creek formed the northern coastline. It stretched thirty miles towards the sunset. A few people managed to live there, for now and again they passed tiny villages, cold, empty and silent on the edge of the marshes. Ploughed fields and peaceful meadows rose inland to meet the sky. Flint church towers were outlined against the late afternoon light or stood pale against deep woodland.

They followed the coast road as it wound along between marsh and hills. The drizzle kept pace with them. After half an hour they came to a village. It lay at the foot of a shallow valley between the sea-rimmed communities of Kelling and Morston. The coast road wound inland around the village but a lane of cottages with a few shops turned off towards the sea. The lane met the valley's river at a neglected little quay before it looped back to rejoin the coast road. Three or four small boats were tied up at the quay and near it stood an old pub, a windmill and a house or two behind high flint walls. The river was only four or five yards wide. Beyond its far bank an eiderdown of reeds covered the marshes. After curling round pub and windmill the little river cut a mile-long slap between mud banks towards the North Sea. Through the winter haze Lawrence made out a trembling smudge on the far horizon. Was that a lifeboat station? And he wasn't sure if he was imagining something else or not, for the North Norfolk coast had already cast some sort of capricious spell over him. But he almost turned to Eve to ask if she, too, felt that the horizon's stained line was dropping away to left and to right.

The drizzle stopped. A few beams of light forced their way through the clouds. Two fishermen in sweaters and thigh boots appeared from behind the windmill. They stomped across the slipway to a boat. Lawrence and Eve walked over to ask about the house they had come to see. But even with a good deal of pointing the fishermen didn't seem to know it even though, apparently, they both lived in the village. Later Eve reckoned they had actually told them where it was but neither she nor Lawrence had realised it. In those early days the Norfolk accent had seemed to them like a blanket. It was warm and friendly – but impenetrable. Later they came just to call it Norfolk, as one might refer to an old language, like Occitan or Gaelic, rather than to an accent. They felt they could have been in western Ireland or the Outer Hebrides – certainly a long way from London.

Eventually they found the house. It was only a few yards from wind-mill and marshland. But flint walls and long grass had hidden it well. An old brick archway reached over the entrance to its drive. A faded board was tacked to the arch, half hidden by Virginia creeper. They could just make out the name cut there: "Gibraltar House".

As they walked down the gravel drive the crunching of their boots echoed against the walls on either side. Lawrence didn't know why but he loved that sound. A year later he still loved it. And by then he did know why.

Before knocking Eve paused, glanced round at her husband, beck-oned to him and walked quickly past the front door to look at the garden beyond. It faced south and was hardly bigger than a couple of tennis courts. Ivy covered its high flint walls. They embraced the garden as if protecting a secret. The marshes began beyond them. At the far end of the garden a hammock was slung beneath a great apple tree. Behind pear and plum trees was planted an ancient summerhouse. Through its windows Eve could make out an old croquet set. A brass plate on its box gave the date: 1935. It lay with a pile of parasols, a sun hat and a few deck chairs. Further along she saw an arched door set into the wall. Its rusted hinges tapered to spirals. Its lock was half hidden behind a tangle of hollyhocks. Its paint was faded with age. At the time that door seemed to the couple merely an old door in an old garden wall. It was the sort of door and the sort of wall you would expect to find in an old English county like Norfolk. But later it came to symbolise the decision they were about to make and the life that was to open to them after they had passed through.

They turned to look back at the house. It was then they saw its seven-teenth-century Dutch gable. Its outline traced a voluptuous curve against the sky, a sky clear now of cloud and rain and washed a thin-veined blue. The curve had the seductive beauty of a Rubens model, swelling wide and generous as it neared the ground. The gable was built of small bricks, the sort the couple had always loved. Over the last three or four hundred years the bricks had been drenched by the rain of Norfolk and warmed by its sun, too. Now they were baked to the rich and smoky texture of burnt sienna. A twist of moss had taken hold at one corner. French windows opened to the lawn next to an old Regency conservatory. By now the drizzle had petered out. In the early afternoon air a dozen tiny birds were swooping around the gable after a cloud of midges. Eve reached out and touched Lawrence's arm.

"Listen! Can you hear them?" They stood motionless together and caught the faintest of high-pitched squeaks in the still air.

They knocked and were invited in. The front door opened to a square hall, its low ceiling supported by a dozen beams. Opposite the door a staircase curled upstairs. Beyond the hall they saw the kitchen. To their right a glass-panelled Edwardian door opened into the sitting room, lit by the south light from the garden. And to their left they walked into the dining room and library, dominated by an ancient chimneybreast. It stretched the length of one wall. Recesses on each side were crammed with logs. Two armchairs stood before it. Beams reached across the ceiling. Curtains were already drawn across the windows. The room was a cave, a real winter den.

The style of the house inside was a blend of historical origins – like the mix of the English character. The massive fireplace came straight out of a seventeenth century Dutch interior. In the sitting room across the hall was a moulded mantelpiece that bore the elegant stamp of Georgian England. The kitchen – yes, that was clearly Victorian. Near a stone sink a casserole of pheasant was bubbling gently away on a stove. And all around the house lay clues of its past. They were scattered as if part of a treasure hunt. Here, a corridor lined with old pine had been polished through the centuries to the honeyed texture of pale straw. There, a recess was lined with grainy walnut filigree fleur-de-lys, no doubt carved by a homesick Huguenot refugee. Next to the recess, an ancient leaded Tudor window. By the garden, the Regency conservatory. Upstairs, a vast Victorian claw-footed roll-top bath. And, as with the English character, these origins all mixed well together to produce something stronger than the sum of the parts.

At the top of the house they found a bedroom with a barrel-vaulted oak ceiling. One of its walls was half-timbered. A small amulet-shaped brick fireplace was set in its middle like a jewel.

Eve turned to Lawrence, her eyes shining.

"I've never, ever, seen a room like this."

But it was the view from the window that enchanted her most. Over the garden wall began the marshes that stretched to the North Sea. Nearby were the quay, the windmill and the pub. Now she turned her head and looked south over the garden, with its summerhouse, apple tree and hammock. Beyond its flint walls a dozen rooks circled around the top branches of some elm trees. Twilight was upon them and soon the light would begin to fail. But through the bare elms Eve could still make out a big Georgian rectory. Behind a faded grass tennis court she saw its stables. An imposing clock face was set above the central doors. Through the late afternoon's still air she fancied she could just catch the clop of hooves on the cobbles.

"Well, that's England for us." She turned back from the window and smiled radiantly at him. "Don't you see? There's this house and the sea too."

"Yes," he agreed at once. "You're right. We want to be in a village and on the edge. It's all here. We don't need to look further, do we?"

"But, darling, we can't buy it yet, don't you think?" She smiled gently at him. "Not until we've sold London?"

Lawrence didn't listen. He had moved over to the window. He recognised the view, although he had never seen it before. It was a microcosm of England, an English domestic view that no other country could offer. And it hadn't changed for three or four hundred years. Yes, he knew at once that it was the Englishman's dream.

They looked at each other. They both felt themselves holding their breath in the way a scent, a snatch of music or the sudden glimpse of beauty can catch at the throat. In that moment they felt the first tightening of the history lines that even then drew them into the time warp that was to bewitch their lives.

In the dining room they sat before the fire and sipped tea with the owner. He had spent a year or two restoring the house. Apparently a wealthy Flemish cloth trader had built it in 1620 when he settled in North Norfolk. He had obviously preferred England's security to the more frequent disturbances across the channel. Gibraltar House was one of the oldest in the village. And then, did they want to see the wine cellar beneath the cloakroom? The owner lit a candle and they bent double to creep behind him down some worn steps. The ceiling was vaulted. Only in the middle of the cellar could they stand. He pointed past some cobwebbed wine racks to a bricked-up doorway. It led to an underground passage. Smuggling had been a big industry in the old days, he said over his shoulder. Some creeks on the marshes were big enough to hide a small boatload of brandy. And they'd done so often enough, too. The government had built a customs house nearby but the excise men didn't seem able to catch many smugglers. He shrugged and smiled. Apparently at one time the rector in nearby Blakeney had been a customer.

Back in front of the fire; and the front door opened. In walked the owner's wife with a black Labrador dog. She left her umbrella open to dry on the hall floor. The Labrador's tail swept a couple of books off the table before it slumped panting before the fire. She settled down to toast crumpets and butter them for everyone. Soon she was telling how she had been walking on the beach. Some fishermen had been casting lines into the surf. There had been a high sea running and the wind was strong and wild. She had felt the rain on her face.

The couple looked at each other and smiled.

\* \* \*

"Well?" said Lawrence as they walked down the drive to their car. "It's the dream all right. I only hope I didn't sound too keen. He might raise the price when I make an offer."

He knew the house symbolised the way of life they wanted to lead. But Eve patted his arm.

"Now then, darling," she said. "We've got to forget it. I know the thought of London already gives you claustrophobia. It does me, too, you know, for that matter. But don't forget we'd be crazy to buy this house now, not until we've sold our own house. So what's the point of making an offer?"

"Oh, God!" he groaned. "Then what did we come all this way up here for?"

"Just to look around," she pointed out. "That's what we agreed last week, remember? We've got all the time in the world. We wanted to look at the area, not necessarily buy something right away. You're straining to buy this house but it's the first one we've even looked at so far."

"Well, the boys would love it," he said plaintively.

"Yes, but they're half-way to Columbia or somewhere by now and it's us who'll be living here. And they're not interested in burying themselves in the country, anyway. Not like us." She smiled at him. "And it's a long way from Exeter University, let alone Australia."

"Well, anyway ..." he looked at her. "All right, yes, you're right, but going back to live in London does give me claustrophobia, if you want

9

to know. Yes, just the thought of it, even – now that I've seen this place. And the coast, too, even more."

He kicked at some stones as they walked back to the car. Gibraltar House could not have been more different from their home in London. There, the hall corridor was barely wide enough for two people. Its stairs were like a ladder. And the view from the windows was of other windows and roofs – and only a few feet away, too.

"I know it's tempting," said Eve. "But what's the point? It's no good comparing it with London until we've sold our house first."

"You said that before," he reminded her. "Anyway, remember what Oscar Wilde said about temptation? The only way to get rid of it is to give in to it. And anyway, we had that offer this week, remember?"

"Well, look what happened to Oscar Wilde," she said curtly. "And anyway the offer wasn't as much as we wanted."

"OK, but it was an offer and surely those people wouldn't have made it unless they were going to buy it ... well, would they?"

She groaned slowly, looked at him sadly and shook her head.

"All right, all right!" he grunted. "But anyway, even if they're not serious someone will make another offer."

She dared not admit it, but she was tempted too. They knew they had found the house of their dreams. And it was in the place of their dreams. They had searched East Anglia and they had found it in a village on the North Norfolk coast. It was a magical house in what seemed a magical area. But dare they buy before they sold?

"Look!" Lawrence wrung his hands. "There's a national housing boom. Prices are still going up, aren't they? Even if this offer for London fell out of bed, someone'll buy it soon. Won't they? And some-one'll buy this house, too – if we don't."

He reminded her how the owner had said that several other people were after it. Dare they wait to sell their own house if they wanted this one? He had told them: "such a beautiful house as this doesn't often come onto the market, all newly restored as well. That's why there's so much interest." Sales talk, they knew. But others had confirmed it. By then she had suggested they stay the night at the village pub and explore the neighbourhood before making for home next day. She thought it might take his mind off this particular house. And they could go and see some more estate agents – which would make it more difficult for him to make a decision.

So they checked in at the pub and over a pint or two of warm beer asked a few questions of the locals. Yes, they all knew the house. And they all thought it was something special.

"Well, what of it?" asked Eve later that night. She realised that she might have made a mistake by staying on. "You used to tell me that houses were like girls and there was always another one coming along."

She smiled in spite of herself. "Yes? Was I the first one? Far from it, I seem to remember."

He grinned and went to kiss her, but she leaned away. He persevered.

"You know very well ... sometimes you only want a special one." It was like love at first sight, he told her. You knew it when you saw it even if you couldn't describe it.

"Well," she said dismissingly, "you've said that plenty of times before."

"Well, I will again, too, because it's true."

Over supper in the pub Lawrence remembered that the owner had told them he had bought the house at auction. Apparently it had been a bit like an aristocratic bag lady who had fallen on hard times and was now a bit loose in the top storey. Bottom storey too, according to a survey – for there'd been something unstable in the foundations. Not to mention a few internal complications. But the stains on the bag lady's coat had not concealed its quality and style.

Next day they drove around inland and had lunch at an isolated pub. Even Eve became mesmerised by the peaceful lanes, the flint-walled cottages and the ragged, uncommemorated fields. They visited a couple of estate agents and even went over another house, a barn conversion.

"Very nice," commented Lawrence. "But even you can see the difference between this one and Gibraltar House."

"Well, it shows there are lots of places around for sale," she said lamely.

By now the high winds of the day before had died down. Lawrence insisted on a last walk on the marshes before leaving for London. They saw that a few creeks wound through this waterland. Their brown mud banks glistened wet like the skin of a new-born animal. Purple sea lavender grew at their edges. Between them lay coarse grass and reeds and brackish pools. A few dark cattle bunched together, heads lowered. A galaxy of starlings rose in the distance, circled and faded away into space. A sheet of rain spat down for a few seconds. Soon the couple came across an old wreck half buried in the mud. Was that one of the smugglers' boats? Lawrence glanced at his wife and turned to look inside. She ignored him and walked on and he had to catch her up. But the landscape and its allusions were already dragging their minds back into the past, hers as much as his.

They both watched as a heron lifted into the air above a patch of reeds. Its great wings beat heavily and its legs trailed as it took off. The pale reeds were still now. They stretched so high that a man could hide in them. Near a shallow pool three oystercatchers darted over the mud, their jet wings striped with white.

Clouds covered the sky like an oyster shell. Only at the horizon was there a pale strip of clear sky, where they could see beyond the shell. Suddenly the sun appeared in it like an eye without a head. It glared at them briefly and vanished again behind the clouds.

Birds turned and called. Light was draining away. The wind sighed. Breakers crawled at the far-off sea. The couple shivered and began to feel they had reached the edge of the world.

*　　*　　*

They were very thoughtful as they drove back to London that night.

"Well, you've got to admit it," said Lawrence as they worked their way through East Anglia's empty lanes towards the motorway. "The type of village is all right, too. It has all the basic shops, you know, besides the pub, I mean. Like a post office and a village store. But didn't you see that luscious delicatessen, too? Well," he demanded, "what's that doing in a North Norfolk village?"

Eve shrugged. She was still resisting. She had a sense of danger.

"Yes, well, no idea," she replied. "So what?"

They were both silent for a few minutes. Lawrence was concentrating on driving past a group of corrugated huts at the edge of a flat stretch of ground. Was that a wartime airfield? He thought they had all been ploughed over by now. His mind came back to the village street.

"And I saw kippers and bloaters hanging up inside a crumbling old shack on the road. And there was a second-hand book-shop with an art gallery."

"Probably full of paintings of geese in V-formation at dawn," she said scornfully, "or 'Sunset on the Marsh' watercolours with the windmill in the background. It's all like that up there. Boring."

"But didn't you see that pottery, too? It had windows full of pots and vases. And there's not an estate agent or a boutique to be seen. It's a working village. But it's not dull, it's got quality, too."

"Maybe," she replied curtly. "So what?"

A stretch of straight road appeared. Lawrence relaxed and smiled. "I think it's what we've been looking for. And so do you. But you're not going to admit it, are you?"

In the dark of the car Eve was silent.

They reached the M11 motorway and turned south for London. The driving was easier now and he began to talk about the local community. It was only then that he thought of something else. And it was something that had been staring him in the face.

"Who do all these shops sell to?"

"What do you mean? Customers, of course. So what? What did you think? Birds?" she said.

He ignored that.

"Customers, of course. But what sort? You don't sell a lot of pottery or paintings or smoked salmon in many villages in the country. Let alone vintage port like I saw in that deli."

And he suddenly remembered something.

"Yes, and what had the estate agent told us? Something about a lot of very odd people living up there?"

The agent had told them that it was a strange area that attracted strange people. It sounded intriguing, but why did it attract them? At the time they hadn't quite realised what he had meant.

"Well, maybe we'll find out," he concluded.

"It's no good," Eve sighed impatiently. "Don't you ever listen to me? We haven't sold our house yet, have we?"

He gripped the wheel in frustration and they both fell silent. The motorway passed beneath the M25. Their headlights showed a tangle of concrete pillars and there was the sound of screeching tyres. Soon they began to drive through London's grimy industrial outskirts.

Lawrence began to think again of the village and its tranquillity. That old pub had been so quiet and peaceful.

"You know," he shook his head as if he was talking to himself, "I could quite easily have just stopped there. Stayed put. Never gone home, I mean."

For a moment he dreamed he was back there. With those shops the village was obviously up-to-date. But it had the feeling of time about it, or rather of lack of time passing. They hadn't seen any houses less than a hundred years old. Even Eve had pointed out how they were all different. They had been mostly built of flint, that primitive building material that was everywhere in North Norfolk. And the houses were all beautiful, in different ways.

Then he thought of life in London. A few years after they had been married they had moved to a street in Notting Hill. They had felt attracted by its rough but natural atmosphere. They had bought a big run-down house and restored it. They had seen the bed-sitter tenements converted back to family houses. They had noticed the area slowly become trendy. They had watched as the bankers moved in. They had been to their smart dinner parties and shared their fine wines and polished silver. It had all got so trendy that someone had made a film about it. But there was still the congestion, the noise and the pollution. In fact it had got worse. And there was little space left for thinking. And with all that gentrification the rough edges had worn off. Now it was all much too smooth and packaged.

He remembered how the air on the marshes had been as clear and sharp as the flint in the walls of the village houses. He remembered that rain on his face – how fresh it was, and so clean. He remembered how the village's empty street had curved round like the tail of a sleeping dinosaur, the flint of the walls its scales. At any moment, he fancied, it could have given a flick and the whole village would have collapsed or even vanished. In the still hours after midnight, he thought, they might even hear it quietly breathing, pulsating.

"Don't you realise," Lawrence pointed out to his wife, "when we spend weekends in the country we're always the ones who have to drive home on Sunday night? Thinking about it ruins most of Sunday. Does it always have to be like that?"

"No."

"No? Do you mean that?" He suddenly became hopeful that she was coming round.

"Yes. We can spend the weekends in London instead."

He groaned at her. "What sort of answer is that? Are you crazy?"

"No. London's always emptier at weekends." And she went "hrumph", stared ahead and folded her hands in her lap.

By then they were driving through the City of London. Apart from the cars, all that existed at ground level were empty pavements and blank shop windows. The skyscrapers stretched above them and out of sight. If they spent weekends in Kent this was usually their route home on Sunday night. It usually took them less time to drive from Maidstone to the City than to drive from there to Notting Hill. What sort of swollen monster had they been living in all these years?

He knew he had to persuade her. And in the darkness of the car he began to describe the walks they could take. Perhaps along that wild coastline or on river banks. Everywhere the skies would be wide enough to drown in. In the winter their skin would be tingling with the cold. But it would be exhilarating, he promised. They would come home to a log fire and crumpets for tea. Crumpets!

"Remember that fire and those buttered crumpets that fellow's wife gave us?" He glanced sideways at her in the dark.

And in a rash moment Eve admitted to him that she might enjoy shopping in that ancient town of Norwich. There would be none of the London crowds. And Lawrence told her they'd be sure to need lunch before the strain of driving home through all those country lanes. He said that the village shops would always have time to ask after the family. And he smiled and promised her that they'd have summer tennis parties on grass courts. They'd share a glass of two of Pimms with their neighbours. He looked forward to warm beer and no music in the old-fashioned pubs. They both agreed that the pubs seemed embedded in the timeless days before the War. And, he pointed out with a sidelong grin, they wouldn't have to go back to London on Sunday night.

By now they had reached the Embankment. Fast cars and motor bikes, screeching tyres and hooting, traffic jams and crowds – even though it was long past midnight. They drove past Big Ben, up the Mall to Buckingham Palace, round Hyde Park Corner and up Park Lane to turn left at Marble Arch into Bayswater Road.

"Well, do we just want to talk or do we want to do it? We'll never get another house like that again."

"I know," she replied. "But we haven't sold our house here yet."

"Yes, you said that several dozen times in the last couple of hours. I'm getting a bit bored by it. The housing market's very strong and we're sure to sell it."

"Well, you've said that quite a few times too," she reminded him.

"But if it's that strong someone else'll buy this house in North Norfolk while we just talk about it and do nothing. Is that what you want?"

Eve did not reply.

"Well?" Lawrence asked her. "Do we want to live this dream? Do we want to live a new life? If we do, we've got to do it now – we're not going to live for ever. Of course it's a risk, but living is taking risks – real living. It's not for the cautious. You want to be cautious? Well, you don't get much that way – you get old early, too, sometimes. Anyway, you've just admitted you rather like the idea of shopping in a country town. You know how exhausting London is. Remember last Christmas and that tree I was trying to bring home through the tube? My God! But up there, what about the neighbours and all those country walks? And Christmas in the country, what about that, too? It'll probably snow as well. Lovely crisp snow, not like the slush we always get in London. Hardly the same, don't you think? And think of the fresh air. And what about the boys, huh? Country life'll be good for them."

"You know very well they've left home," she reminded him. "And the last thing they want to do is to find themselves stuck in North Norfolk."

But she hesitated – against her better judgement.

"Is there enough value in our house for the bank to take it as security and lend us the money – allowing for our mortgage with them as well?" she asked. "We don't have to borrow anything anywhere else?"

Lawrence patted her arm.

"Plenty," he told her. "Its value has shot up, especially in the last few years. All those bankers moving in have pushed the prices up." He grinned. "I never thought I'd be grateful to bankers."

She turned to him.

"Yes, but how much will it all be?" she demanded.

"Oh, what? Altogether?"

"Yes! You know exactly what I mean."

"Oh, only a few hundred thousand pounds."

"Only a few hundred thousand pounds!" she said scornfully. "But you'd just make our whole life a misery if we didn't buy it, wouldn't you? But what if we got into trouble? You'd only come back to me and say you couldn't have expected that to happen, it was just bad luck."

"Of course I wouldn't," he said impatiently. "But we won't – wouldn't – anyway."

There was a long pause in the darkness of the car.

"All right, then," she said. "OK."

"Good!" he replied. "But, Eve, my darling, you wanted to do it all along, didn't you?"

"Well of course I did. Of course I wanted the house! Who wouldn't? But I've got more sense than you," she said. "It's dangerous, risky. And I'm worried. Please don't make a mess of it."

They reached home, parked the car and walked into their empty house. Their boys were no longer around. Now it was too big for them. And it was silent, which made it seem even bigger. They went to bed almost at once. After he put out the light and they had settled down together to sleep, she told him:

"OK, now you can try to bring the price down."

And they both smiled in the dark and went to sleep in each other's arms.

So Lawrence and Eve bought Gibraltar House before they had sold their own house. It was against everyone's advice. And so what, they told them all! If you're not prepared to take risks for your dream, they said, you might as well lie down and pull a blanket up over your head.

*     *     *

They were sorry to be leaving London. It had been exciting and full of opportunities. Notting Hill was a tapestry of people from all over the world. The tapestry flowed over the pavements and even the streets and for twenty years they had lived in its centre. And all that time they had known, too, the deep contentment of being a self-contained family unit in a big city. During those years they had been caring for their sons as they grew up. They had shared the joys of parenthood and all the trials of childhood – from their sons' infancy through to secondary school. Slowly the boys had begun to shape their own lives. But still every night all four would be home from work and from school. They would make supper and discuss things together around the kitchen table. And they had known that although their family was part of that big city they could still close their door and be private too. And that intimacy had welded them all together.

But now their boys had left home. And this had changed their lives. For the gap they had left had made Eve and Lawrence aware of other changes. They began to notice how the dirt and the noise had increased. The crowds they had once found fascinating were now claustrophobic, even alien. Yes, the packaged food had been conven-ient and the controlled environment had been comfortable. After all, life had been very busy. But when the boys had left Lawrence and Eve realised that London's sophistication had polished smooth their rough edges. And now they wanted them to grow back. For years they had taken food and shelter for granted. Now they wanted to live closer to the land and to learn their true values again.

There were other changes too. And these changes were worse than the packaged food and the noise. For British society had deteriorated into a condition described even by a  prime minister as a yob culture, the result of two generations of faulty education and upbringing. It had gone on so long that now the blind were leading the blind. And the growth in violence and selfishness over the years now seemed more and more accepted every day.

Then something strange was also happening. In the last few years they had noticed that England was no longer being respected as much as before – even by itself, even by those who were English themselves. That worried and puzzled them. Guilt of empire had been the trendy British ailment since the end of the war. Now they were almost expected to feel guilty for being English. And Eve and Lawrence felt that was complete nonsense. Compare that with the French, Lawrence pointed out to his wife. It was the British who alone saved the world in a war when France's contribution didn't last much longer than a good lunch. Yet they were always demonstrating their national pride and never got questioned – unlike the English. The couple knew that the English sense of tolerance, fair play and individuality were admired around the world. It had been England that had developed democracy. And England had given the world the idea of freedom under the law, not to mention the language. "It couldn't happen in England," was what people used to say. And contempt for all of that was absurd – but very odd, too. Lawrence and Eve sometimes felt undermined from within. They felt that something strange was happening but couldn't work out what it was.

Perhaps worse, the government sometimes seemed to ignore parliament and even seemed to be co-operating with the European Union about all the regulations they were imposing and about its attitude to England, too. Lawrence and Eve didn't like that but felt unable to change the way things were going. So they thought everything over, shook their heads and decided it was time to follow the advice of that great Frenchman Voltaire and cultivate their garden. They would turn their backs on the government and London, move to the country and find a place where English values still existed. Perhaps they could even take root in a community that would lead a revival of English culture that might once again flourish throughout the country.

In any case they had already realised that at different times in your life you did different things. The times for action and taking risks were gone. Now it was time for taking stock – time for contemplation. They wanted to think of what had happened in their lives and perhaps even to make sense of it. And for that they needed to leave London. They needed the peace of a quiet night, the fresh grass underfoot and the calm that comes as the sky opens out beyond the houses at the end of the road. Lawrence needed the solitude of a tramp over the hills or across a frozen salt marsh. And he needed to come home to a book-lined study and gaze into its blazing fire. He needed to walk in the night's silent bowl and listen while an owl's hoot filled it. He needed to stand beneath a full moon hanging over a water meadow, its face cracked across by a tree's bare branch. Eve it was who needed the satisfaction of growing her own vegetables. And she wanted to cook them with herbs picked from her own herb garden. She wanted to make rich bedding and to plant bulbs, to drain and dig and manure, to prune and plant out, to weed and to water, to stake and to mulch, to plant fruit trees and to bottle her own fruit. She wanted to care for her garden throughout the year. She wanted to prepare it for the miracle of spring, to relish it during the joys of summer and in autumn to strengthen its defences against the "furious winter's rages."

And they both wanted to fold into an English village community where everyone was mutually dependent and so understood what was expected of each other. They wanted to live where the seasons dominated their lives, to experience life on the edge and close to the earth. A generation or two in the Smoke was quite enough for someone who got a bounce out of a rough track through an English wood and a few rooks circling overhead.

"I've often spent the whole day in London without really knowing what the weather's like," Lawrence pointed out to Eve. "I want to feel the rain on my face again."

So they had decided to leave. But had it all really begun long, long ago – maybe even in the cradle, when Englishness, so derided today, had come with mother's milk? For underneath it had lain the dream that Lawrence had dreamed abroad and far from home, the dream that sooner or later comes to all good Englishmen.

It was of course the dream of settling in the English countryside, of finding an old vicarage or just a cottage and there putting down roots. It was an Englishman's dream but it was a dream of England, too.

Lawrence wanted to live his English dream, not dream away his life. And he wanted to do it before it was too late.

*     *     *

Meanwhile Eve was proved right – as wives often are. After the buyer for their house in London pulled out the property market began its biggest drop since the war and they had no other offers. But in those days everyone thought it would shortly pick up. It always had before, hadn't it? But the drop became a dive. And they were stuck with two houses and a mortgage the size of a City trader's bonus.

Eve couldn't avoid reminding Lawrence of his rashness. For it had plunged them headlong into a financial nightmare full of anxiety and stress. But they were husband and wife and together they did their best to keep afloat. They told themselves that it wouldn't be long before they found a buyer. But no buyer appeared and they dropped the price a bit. And it made no difference. And a bit later they dropped it a bit more. And it didn't make a bit of difference either. To make matters worse their bank wrote asking them to pay off the mortgage on Gibraltar House. Lawrence knew it wouldn't be long before they were going to insist they sell it – or their home in London, one or the other. And complaining wouldn't make a bit of difference, either.

"The trouble is," he told Eve, "they've got a charge on it. And that means that if they demand their money back they can sell it for only enough to cover their own costs – not for the best price. And we can't afford that. They've got us over a barrel."

"That's pretty obvious," she snapped at him. "Well, why didn't you think of that before we bought it?"

And she insisted they make the supreme sacrifice. They put their dream house back onto the market. Yes, the house they had just bought on the North Norfolk coast. But it didn't really help. There were no buyers for that either. And still none for their London house. Lawrence regularly changed agents and cut the prices of both. And none of it made the least bit of difference. In fact one agent actually claimed that the market might never recover at all.

"What if they're right?" he thought to himself. And he hid the article from his wife.

"Well, we've got to do something about this mess you've got us into," said Eve. "We've got to let it out while we're trying to sell it. At least that market's not dead – yet," she said.

"Yes," he said brightly. "Apparently everyone's renting instead of buying at the moment. No long-term exposure, someone said."

She laughed in spite of herself.

"You're incorrigible!"

"Oh, I don't know. You've got to prepare for the worst but you've got to hope for the best too. Praise the Lord but pass the ammunition," he told her. "Something will turn up. You wait and see."

So they advertised for tenants. Someone took the house for a few days but otherwise the enquiries were for the summer. "We'll be bankrupt and homeless by then," as Eve told him. So they spent a weekend or two at Gibraltar House themselves. At least, he agreed, they were one step closer to their ideal way of life. But a weekend gave them little time to live that life. They might meet pub regulars but no one else, although by closing time they for some reason began to be sure that one day all would be well. But still no one wanted to buy either house. And when they were up there they still had to leave for London on Sunday afternoon. Even the thought of it stained their weekend's pleasure the way red wine stains a white carpet. And it added a sharp pain to the underlying anxiety about money and their home and where they were going to live if the worst happened.

*   *   *

It was during their first weekend at Gibraltar House that they made an important discovery about North Norfolk. It was a sort of initiation – because everyone who has spent a winter's weekend there knows it anyway.

What is it? Well, what do you need most if you live in North Norfolk? Friends? Transport? Shops? The telephone? All important – but no! None of these. What you need most is to keep warm.

The solid-fuel stove that came with the house wasn't really good enough. When they arrived for the weekend, even if they got it going at once, it took twenty-five minutes to warm the place. And in any case the soot it gave off covered everything in the kitchen. It got so bad that one day – it was just after he had kicked it because it had gone out and he had bruised his toes – Lawrence realised that he hated the stove with an unparalleled virulence. But it had been the morning stove that had turned the worm, rather than the arrival stove. Late at night and full of food and wine, they were often drowsy before the fire. So he often forgot to dampen it down before going to bed. So it often went out. So he often shivered in next morning's winter dawn as he scrabbled up a bucketful of coal and kindling to relight it. So one such morning he asked himself: "do I really want to go on living like this?" And he answered himself: "No!"

So they bought an oil-fired Aga. And when they arrived one Friday night a fortnight later a huge squatting beast the colour of vintage Burgundy was throbbing away in the kitchen. It radiated pleasure like a dionysiac god and embraced them with heat as they opened the front door. The tea towels on its rails were warm. The house was hot as toast. Their cat was purring. And, after two very big whiskies, so were they.

But still they hadn't sold either house. The mortgage was piling up with interest on the interest. Both houses were now worth less than their mortgages. But their value was guesswork anyway because no one had made them an offer and no one believed in estate agents' valuations any more. Even if they sold Gibraltar House they would still owe hundreds of thousands of pounds and that meant they would have to sell their London house to repay it and then where would they live?

Their mortgage had become an albatross, that bird of the oceans, the curse of any doomed sailor who shot it whereupon, said the legend, it wrapped itself around his neck and did not release him even when they sank locked together below the surface and vanished into the cold and merciless depths, never to emerge again.

Often Eve and Lawrence awoke before dawn, troubled and uneasy, to ask each other in the chill half-light if they really could hold on until the market rose again. For it had to rise again. Didn't it?

Those few weekends in Norfolk were havens, boltholes from the bank and the dead market. All the more was treasured every hour there. And so they lived those anxious days of stress.

*　　*　　*

That tenant was the only one they had. For some reason it was difficult to find a tenant during the winter. And they – Eve too, for she wanted to make the best of things – still disliked leaving for London on Sunday night. It was bad enough being the victim of the market. But now they were doubly frustrated. And then they looked at each other and said they had no right to complain. They were lucky to be in England and not to suffer the risks of living in Afghanistan or, well, so many other places. Still, it was almost unbearable. Except, of course, that they had to bear it. And then, after only two or three weeks, Eve had a brilliant idea.

"All right. You've won," she said. "We're in up to our necks anyway. So why not live our dream now? We couldn't let Gibraltar House every week of the year, but we could with Notting Hill," she told him. "Stuff it. We might as well try for our dream when we can!"

This really was plunging in – but they did it. An agent soon found them an Arab diplomat for a tenant. Their house was just what he wanted. He had four wives and nine children so he needed all of its five storeys. He was in the Middle East at the moment. But he had paid a deposit and would move in two months later. Meanwhile Lawrence and Eve would make an inventory of the furniture.

So one wet and windy afternoon they drove up to North Norfolk, there to live, they hoped, for ever.

\*     \*     \*

They certainly never forgot how exhilarated they'd felt that first morning. Yes, they were very cold. Yes, their books were piled everywhere, the furniture was stacked in heaps and they had spent the night on a mattress on the floor. And yes, clinging round their necks was still the albatross of their enormous mortgage, their Siamese twin with elephantiasis that they could never part from and which weighed them down every time they thought about it. Even their cat – name of Sphinx – had taken offence at the move and hidden herself in the airing cupboard. But they had moved in and Lawrence was sure that something would turn up.

So they couldn't stop smiling, even Eve. In for a penny, in for a pound, they said. Or, at least, Lawrence said. They walked on air. Everything seemed new. He smiled as he felt the rain on his face. And their boots crunched on their gravel drive as they began their first Monday morning walk down the village street.

"Look, no double yellow lines!" said Lawrence, "not even single ones. No street lights either!"

"Yes, I suppose so," she agreed reluctantly. She was still cautious about having moved up.

Months later, after dinner with neighbours, they both came to love walking slowly home in the middle of the empty village street, the beam of their torch wavering ahead and the noise of their boots echoing off the walls of the houses.

"And can't you smell the wood fires, too?" said Lawrence. Smoke was gently rising from a few chimneys. And there was no hint of exhaust fumes.

The village street curved round like the dinosaur's tail Lawrence had imagined on their first visit. The houses lining it were all built in different styles. They showed how through the ages English architecture always lived easily with whatever came before it.

"Look!" Lawrence said to Eve. "Look at them – that Tudor half-timbered house across the road, near the pub with a gable like our Dutch one."

And round the corner of the road from the pub a simple Georgian facade was squeezed between a Victorian villa and an Edwardian cottage.

"There's even a Regency bow-front. They're all next to each other, all different yet all mixing together."

"Part of the English architectural genius," smiled Eve at last.

"But what about council houses?"

"Can't see any, maybe just outside the village. But just give even those a couple of generations and they'll be OK too."

"You know, we've got the same sort of thing inside our house here, not the furniture but the rooms, the big Dutch fireplace and our sitting room, it's eighteenth century. And the top floor – it's half-timbered Jacobean." Eve was becoming enthusiastic, for she was practical and made the best of things.

"And for that matter," pointed out her husband. "It's like all the mixes in English society, all the refugees escaping persecution from way back, the Huguenots and the German Lutherans – the religious ones, and everyone who came here to escape the Nazis from everywhere in Europe, not to mention the West Indians and the Pakistanis later on. Oh, nearly forgot the Afghans and the Rumanians and now half Europe all over again."

He paused for breath. "Somehow they all fit together."

"Well, after a generation or two, anyway," Eve smiled at him. "But what about the Australians? Remember how so many of them came over in the '60s. What were they escaping from? The six o'clock swill?" They both laughed. He was relieved that she was beginning to take it more lightly. He knew he had made her agree against her better judgement. It was bad enough having such a big mortgage. He had to just hope for the best – that she'd hang on and see how wonderful it was going to be to live on this coast.

"But no wonder there's no such thing as a pure-blooded Englishman," he said. "And the oldest mix is the strangest one of all – the Anglo-Saxons and the Celts – the soldiers and the poets. It's why foreigners used to think the English were mad. But it's true! English is as English does." He paused – and then added, "and not as Europe does. Most of the refugees came here to escape from one battle or other in Europe. Funny how you don't get many refugees from England to Europe – except Oscar Wilde and Bonny Prince Charlie, of course."

"Well, don't forget Lady Hamilton, Nelson's lover," she reminded him. "You know that when he was dying he asked the Government to look after her? Well, they got all moralistic and ignored her and she died in poverty in Calais. Ugh ... men!"

They noticed that a couple of shops were closed. The weekend visitors were now no doubt back at work in some big city. Later on Eve and Lawrence came to like Mondays best of all. They looked forward to having the village to themselves in the way that one looks forward to the evening and the first drink of the day. Maybe it was raining, but on Mondays it would be quiet. Even if the street were a wind tunnel, it would be empty. And the village would belong to them a little more. And they would know that anyone they saw would live here. And, as time went on, be more and more likely to be a friend.

And their first stop that first day? The pub, of course, name of the George and Dragon, on the banks of the River Glaven as it passed the village's northern outposts of quay, windmill and Gibraltar House to wind through the marshes on its way to the North Sea. Eve noticed a large sign in the pub's window. 'No Vacancies', it said. Full up? That was odd, she thought. The weather was wet and windy. Not exactly holiday conditions. Perhaps some bird-watchers were here on a special tour. The marshes were a well known meeting-ground for thousands of birds. But the bar was empty.

"Having a long weekend?" asked the landlord laconically. He was lean and phlegmatic. He had a crew cut and narrow crab-like eyes. He stalked up and down behind the bar and flicked at the counter with a damp cloth. He didn't seem too pleased to see them and didn't bother to disguise his general boredom.

"No! We've moved up," they told him. "We've put our house in London on the market and brought everything up over the weekend."

"Oh, really? Very good!" He grinned and seemed to relax. "Well, I'd better give you a drink on the house. What'll you have?"

This initiation rite was a good start, thought the couple. They ordered drinks, beer for him (warm again, he noted with satisfaction) and a gin-and-tonic for Eve. Drinks from the landlord! Maybe behind that crustacean exterior beat a heart of gold – even though he was doing his best to conceal it.

"Well, you seem to have plenty of business." Eve was thinking of the bird watchers.

"No, the place is empty."

"But you've got that board outside saying 'No Vacancies'. "

"Oh, don't take any notice of that. We just don't want to be bothered with people in the winter." He rolled his eyes and jerked his head backwards, clearly overcome by uncontrollable nausea at the thought of customers. "It's even worse in the summer. The place is swarming – absolutely hopeless. You wait."

He flicked at the counter again and stalked off down the bar.

As they left the pub towards the pottery shop, the one they had seen on their first visit, a tall and handsome woman emerged from it and strode away down the middle of the street. Her auburn hair rippled down her straight back. Lawrence opened his mouth, looked at his wife and closed it again. At that moment an old blue car, the first car they'd seen that morning, swept past him rather too closely for comfort.

"Watch out!" cried Eve. "You nearly got run over. And it's only our first day."

"Do you realise that was a Morris Minor?" he told her. "You don't often see them nowadays. Good condition, too."

"Yes, and it looked like there was a vicar in it," said his wife. "I saw his dog collar. Well," she smiled at him. "You'd have seen it too if you hadn't been looking at that woman."

By then they were opposite the pottery's big show-room windows. Through them they saw a balding man with a beard and side-whiskers. He was smiling gently to himself as he sat reading a newspaper, The Guardian. He sat cross-legged, wearing corduroy trousers and a tweed jacket patched at the elbows. He was smoking a pipe. While they were watching he took it out of his mouth, looked at it closely, tapped it on an ashtray and slowly put it back in his mouth. He seemed so relaxed that he could have been in his London club. Behind him a beautiful young woman was sitting at a potter's wheel where she was turning a lump of clay into a vase. She had waist-length pearly hair and a serene smile. Her skin was the colour of milk and looked as smooth as alabaster. She reminded Lawrence of a Rhine Maiden, a model for one of those old German posters demonstrating health and beauty. Standing in a doorway to a back room was a youthful man with dark curly hair. He had an electricity plug in one hand and was wiring it up with a screwdriver as he talked to them. From time to time he waved the screwdriver as if to emphasise a point. Through the open door they caught a phrase: "the theft that is property ... a canker to the body politic."

They all seemed rather like a family, as if Lawrence and Eve were watching them inside their home. Later they discovered why.

Through the showroom's windows they saw chunky dishes, salt holders like diver's helmets, cutlery drainers perforated like sieves, vases the shape of divas – tall, eloquent and commanding. Everything was slightly on the heavy side, grainy brown and thick like a crust of wholemeal bread, or opaque-white or sable. And no patterns, just a surface texture varying between salt, pepper and sand.

"Look," said Eve. "It's solid but it's really beautiful, harmonious as well as functional, both at the same time."

Lawrence smiled to himself. She liked it! Things were improving.

Months later they sometimes felt they could hardly travel down a remote lane in North Norfolk without coming across a potter crouched over a wheel producing some grotesque object such as a teapot shaped like a cat. But this pottery was different.

And there was something else, as Eve pointed out.

"Don't you see?" she said. "The style is like the North Norfolk coast – earthy. Oh ... " she tried for the right words, " ... rough, tough, strong, basic ... as well as beautiful. Certainly not genteel or delicate."

"But what are they all doing here anyway?" asked Lawrence. "I mean, most potters are quite solitary, aren't they? But these aren't."

"That's right," commented Eve. "And did you hear that man talking about the theft of property? We must be real crooks to him – we've got two. He must be a Marxist, the village's Marxist, that's it!" she giggled.

Lawrence grunted.

"You mean it's our bank that's got two, not us. Anyway, if he is, he's probably the last one left in East Anglia."

The smoke house next door looked a tumbledown shack – and it was locked. They gazed through a cobwebbed front window. A counter was crammed with bloaters, smoked salmon, mackerel pate, potted shrimps and pots of pickled herrings.

"But look at the back room!" said Eve. She had seen a Moses-like figure with a bushy beard and towering shoulders. He was hooking a pile of kippers onto some metal bars inside a chimney. They gazed at him but he looked blankly through them over his beard and looked away again without pausing.

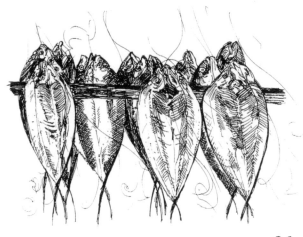

BL

Across the street was a bookshop with an art gallery. As they walked towards it a man inside took hold of the "OPEN" sign hanging on the door, turned it over and hung it up to say "CLOSED". He was short and dark and glared at them through the glass door before he turned away.

"Good timing, anyway," laughed Lawrence. "But a bit odd."

In the art gallery he saw some brightly painted and even wild looking pictures on the walls. He called to Eve again.

"Look – all primitive, sort of. They could have been painted by any of Stanley Spencer, or Grandma Moses, or Lowry, even Blake."

"Except," she pointed out, "that they're all dead."

"What about Beryl Cook, then?" asked Lawrence. The pictures showed dinghies with sails like shark's teeth, clouds like tears, seals like Harold Macmillan and weird perspectives. Several featured an odd-looking man with a pigtail leaning forwards at an impossible angle. So who was this fellow Brian Lewis anyway, the name shown on the easel in the window? Was he one of the odd North Norfolk types mentioned by that estate agent?

"Anyway, it's obviously not all boring bird paintings up here," he told her, grinning. "Despite what you'd said."

"Well!" She paused. "OK, but they're sure to be around somewhere."

"But not in this village. Which is where we live, remember? Come, darling, you've got to be fair!"

He left it at that for the moment. He felt he was gaining ground. She liked living here. But she wasn't going to admit it – not yet.

Near the gallery beckoned a delicatessen. It had a stable door that glistened black and was barricaded with huge bolts. As they approached, two of the bolts shot back with a clang, the door's top half swung open and a well-built man with a black beard leaned out. Several buttons of his white shirt were undone and a good deal of curly black hair was struggling to escape. His top half – the part they could see over the stable door – showed a lot of physical presence. Rather like an Ancient Greek, maybe even a Greek God, thought Eve secretly. And what was that above the door?

"Morning!" he called with a twinkle and a grin as he caught sight of the couple. He had a bottle of wine in one hand. "You're just in time! We've just opened up for the day."

"Well, we've just moved up – for ever!" announced Lawrence, with a confident smile. Eve gave him a despairing look.

"No! What, to the village? That's wonderful! Come in and look around. I've got some new Shiraz red wine delivered here today from Australia and was going to try it out."

Lawrence glanced at Eve and she shook her head at him despairingly but smiled too. So he smiled too.

The owner swung back the lower half of the door and stood aside to let them in. Behind him stretched an irresistible glutton's trap – at least for Lawrence. Sugar shack chicken mole, lavender tapenades, chilli chocolate risotto with prawns, pastel de choclo, Moroccan fish tagine and Harissa paste, not to mention olive oil from everywhere in the Mediterranean. Lawrence began to feel faint. Then there was a lot from Norfolk – stone-ground bread, amber honey, rich and strong cider and clear white wine. And strange liquids glittered in exotic phials shaped into tall tubes, squat bombes and smoky pyramids. A dozen speckled bowls (from the nearby pottery, thought Eve, judging by their texture) spilled over with half a dozen sorts of olives – black, green, pitted, stuffed and marinated. Scattered over a spread of spinach was a cluster of deep yellow Moroccan lemons as firmly knobbled as a kutch girl's nipples. Then there were stacks of rich and creamy foie gras, rillette d'oie and terrine de canard from south-west France, marinated lemon, bowls overflowing with oriental spices, succulent stuffed vine leaves from Greece, oily gunmetal slices of baked Spanish aubergine edged black like a bereavement card and handfuls of nacreous and writhing octopus and squid. Behind the counter an amphitheatre rose up of more than forty cheeses. Dominating them at centre stage was a large wheel of Roquefort. Many varieties of local cheeses were grouped round it like cottages around a church. Even Eve had never heard of some of them. Above them stretched a vaulted whitewashed roof ribbed by black beams. From one of them hung a red cartwheel and a crimson horse collar gleaming with brass studs. Two long sides of pork swung gently next to them.

And near the pork were several lengths of what looked like green garlic. 'Green garlic?' thought Eve. She looked closer – and saw Brussels sprouts sticking out of a vertical spine. Below them a big furnace cavity had been given a silver lining and now overflowed with a tumbling cornucopia of a dozen different shades and shapes and bakes of bread. Behind it was a wine department of bottles from all round the world. In one corner an upright barrel was draped with a red-and-white checked cloth. On top were three empty glasses and a bottle of Australian Chardonnay. It was straight out of the fridge, too, for a coating of tiny beads decorated its surface. The wine's rich lemon-grass texture turned the beads into prisms twinkling with light. Lawrence felt that Chardonnay was as much a food as a wine – and suddenly felt hungry as well as thirsty. It was hardly past noon and they had just had a drink in the George and Dragon. But he suggested to Eve that they might consider trying a little taste.

"We could use a few stuffed vine leaves to go with it too."

"Stupid!" She said caustically. "Can't you see the closed circuit tv?" A camera in the ceiling was pointing at the barrel. She was enjoying this. "We don't want to create a bad impression. We've only just moved up."

She was hiding her delight in finding such a shop in their village.

"Don't worry about that camera," smiled the owner, as he suddenly appeared with a bottle of Shiraz and put it down next to the Chardonnay. "We're all like that here. Anyway, that's for visitors and you deserve a glass for moving in. But would you prefer Chardonnay? It's a bit early for red, I suppose."

Lawrence could never make a decision like that so Eve chose Chardonnay for him – rather absently, for her mind was on something else. She was deciding that the shop owner really was remarkably like a Greek God. She watched him fish a corkscrew from his pocket and bend over the barrel. But, as he explained, it wasn't a barrel.

"Did you know that this place was once a forge?" He grasped the bottle in a hairy fist and delicately drew the cork with the other. He pointed to the barrel. "This may look like a barrel but it's actually the bellows for the forge. If you had a horse you wanted shod I could do it for you. Everything still works, you see. Mind you, we'd have to wait until the shop closed. EU regulations, you see."

He grimaced, winked and put the bottle down on a huge black anvil in a nest of straw and almost hidden beneath a pyramid of Veuve Cliquot magnums, Chateau Lafitte 1982 and Coleman's English mustard. The anvil protruded like some sort of uncircumcised priapic growth, property of an un-gentlemanly Greek God, perhaps – and about to leap out at any moment and frighten the horses. He slapped its blunt end.

"We'd put its foot on this," he pointed out. Was he serious?

"I was wondering about those sides of pork," said Eve as she accepted a glass of wine.

"Oh, yes. They're Hector's pigs – were, I suppose. We try to sell as much local food as we can. And there's a lot of it round here."

"Well, who's Hector?"

"He lives a mile away across the valley at Hector Hall ... rears pigs and pheasants ... always wears an old service greatcoat ... it'd been one of his ancestor's, he says."

Fresh local food straight from the ground or the chopping block! And next to it were delicacies from all over the world. Eve had become thoughtful when she saw all this, noticed Lawrence. But who were the customers for it all? And then Lawrence remembered what he had worked out that night they had driven home after their first visit. Those people, they had to be around here somewhere.

At the delicatessen the village street met the Cromer coast road on its way west to Blakeney. The street crossed the coast road and became a lane that passed the village post office and ambled a mile inland up the valley, keeping company with its water meadows and its river. Cottages lay peppered along the lane like shot from a 12-bore. Finally it reached the village green. Another pub, the Three Swallows, stood duty at its edge. Four seagulls, blank white against the fresh wet grass, were pecking about for worms. They were in a roped-off enclosure in the centre of the green. As the couple approached they flew off with a flash of deep red legs. They swooped up to perch on some tombstones in the graveyard of a giant church rearing up behind the pub. That church was tall and ashen, like the ghost of Christmas Past. It dominated the pub and the cottages below. Its slender gothic windows and buttresses, flying light and heavy at the same time, showed the authority of centuries. But now it was crumbling and decaying. The carvings and traceries were eroded by the weather more than by the abandonment of faith. For their classical proportions still proclaimed truth, if great power no longer. This dowager was long past her prime and her retinue long since departed. But still she displayed the bones of classic breeding and disdained the secular forces that had diminished her influence. Her role seemed to have been long obscured. The religious landscape had been invaded by a secular flood that concealed its valley of faith. Now the faith's existence was revealed only by its symbolic peaks – the Sunday services, the weddings, baptisms and funerals, the annual Church Fête and the Christmas carol service. Nevertheless, as Lawrence and Eve were to discover, those rituals linked the travelling song line of the faith they represented and bound together the people of the village.

But today the graveyard's only living occupants were a dozen sheep. Oblivious to a slight drizzle they munched for eternity on the long grass between the tombstones.

The drizzle grew to slashing rain and the couple dashed for cover. The pub's bar was as empty as a rifled tomb. A log fire hissed at one end. Lawrence looked at Eve and smiled. He clinked a couple of coins on the counter and a young man appeared from the kitchen, rubbed his eyes and pulled on a jacket. Lawrence ordered a mug of warm beer and a gin and tonic for Eve. They stood together before the gently burning logs. Silently they gazed out at the bedraggled village green. The rain was falling on it with ruthless monotony. The seagulls had returned and were again pecking for worms. Together they watched raindrops dribbling down the windows. Lawrence considered betting on which would reach the bottom first. And they listened to the silence behind the crackling of the fire. He began to understand the phrase: "buried in the country." And he loved it.

It was then, standing before the logs and watching the rain, when they caught again that feeling of Eve's when she had first looked out of their top floor window and seen the rectory, the stables and the woodland.

"It's not just our house, is it?" she turned to Lawrence. "It's the whole village, you know."

He looked at her and nodded.

"It seems ridiculous," he said. "But we seem to have fallen into some sort of pre-war time-warp ... some time in the mid-thirties, like maybe 1935. And are you actually telling me that it might have been worth the risk to come up here?"

She tossed her head and shrugged nonchalantly.

"Possibly ... maybe. But the jury's still out."

They sat quietly, as if not wanting to break the spell. The mid-thirties, those were the days when all was well with England, weren't they? Those shops, shops that they already felt they knew well – the Deli, the Pottery, the Smoke House, the Bookshop and the Art Gallery – they wouldn't have existed before the war. But that enhanced the feeling that the village seemed self-sufficient – as villages were in those days. Yes, people's needs were a little more elaborate nowadays – but the shops met them, as they had before. So they helped to give the village the atmosphere of an isolated paradise. Eve and Lawrence had already begun to realise that North Norfolk existed inside some sort of bell jar. It seemed forgotten and isolated – but independent, even protected. Norwich Station was a terminus, so nobody travelled through it on the way to anywhere else. And there was no point in having a motorway in Norfolk. It all added up to a backwater – like an island. It helped to create for them the absurd but irresistible illusion that they had come to live in a golden age before the war. It was an age that, like all golden ages, radiated an intense feeling of security, contentment and belonging – after the age had passed. They both secretly knew the golden age had never actually existed. But that didn't worry them at all.

Soon the rain stopped and they ventured out. Westwards, beyond the valley's river and its water meadows, stood another old church. The couple decided to save that one for another time and climbed up past the grazing sheep and their church. A lane led north towards the windmill and home. Outside the lych gate they met an elderly man wearing a battered overcoat. He had just arrived at the gate and was climbing very carefully off a little scooter. Unlike them, he did not seem a visitor. In fact he seemed almost as old as the church. His overcoat ended in tatters above a pair of bare ankles and untied boots. Bristles grew round his face like an unkempt and displaced halo but he gave them a generous smile. He welcomed them with polite queries about their health and they were touched. He beckoned.

"Look at these little things here. I've just come over to check up, see if they've arrived yet." He pointed down to a patch of south-facing grass. "The winter aconites, see? There they are, too! They're coming out already."

Eve crouched down, saw the yellow buds beginning to open and looked up at him, beaming.

"Yes, you're right. They're here already!"

"A miracle, I call them," said their new friend. "And there'll be a violet or two soon. It's a miracle, a promise. Every winter after the turn of the year. I always tell Philip when I see them first."

"Philip?"

"Yes, our rector. You know?"

He looked towards the church and smiled happily. They introduced themselves. After a few moments of awkward but friendly talk they walked thoughtfully home down the lane. At last Eve said:

"That old man, he's part of it, too, you know – somehow."

And Lawrence knew that he was – somehow.

Clumps of wild thyme grew on the banks of the lane. The rain had released a rich bouquet of their scent. But now it was dry and even the sun had appeared. For a moment they almost felt warm. It was their first lesson on how quickly the weather changed in North Norfolk. The lane led them to one of the narrow alleyways that connected one part of the village with another. They ran between the gardens of various houses and their walls were eight or even ten feet high. Often they were overhung with ivy. Always they were dark and gloomy. They were only just wide enough to allow a smuggler to escape from an excise man, a barrel of brandy on his shoulder, his greatcoat flapping round his thigh boots and, no doubt, his cutlass gleaming in the moonlight.

Soon the alleyway ran along the wall of their own garden. After a few seconds they reached their door. It was the faded old door with the rounded arch they had seen that first day. As he put his hand on the latch, Lawrence looked at Eve and smiled.

"Now!" he said to her. "Wait for the miracle, our miracle! And it really is our miracle, darling." And he put his arm round her and opened the door.

Behind them was the dark and gloomy alleyway. It was useful when travelling on the way to somewhere though not a place to dally in. But on the other side of the doorway was their garden, now sunlit too, with the lawn and the croquet hoops, the fruit trees, the conservatory and their own house with its Dutch gable.

They had come to understand the symbolism of the door. If it had been ajar, anyone walking down the alley could have looked into the garden. Perhaps they might have glimpsed someone dozing in the hammock. Or maybe a group of friends drinking wine and laughing together at the table under the blossom that hung on the apple tree's bough. And was that a tame panther lying asleep in the grass? They might have been tempted to venture inside, guessing that adventure and fulfilment lay beyond. Lawrence and Eve had opened that door when they bought Gibraltar House. They had accepted the risks of doing so. After all, they had bought it before they had sold their own house. So they had risked losing everything. But that risk was the price to be paid for living their dream. Opening that door in the wall had become the symbol of their new life in North Norfolk. But what if they had been more cautious – had not dared to take such a risk? Then they would have turned their backs on the chance for adventure. They would have walked on, away from the sea and the edge, the edge of risk – of living – as well as of landscape. And their life's course might have remained the same, living in the same house in Notting Hill that they had always lived in with the same habits and seeing the same faces that they had seen for decades except of course that they would all be slowly growing old. But Eve and Lawrence had opened that door. Yes, their mortgage kept them in constant anxiety. But that anxiety made them appreciate all the more their style of life. And it made them appreciate that next door only the pub and the old mill, that eighteenth century wind-catcher, separated them from the marshes that stretched away under the bowl of sky to the line of far-off surf.

They watched huge footprints planted by the wind on the carpet of reeds and now weaving towards them. They stood mesmerised by the sight of that ancient movement. A few hundred yards away a herd of cows huddled together against the wind. Far beyond trembled the horizon.

Lawrence was excited and liberated by this wide expanse of water-land and sky. The unfamiliar feeling the landscape gave him seemed to

reflect the risks they had taken to move here. For a moment it made him dizzy as if the feeling were a drug. A far-off tuft of reeds seemed to lie at infinity and a remote bird-watchers' hide to become a speck of dust in the iris of God's eye. Even eternity, he felt, was only an hour away. He knew that his intense consciousness of it all expressed the rich quality of their life on the coast. He shook himself down to earth and turned to Eve.

"It's the edge all right, darling. That's worth a bit of risk."

She looked at him and smiled. "I know. I love it too, you know."

And then –

"But still. There's still that awful bank."

He smiled.

"That's the other edge. One sharpens the other."

"Yes, but will they really kick us out?"

He embraced her.

"Over my dead body," he told her.

She looked at him for a moment – then made a face and laughed.

"Don't chance it," she told him.

Silently they linked arms and she rested her head on his shoulder as they walked down to their house together. Again their boots crunched on the gravel of the drive.

"You don't get that sound on London pavements," remarked Lawrence.

"No," his wife replied. "But there's something else to it. I can't quite work out what. But whatever it is, I know it's important."

"Worth being here?"

"Of course. But not worth going bust." Then she paused. "Well, probably not."

And then: "You know that prime minister, the one who said England had a yob culture? When he resigned from politics didn't he move up to North Norfolk?" She turned and looked at her husband.

"Oh, yes!" said Lawrence. "You're right. He bought a place on the coast somewhere round here, I think," he paused. "Well, it's obviously catching!"

She walked over to a nearby flowerbed.

"What are you doing, darling?" he asked, puzzled.

"I think I'll have my vegetable garden just here. Where that flowerbed is. I can easily move the flowers."

He laughed and she turned.

"What's so funny, then?"

"Nothing! Nothing at all!"

And he kissed her.

So they had completed that Monday morning paseo down the village street. It was the initiation and privilege of incomers – not for week-enders. But no one had much responded. The George and Dragon didn't like its customers, the Pottery only spoke to its own family, Moses at the Smoke House had looked through them and the saturnine character at the Bookshop obviously disliked customers too. Only the Deli was friendly, that man looking like an ancient Greek God.

"We go bust coming up here and they won't even talk to us," said Eve miserably.

"It's our first day," Lawrence told her gently. "This isn't America. It's England. It takes longer to get to know people. But maybe it's more worth while when we do."

*       *       *

Later they left their unpacking and gathered in the conservatory for the first evening drink of the first day of their new life. Lawrence turned on the radio. It was just before the news – with AA Road-watch, the programme reporting driving conditions.

"Both carriageways of the M25 are blocked near Caterham between junctions 6 and 7 due to a collision between two articulated lorries. Drivers are advised to leave the motorway at those junctions to avoid delays. An accident near Milton Keynes at Junction 14 on the M1 is causing a 12-mile tailback south."

Slowly Lawrence poured a gin-and-tonic for his wife and a whisky for himself.

"Doesn't sound too good," he said laconically, as he passed the glass to her. He sat down, took a sip of his whisky and gazed out over the garden. A thrush was pecking at a worm near the forsythia bush on the lawn.

"Goodgie, goodgie, goodgie," went his wife as she stroked their cat. It lay stretched out on her lap and was purring like an engine. "Lovely pussy-wussie. Does a Sphinxy-winxy like her new home, then?"

A dozen rooks perched motionless in the elm trees near the rectory.

"London now and an accident at the Cromwell Road and Earls Court Road junction has caused a long tail-back to Hyde Park Corner. The Bakerloo Line is not operating between Piccadilly and St John's Wood Stations due to a signals failure. The City is indefinitely closed to all traffic following the discovery of an unexploded bomb in Threadneedle Street. The IRA has claimed responsibility."

Eve looked at him over her glass and raised her eyebrows.

"Well, we obviously got out just in time," she said. "Didn't we, Sphinxie?"

She held the cat with one hand, leaned over to take a sip of gin with the other and sat back to paint her fingernails. "I suppose it would be too much to ask the IRA to blow up our bank?"

*    *    *

Winter dragged on. Dusk still came early. Before the light failed in the afternoons they sometimes saw snowflakes swirl in a faint gust of wind. Those were the days when the frost never left the iron ground. Often snow lay upon it all night, an embroidered shroud for its eiderdown.

That winter was their first in North Norfolk. And it was cold – very cold. Most mornings the fields were rimed with white frost. They knew few people so they walked alone and the wide and empty roads echoed to their boots. Often they crossed the marshes to a reed-bordered lagoon, there to watch wildfowl feeding in the cold morning air. Later they would make their way home past the windmill, its sails spread wide and high above them. The washed-out February light faded early. Sometimes, as if to emphasise the emptiness of the marshes, a few hundred black Brent geese gathered near the beach road. Their heads nodded as they rotated anti-clockwise in a solid circle. Every now and then more geese joined them. Turning into the wind, they landed feet forward, wing flaps down, and were lost quickly in the crowd. And the soft clucking of deep and guttural muttering came to Lawrence and Eve over the pale marsh reeds.

Despite the cold they kept warm by making a good pace over the bank to the flint beach. They often took a three-mile hike along the river to Blakeney and back through the water meadows. On the edge of the marshes tall chimneys behind some trees were all that showed of a hidden mansion.

Their path home led past a stack of reeds by the river's sluice gate. There they often saw someone cutting bundles of reeds. They kept up a good pace and on the last lap along the edge of the marsh and through the village they knew they would be returning warm. But once home the central heating was not always enough. They needed fires in their rooms too. And for that they needed firewood. In London you

could always find free wood. The building skips in every street were often full of wood. There were other treasures in them, too – filing cabinets, electric sockets, a wicker chair, yards of almost new wiring and even a large Modigliani nude (copy). Lawrence had long learned that a carpet in a Knightsbridge skip was worth more than a new one in a Neasden lounge. But their village had no skips. So he spread out their local paper and turned to the advertisements. The Eastern Daily Press has a wide coverage. It even reported events outside East Anglia, where bin Ladin and Bush were likely to be confused with a new kitchen gadget and something in a garden centre. But the small adverts were much more important. And there in the 'FUEL' section, sandwiched between 'Thatched Roofs' and 'Top Value Firewood,' was 'The Log Lady'. How could Lawrence resist?

Two days later a yellow truck of logs backed and bumped down their drive. Here and there on the walls it left paint before shuddering to a halt by the conservatory. Both doors opened and out jumped the Log Lady and her two small boys.

"Karina!" she announced with a broad grin. And stuck out her hand.

Lawrence was puzzled by her clothes. She seemed about to jump from a US chopper in the Vietnam War. Her trouser fatigues were in a charmingly green and brown camouflage motif. As an accessory an ammunition belt (optional loaded, perhaps) encircled her waist. The ensemble was completed with a top that matched the camouflage motif fatigues. As a novel feature, three inverted red stripes were sewn on her shoulder. They indicated, of course, that she was a sergeant in the US Marines. All of which would no doubt have scared the Vietcong to death and forced them to order several tons of wood from her every day. And that, more or less, was what happened to Lawrence. She was about thirty – or was it twenty-five? She had twinkling eyes and confident charm. And she was as fresh as the morning dew. She may have been wearing combat gear and an ammunition belt, but she walked with simple elegance. She could have been sauntering down a Paris fashion catwalk. Even, come to that, with the same clothes. It was the weekend and their first London visitors were there. Karina moved amongst everyone to the manner born, bestowing small talk and compliments like the Queen at a Buckingham Palace garden party.

"Have you come far?" she asked the guests. Then -

"Oh, isn't it nice to have a house where you can invite your friends to stay!" She smiled at Lawrence – who melted, lost his grip on a wooden spoon and dropped it into a casserole of rabbit simmering on the Aga.

"Oh, what a pity! But it smells lovely. You must be such a help to your wife," she told him. He had bought the rabbits the day before from a fellow in the Dun Cow in Salthouse, a village a few miles along the coast. They had cost him a pint and another pint to have them skinned and gutted. Later he discovered he had paid twice what a butcher would have charged. Back home he had poured a bottle of red wine into the casserole after mixing in five tablespoonfuls of mustard and twice as much sugar. Later he would cool it down and pull the meat off the bone. He had thought up that mixture of mustard and sugar by pure chance. That morning he had opened his food cupboard and then found himself frowning because he had forgotten what he had opened it for. Later he remembered: he had a lot of excess sugar and had been wondering what to do with it. So he used it to take off the sharpness of the mustard. Meantime he was baking some vegetables in olive oil with plenty of whole garlic cloves.

"Can I taste some?" asked the Log Lady. He found another spoon and dipped it into the casserole.

"Oh, lovely!" she exclaimed. "How did you manage that taste?"

Eve was shopping at the time, buying kippers from the Smoke House for their guests for tomorrow's breakfast. She would have been home in time to meet the Log Lady but had gone on to the Deli, partly for some olive oil but really because she was curious about the owner, the one who looked like a Greek God.

Lawrence showed the Log Lady round the house. Catching sight of the bookshelves he was building, she turned to him.

"I'm going to make sure my boys read every night before bed."

At the time they were busy watching television in the next room. He wrote her a cheque.

"I had to go deep into the forest inland for this load." She smiled at him as he wrote and his pen spluttered and he had to re-write the cheque.

"It was very dark and I nearly got stuck." She made it sound like the Wild Wood. He shivered and almost clutched at her hand.

As one of their friends said later: "You don't get them like that in London."

Yes, they were all familiar with the class resentment that came only too often with the Greater London accent. They had found none of that in North Norfolk. The Log Lady was confident – and happy, too. She admired success, complimented it and did her best for herself. And then Lawrence suddenly realised that this must have been how Nell Gwynn got started – oranges instead of logs, though, of course. To him she combined Nell Gwynn, Eliza Dolittle and the Queen. It enchanted him so much that over the next fortnight he ordered four more loads. Eve, who had missed meeting her, told him tartly that it was just as well that it was too cold to sit in the conservatory because he'd filled it with logs.

"Well," he said, "if it had been warm I wouldn't have had to order the logs, would I?"

The logic of that did not appeal to his wife. And when he told her that the Log Lady almost made him forget their mortgage she replied: "Well, that woman didn't help me forget it, that mortgage I was talked into, you can be sure."

And when the rabbit he had cooked with his recipe of mustard and sugar had been a great success with their weekend guests his wife was not amused. No, not at all. He couldn't understand why.

When Lawrence rang Karina to deliver the last load he mentioned that Eve would be at home this time. This can't have been why she had put her hair up, painted her nails and put on a pair of high heels with a long hobbled grey skirt. They forced her to take eight-inch steps. Difficult when you're carrying an armful of logs. But it had no effect on her smile.

Eve's comments?

"If you want any more wood you'd better go and live in the Wild Wood yourself. And I'll go back to London."

For a moment Lawrence was upset. Then he remembered.

"What, with that Arab who's moving in?" he laughed. "You'll be lucky. He's got four wives as it is."

Lawrence gazed every day at his logs, as countrymen do. He gloated over them as if they were treasure trove. The very sight gave him security for they represented energy as much as oil or electricity. And they made him feel nearer the edge.

The driving rain could lash the coast all it wished. And the frost could freeze the marshes' swampy pools all it wished, too. The gale could chill to death the helpless birds that tried to shelter in the grass. But Lawrence and Eve were all right. Inside, no matter how harsh things were outside, they could lie warm in bed at night. For the fires were lit and the central heating was on. Once between the sheets they stretched their toes as warmth spread over them like a blush. And they lay quiet, smiled at each other and listened to the wind buffeting around the garden outside and booming down the chimney. Inside, it was like being in a padded cell. The air in their bedroom was still. It almost made them hold their breath.

"Don't you think it's worth leaving London just for this?" Lawrence asked his wife. She raised her eyes to the ceiling, heaved and gave him a look.

"But, darling," he protested. "The closest anyone ever got to the weather there was watching the forecast on television."

Sometimes they would both waken in the dark, a little puzzled because they couldn't work out what had woken them. And then the window frame would rattle again and they would realise that the wind had changed.

So they had become very conscious of the weather. Often now they would look out towards the marshes and say something like, "I think the fog's lifted a bit ..." or "... those clouds look like clearing." These were phrases that made them feel close to the earth and they were very satisfying. And they discovered few pleasures were deeper than lying in a warm bed and listening to the rain beating at the windows. Idly they would say to each other: "d'you hear the rain?" And they would smile, for they knew it couldn't get in. They felt all the warmer for that.

One morning Eve woke early and prodded Lawrence. He groaned.

"What is it?"

"I've just thought ... why did those geese sometimes walk round anti-clockwise? I mean, why do they walk round in a circle at all? But why anti-clockwise, anyway?"

He groaned again. Then –

"It's obvious." He was annoyed and wanted to go back to sleep.

"Well, why is it so obvious?"

"Because ... because it's Wednesday," he said, turned over and pulled the sheet over his head.

"What?" She peered at the calendar on the wall. "It's not, it's Thur- ... ahhh." And she prodded him again and turned over too.

Slowly the wind became a little warmer. One morning the air was a little less frigid than the day before. And so the earth began slowly to tilt towards the sun and greet the spring. But shortly after that gradual improvement they discovered again how swiftly North Norfolk's weather could change. One night it had been particularly stormy. The clouds were racing each other across the moon. The elm trees were waving excitedly. The shrubbery was being ransacked by a pack of wolves. But next morning the whole garden was motionless. They were amazed! Clearly time itself had stopped. For nothing was moving. Every leaf on every tree was still. The evergreens were like pillars of salt. All the birds had vanished. The air was clear. There was no wind. Smoke rose vertically from a next-door chimney. And everything was silent. They could both have gone deaf overnight.

Even more fascinating was the hour before dawn when a heavy frost gripped the earth. It lined the ground and turned the trees and the garden walls into silhouettes. Sometimes a heavy sea fog moved inland. Everything turned vaporous and the air became damp and grainy. Neighbouring houses were indefinite shadows and bulked near like ships in a Channel fog. Eve said she could hear birds beginning to try to sing. Not many, perhaps one or two. They battled against the dank vapour for a time and then subsided. Only a curlew's rising lilt came clear through the fog from somewhere distant on the marshes.

\*     \*     \*

It was the village's general stores nearby that at last led them into the labyrinth of village life. Tom, its owner, was a former naval person, proud, square-shouldered and fit. Rumour had it that he had been in the SAS too – and perhaps still was. But he smiled mysteriously and told everyone that his lips were sealed. In the last twenty years he'd seen service round the world before coming home to his roots – as the English do. It seemed he kept his fishing boat at a port along the coast. Most days he went out at high tide – the only way to clear the bar at the harbour's entrance. And to get in again he had to wait for the next tide twelve hours later. But by then he would have an abundant catch of fish – and cages filled with crab and sometimes lobster. He ran the shop like a quarterdeck. He wouldn't be long back before the fish would be stored away and a gaggle of local girls set to work dressing the crabs for sale. His wife Jill served the customers. She was a tall and lanky north-erner with a resounding laugh and no nonsense. She kept a horse and often rode to work, although they only lived a few hundred yards away. It was usually tethered to a bolt by the window with a bag of feed round its head. Through them Eve put names to the George and Dragon's landlord – Ronald. And she heard some gossip about the owner of the Deli and more of the youngish man with curly hair they had seen in the Pottery, the one she had suspected was a Marxist.

"Basic stuff," as Eve told her husband. "All about the women in their lives."

At one of those early visits to Tom's shop she bumped into a friend from London. This was a plump and affectionate artist and poet who had a cottage somewhere near the village.

"So you're up here at last! Wonderful! Have you really moved up for good or is this just a visit?" asked Pippa.

"Well," replied Eve, looking daggers at Lawrence. "Well, we've moved up for a time anyway."

"Oh, well, you're here," she giggled. "That's wonderful!"

She sounded really pleased.

"Maybe for ever, too," broke in Lawrence. He grinned, "Or at least until the bank moves us on."

"Oh! Ah, well, I understand." She shrugged. "Oh, those banks! I'm having trouble with mine, too. They want their money back. So unrea-sonable – I ask you!"

She giggled again. "Well, before they get it I'll give you a ring and you must come and have supper. I've just finished a couple of new poems."

She bought two dozen mussels ("No, dear, just for me," Lawrence heard her say to Jill), a bottle of wine and two handfuls of parsley before bustling noisily out, waving and calling "Good-bye" to everyone.

Tom's family had lived on the coast as fisher folk for generations.

Apparently their name was similar to that of another no more ancient but ducal family living in a stately home beyond Wells to the west. No relation, what with all that land, supposed Lawrence. But he was already realising you could never be sure on this coast. Much later Lawrence and Eve visited this stately home, an alien Palladian pile gestated during a Grand Tour to Italy and now squatting like a sandstone toad by its waterhole on the marshes. Not at all a Norfolk style. Its owner was the earl of somewhere in the Midlands with an ancestor who long ago had made himself a great reputation as an agriculturalist.

A few evenings later in early March Pippa was as good as her word and invited them to dinner. Her cottage was only a mile or so up the valley. It had been built for a farm labourer two hundred years ago. The woods had sheltered it all those years. By now its flint walls had absorbed the tones of the trees that surrounded it. Ivy had assaulted the walls, besieged the windows and taken possession of the roof. Tufts of grass had marched over her porch and surrounded her water butt. By now the cottage was smothered by nature and as firmly rooted into the ground as a tree. And the only change since it was built had been the installation of some rudimentary plumbing. Even Pippa cheerfully acknowledged that this was little more than the merest of gestures.

"A tap like a watery nose," as she put it, "a drain like a stain and a bog unfit for a hog – let alone a dog!"

And since she was a poet and a painter, she was probably just as hard up as its first tenants, the farm workers. Her poetry was simple and profound at the same time – like that of Blake or Robert Frost. She painted North Norfolk in the same way. Like all the local artistic demi-monde, she drew her inspiration from its austerity of its landscape.

On the couple's walk to the cottage the weather had been cold, almost paralysingly cold. It was the sort of climate you had to keep moving in if you didn't want to freeze. But once indoors the warmth thawed them out. One reason why they had wanted to live in North Norfolk was because they had wanted to appreciate the contrast between cold and warmth. Now they had discovered how cold it could be. And they had decided that warmth was better.

Tonight was their first dinner invitation. They were crammed shoulder to shoulder with their hostess and another couple at her table in the kitchen. Thick and frayed curtains were drawn tight. An old stove glowed. Candles were jammed into empty bottles. Shadows shrouded everyone. Lawrence and Eve saw that the walls were covered with paintings – here landscapes, there figures – and all merging into each other.

Some were as small as postcards, some were magnificently large. Flourishes of wild stencilling dealt with any undesirable empty areas of wall. Hand-painted plates and mugs in varying sizes and patterns were stacked on the Welsh dresser. They shared space with bric-a-brac, cards, shells and objets trouvés from the beach that Pippa had clearly felt to be indispensable sources of inspiration. The room was like one of those glass paperweights full of little images that are obliterated by snowflakes when you shake it. At any moment Mary Poppins and her umbrella might come sailing in through the window. And nothing existed outside the cottage.

Pippa filled everyone's glass with wine. The other guests were a couple from the Pottery. Eve recognised them from when she and Lawrence had looked through its window that first day. They were the beautiful alabaster-skinned Rhine Maiden (a German girl, a potter who, Pippa explained to them, had come to live in the village some years before) and her friend, the man who had been reading The Guardian. The Rhine Maiden handed over a little package to Pippa.

"Just something I cobbled up," she said with a modest smile. She was clearly already familiar with a few English idioms. Her present was a tapering wall-pot, the sort you would hang from a hook on the wall. It was wider at the top than the bottom and its surface had the North Norfolk salt-and-pepper style they had seen in the Pottery.

"Oh," cried Pippa ecstatically. "How beautiful, my darling! It could have been dug up in ancient Troy."

"Well, it's not as old as the hills!" she laughed. "I only made it last week. But I thought you could put some flowers in it."

Her long pearly hair was now tied back with a blue silk ribbon. She was sitting with elbows together, hands supporting her chin. Her slim eyebrows were perfectly arched above a calm and steady gaze. Besides her sat The Guardian reader. Pippa explained to Lawrence that he looked after the business side of the Pottery. He smiled depreciatingly and stroked his beard.

"Such as it is," he said with an ironic smile. "Not exactly rocket science." Now and then during the evening he brought out a pad and made notes. Eyes briefly twinkling, he threw brief comments into the conversation and sat back in the way that one drops a pebble down a well and waits for the splash.

Pippa had let down her shimmering jet-black hair and her eyes were sparkling. She poured wine for everyone again and talked of her recent visit to an exhibition of Gainsborough's paintings at the Royal

Academy in London.

"He was so English. You can see English history in his paintings and not just the landscapes, either," she announced. "It's the way of life."

She began carving slices from a shoulder of lamb. Buried deep below the surface were dozens of tiny lumps of garlic. By now the whole shoulder was oozing with rich juice.

"Mint sauce!" she announced, putting a pot on the table. "This poor little thing was alive a couple of days ago, John Hurlingham my butcher in Holt he told me, so we've all got to drink a toast to this little lamb."

Everyone raised their glasses for a moment and nodded compassionately at the shoulder of lamb before them.

"Wham bam, so sorry, lamb," sighed the Guardian, who then cocked his head to one side and made a note in his pad. The Rhine Maiden shook her head and smiled at him. But Pippa went on without pausing. "Lamb of God – I should have painted it. Anyway we've got Brussels sprouts in a cheese sauce with things in it."

She put another dish on the table. Its sides were painted with freestyle carrots and mushrooms even though it was full of sprouts. She had drizzled them with flaked cheese, grilled them and then scattered a cloud of ground nutmeg and almonds on top. The nutmeg speckled them like the surface of some of the dishes at the Pottery.

"As for the sprouts," said Lawrence, "no doubt Brussels will have us all conforming to artistic uniformity one day. Remember what the communists tried to do!"

"Don't say that. They can't do that," protested the Rhine Maiden. "Artistic integrity ... it's part of what makes a country tick."

"Well, they're making us do everything else the same nowadays," said Eve. "Look at vacuum cleaners!"

Pippa laughed, took a gulp of wine and put her glass down with a thump. Some drops splashed onto the tablecloth.

"Bugger!" she said, wobbled slightly and wiped it off with a scarf.

Eve could not help herself and thought 'what about some gossip?'

"There was a woman we saw leaving your Pottery," she said. "On our first day after moving up, she was walking down the street – by herself, she was. She had a very straight back and lots of long wavy hair."

"Ah!" began the Guardian, "That's Justine. Yes, she's rather ... ouch!" He jumped and looked painfully at the Rhine Maiden. "What d'you do that for?" He leaned down and rubbed his ankle.

"Oh, her!" sniffed Pippa. "Her ... just someone who used to work in the Pottery. We don't have much to do with her nowadays, do we? Would anyone like some more wine?"

The Guardian winked at Lawrence, everyone held out their glasses and the identity of the woman with the straight back and the cascade of long wavy hair was not revealed. Not that night anyway.

"What wine are you giving us, Pippa, anyway?" asked the Guardian, by way of distraction.

"I can't remember," she admitted. "But it's red. I know that."

"Ah!" he grinned, brought out his pad again and made a note. Later Lawrence learned that he was the village historian and these were notes for a book.

Dinner continued with a slab of Brie cheese from the Deli in the village. And the conversation continued with a good helping of more gossip. It was an ingredient as vital to a local community as yeast to the making of bread. Good for exaggeration, too. Eve and Lawrence were silent for much of the evening. Her brief effort had fallen upon stony ground so they mostly just sat and listened.

The owner of the Deli and one of the girls there? Yes, there was certainly something between them. And then there was the dancer called Marilyn, they told Eve. She was a friend of his too – like most of the women in the village, apparently. Who was Marilyn anyway? Oh, just some connection. Same with Justine, thought the Guardian (checking with his notes) but Pippa and the Rhine Maiden refused to discuss her.

"Well, he certainly seems popular," remarked Eve. "And he looks a bit like a Greek God. Which was the one who was always chasing women? Haephestus, wasn't it, the black-smith? That's what he looks like, anyway?"

"No, it was Zeus." The Guardian was riffling through the back pages of his notebook. "Yes, here we are – Zeus ... yes, got himself up like a swan because he fancied a girl called Leda. Just as well, too." He looked up and winked at the Rhine Maiden who smiled back. Eve caught the exchange but did not understand it. The Guardian went on.

"Leda, yes – she was partial to swans, according to Homer."

And the Bookshop's owner? Who's that? You'll find out – and watch out! Well, that bearded fellow at the Smoke House, looks like Moses? Ah, an enigma! And someone mentioned something about someone called Prospero, a weird man who always wears his coat over his shoulders, had a sort of servant and a golden retriever who leaped about all over the place. And then a formidable lady called Millicent, she was the parish council chairman and hadn't she bulldozed through some infilling in the village for someone who wanted to build a house? And hadn't Ronald at the George and Dragon been for a drying-out session last month? Lawrence and Eve had hardly heard of some of them. Eve certainly glowed as the evening wore on.

Eventually the plates were cleared away. The talk had slowed a little. Some one replaced a guttering candle. Pippa reached behind for a book on the Welsh dresser. Lawrence and Eve shared a smile. They had been warned that she might perform. And they wanted to be enthusiastic.

"Well, before you all go, I'd just like to read you this," she coughed, clearing her throat. "I wrote it this afternoon when I'd come back from exercise in the pool near Cromer."

She brought out a sheet of paper and looked round, eyes gleaming again.

*"Sensible girls go nowhere*
*they sit in the bar*
*looking like Edward Burra*
*or Matisses*
*red lips ajar*
*not caring what passes*
*not talking to people.*
*I wish I too*
*Could be pale and trim*
*With a gash of red*
*Sitting on a bar stool looking thin."*

"Oh, but Pippa," protested the Rhine Maiden. "I think you've lost weight."

"Well, thanks, dear," laughed Pippa, wobbling slightly. "But what about the poem?"

"Poignant!" decided the Guardian, nodding sagely.

"Thank you, darling! Well, since you like it so much, I'll read you all another one. It's called" – she searched for the page – "ah, here it is! 'Holiday Snap' She held her arm up as if she was holding a starting pistol. Then she waved her hand gently.

51

*"Oh woman among the sunflowers!*
*Oh crush of sky!*
*Your soul is a peeled grape*
*Your skin is brazed by stardust and cobwebs -*
*Smiling lips held together by gravity -*
*To force them apart would make you cry."*


There was a silence.

"Ah..." At last the Rhine Maiden breathed out. "That's beautiful."

"Yes, it's so lovely, so gentle," agreed Eve.

"It's like a Chinese painting," remarked Lawrence. Pippa blushed and put her arm round him.

"Oh, Lawrence, you're so sweet. You all are!"

The guests refilled each other's glasses. Elbows planted on the table, they huddled together, heads almost meeting, joking gently. Candles and empty bottles crowded the table. Voices dropped and the silences became longer. At last someone sighed and slowly rose and everyone followed suit. They sorted out their coats and scarves from where they had been dumped in the downstairs bath and kissed their affectionate good-byes.

Their new friends from the Pottery had a torch. They led Lawrence and Eve home along a path through the woods to a water meadow. Beyond was the river. They followed it down the valley towards their village. It was midnight, and midnight cold. The full moon overhead was cracked across by a willow's bare branch. Overcoat collars turned up, scarves muffled faces, hands plunged into pockets. They walked silently in the night's bowl. Suddenly a tawny owl floated over them to the treetops ahead. Its wings flapped slowly and its hoot filled the night's silence. The Guardian pulled out his pad, shone his torch on it and made a note.

"Here I couch when owls do fly," he smiled, looking round to them as if apologetically. "Remember that?"

"Yes, that's ... " Eve looked at Lawrence, puzzled. "I know that from ... somewhere ... sometime at school?" She thought for a moment, then gave up and walked on.

They began to talk together in low voices, as if in a mutual trance. Their breath condensed into vaporous clouds.

The Rhine Maiden told them that besides the windmill in the village there was a watermill in the little village of Letheringset at the head of the valley.

"So we live between two mills," she smiled. "The river runs below the watermill. It uses the water's power to turn the stones, of course. So the local bread – brown, naturally – it's made from stone-ground flour. It's very creamy and uneven. It's difficult to find this in England. But this is the only sort of bread we eat here. And, of course, at the other end of the valley is the windmill near your house and it ground wheat too until a few years ago. But the miller left. He had become disillusioned with life in England and even our village couldn't hold him. He emigrated to Australia and no one else has wanted to work there."

So they all lived in the valley of the two mills! A Shangri-La, a setting for some lady novelist's historical romance of an isolated valley and a community that few joined and fewer left. The mills stood guard over the valley, one at its head and one at its foot. They took their power from wind and water to provide bread for the people. But the mill that no longer operated, did that forecast a decline of their paradise one day? Nothing stays the same, says the wind to the reeds. Meanwhile five churches in Letheringset, Glandford, Wiveton, Blakeney and their own village looked after the souls of the valley community. Lawrence stumbled and shook himself out of his romantic dream. He remembered how he had felt almost hypnotised that day he had watched the wind planting giants' footsteps on the marshes. He realised again that this coast had a quality that disturbed the mind.

The source of the River Glaven? The Guardian pointed back over his shoulder.

"That's a spring in a field a mile or two above Letheringset Watermill," he said. "After turning the mill's wheel and its heavy stones and so on, it flows under the road into the valley."

At first, he told them, it flowed fast – a young river in a hurry. It left its origins without a backward look. It flowed noisily, full of energy. It took the easiest path, a shallow but swift course between narrow banks. It was eager to seek new channels and get there fast. So it cut brashly through sloping pastures hemmed in by steep woodland. Soon, far from home now and meeting obstacles in its path, the Guardian told them how it changed direction a few times, swerving to avoid a round-towered flint church, crossed and re-crossed the valley at a couple of shallow fords and rippled past a hamlet of flint cottages. The hills levelled out further down, he explained, the valley widened and another stream joined it. Now wider than before, their mingled waters flowed past well-established buildings unknown in its more unstable youth. At one point it widened to a narrow lake and ran below the long windows of a grand country house. "Some landed gent," smiled the Guardian – and looked at his notebook again. "Or was it the beerage?"

Later it made a slower pace through woodland towards flat water meadows. "We'll be coming to them soon," the Guardian told them over his shoulder as he led the way. Soon it passed signs of relaxation – a punt tied to a landing stage and a diving board over a deep pool. Later thick weed slowed its pace and froth lined the widening banks.

A church loomed up before the group of walkers and it was here that they turned to cross a hump-backed bridge. As it meandered through the water meadows the river was now in the final stages of its life-cycle from youth to old age and drifted away from them through a ruffled sleeve of reeds towards the quay and the village's outposts of pub, windmill and their home before its final journey through the marshes to oblivion in the sea.

Their backs to the river, the walkers followed a lane across the valley.

"These water meadows," announced the Guardian and waved his torch around. "See them? All flat? Well, centuries ago they were all underwater – it was all a wide estuary here, where we're standing now and right over to the Three Swallows below our church – the other pub, you've been there yet – yes? Well, you'll see it in a minute and you'll know where we are then. They brought quite big ships up the river in those days." He fished out his notebook and shone his torch on a page – "yes even 100 tons, apparently. That was where our port was then, by the pub – well, just a quay really, and there was another one behind us," he waved his torch over his shoulder, "just below that other church near the bridge we just crossed. So there was a quay on each side, one for each village ... " his torch flashed left and right. "But a few hundred years ago some capitalist decided he'd like some more land – without paying for it, of course," his eyes twinkled at them. "Paying was only for the proletariat – not for the nobs. So he banked it across downstream – this side of the windmill, it's where the coast road is now – and he just left a gap for the river flow. And that made the estuary silt up – no tides to scour its bed, you see, to keep it deep. So it all became his land and the pub lost the port. That's why the quay's now where you live."

Lawrence took some time to digest all this. But the shining of the moon on their church's west window soon distracted him. Below the church sat the Three Swallows pub and the group of village houses they had seen before. Now on hard tarmac they walked more quickly and it was not long before they crossed the coast road and reached the Pottery. For a while they stood there, talking together while the night mist swirled about them. At length Eve and Lawrence exchanged farewells with their new friends and walked the last few yards home. The sound of their boots rang against the walls on either side.

"You know," said Eve thoughtfully. "I've just realised we've been talking about the people rather than the food. It's a good sign. So things might be opening up a little."

"You mean you like it here?" Lawrence smiled at her.

"Well, who wouldn't? But it's not us or our friends who decide our lives. It's that dreadful bank."

But she linked her arm round his and their boots crunched together on the gravel of their drive as they walked the final steps to their own front door.

On their telephone answering machine they found a message from their sons.

"Hi, Mum and Dad, we're in Rome, please send us £300 at the Banco Ambrosiana as soon as you can, we're starving. We crashed a scooter we bought but we're OK and anyway it's warm here. Great ruins, too, they're really old! Bye ... Oh – hope you're both OK too?"

*       *       *

Next day they drove to Norwich to buy some stair carpet. What they had found in Gibraltar House was as thin as wallpaper and just as frail. So to find out how much carpet they needed they had to count the number of steps in the staircase. And that led to a happy co-incidence.

For if Lawrence and Eve had ever doubted that this was the house of their dreams, the business of the stair rods would have proved it – good and proper. Many years ago, before they had moved to Notting Hill, their first home had been a workman's cottage in Fulham. It was Edwardian, built in 1905 or so. They had paid £3,000 for it – not bad, even 60 years later. And in a Fulham Road junk shop Eve had found seventeen stair rods – complete with their screws and brackets. The rods must have been made around the time it had been built. She didn't really know why she had bought them because they didn't have any carpets on the stairs then either. And after Lawrence had paid the deposit for the house they couldn't afford to buy any. And that was even before the boys had arrived. But the rods were very pretty. Their ends were shaped in beautiful arabesques. And the brackets were delicately worked with little twists of fleur-de-lys. Everything was made of gleaming brass and chunky in the way things were made when "Made in Britain" meant something. They weighed a ton and cost £3 the lot. But Lawrence never fitted the rods into that house. In the first place there were seventeen rods and only eleven stairs. And in the second place, even after a couple of years of trying to save up, the only sort of carpet they could afford wasn't anything like good enough for the rods.

Then they had moved to Notting Hill. But that house had about sixty stairs and it would have been wrong to have the rods fitted to only seventeen of them. So they remained tied together by their loops of ancient string and with their brackets and screws in their ancient bag. They lay for years in a dark cupboard full of 'Things That Will Come In Useful One Day'.

And then they had found Gibraltar House. So now the stair carpet had to be replaced. Compared to their mortgage the new carpet cost nothing so the price didn't hurt. And before they bought it Lawrence counted the number of stairs – and there were seventeen! So, no doubt about it! They now had mathematical proof that this was the house for them.

Next morning Eve was describing this in some detail to Jill at the grocery shop beyond the George and Dragon when she met Tom's mother. Iris was small and round, gentle and white-haired. And she had a warm slow smile. Lawrence and Eve soon came to know her well and were proud of it. She and her husband Harry both spoke "Norfolk," that almost impenetrable accent that they were still struggling to understand. Harry was the younger, a good-looking fisherman in his late fifties with tousled hair, a grin and a cigarette stuck in one corner of his mouth, even when he was eating. They never saw him wearing anything other than a peaked cap and a sou'wester with mole-skin trousers tucked into a pair of sea boots. Every few days – whenever there was an 'R' in the month – he appeared in the shop with a sack of mussels. He dumped it in a big bowl in front of his son (he of the SAS), sniffed heavily, leaned on the fish counter and lit a cigarette. The sack always dripped with seawater and always smelled of seaweed and mud. And always Tom complained about it. And always Harry flicked his cigarette ash all over the floor, coughed as if he was about to bring up half his lungs and said something in "Norfolk" which as usual Lawrence and Eve couldn't catch. He had the independent Norfolk temperament that said: "take it or leave it." And they took it – every time.

Soon Lawrence and Eve began to hand out gossip as well as merely receive it. Standing at the till waiting to have three dozen fresh mussels weighed out, Eve might be joined by someone wanting to buy a couple of mackerel. Jill would introduce them and gossip would sprout over the sea food. Eve said she had seen a removal van on the green by the Three Swallows. Yes, that's right, it was a big van from London. And they were unloading a grand piano. So in return she was given some tit-bits about laconic Ronald at the pub.

"And what about that chap who looks like a Greek God, the one at the Deli?" asked Eve. "Isn't he rather friendly with one of his assistants?"

That produced a resounding laugh from Jill – who then told them a few tales. And some of them might even have been true.

Others they met in the pubs and in the shops slowly filled in a few of the gaps. They met an elderly man in the Three Swallows by the church. He told them that his family had owned Gibraltar House for generations – name of Stangroom, or something like that. Lawrence hadn't been sure but it sounded copper-bottomed Dickensian. But yes, he confirmed, that secret passage from their wine cellar had gone under the road. It led beyond the mill to a creek on the marshes where they used to hide the brandy in one of their boats.

"They found it when they were putting up a telegraph pole to the coastguard station," he said. "It must have been a hundred year back now. But it was then they blocked it in. In the old days the family had got a lot of business out of that passage. I still remember old great-uncle Norman, he was fair peeved about what post office did."

And then the next day, buying stuffed vine leaves in the Deli, the Greek God Zeus (as Eve now imagined him, remembering what the Guardian had said) introduced them to the tall and dignified man they had learned about at Pippa's supper party. His short grey hair was tight and curly and his eyes were thoughtful. And, yes, he did wear his coat draped around his shoulders, leaving his arms free. And he seemed to appear remote and still as if he never moved.

"This is Prospero," Zeus told them. "He lives up on the hill here."

Prospero bowed his head slightly and gave them a dignified smile.

"Greetings! This Deli ... it's our meeting place."

He spread his arm around the shop. It hovered over the cheeses, the olives, the sides of ham hanging from the beams, the stuffed vine leaves, the marinated lemons and the shelves of fine wines. He turned to them with a smile.

"Here's everything advantageous to life."

Zeus undid a shirt button, scratched his chest and winked at them as Prospero continued.

"In North Norfolk you will live merrily," he promised them and smiled. "For there are so many good creatures here!" He smiled at Zeus and laid his arm lightly on his friend's shoulder.

"Thank you," answered Eve, a little puzzled. She watched him as he left with a golden retriever on a lead. The dog was leaping around excitedly. Behind him walked a friend, or maybe some sort of assistant. He was dark and short with round shoulders, almost hunchbacked. He carried the groceries that Prospero had just bought – Parmesan cheese, Parma ham, a bottle of Chianti and some spaghetti. All Italian, noticed Eve.

She turned to Zeus.

"Who is he? And how has he come to live here? And what did he mean 'merrily'? It reminds me of something but I can't quite remember."

"Well, he'd been living in the Mediterranean for years," he told her. "On an island I think but I don't know where. In fact, well, I've known him for some time but I don't know a lot about him. But it's been some years now that he came back to England. He told me he came up here because it was somewhere free from interference, he said, or something like that, outside influence, maybe, the nearest place to an island that he could find but in England, I don't know, can't work it out. But he'd had a commune and he started the Pottery here and brought in the others who live there, have you met them yet? And then he moved out, he said something about having a new stage in his plans whatever that meant and he now lives on the hill behind the village. As for 'merrily' ... well, I suppose we all love it here."

He grinned at her. "And you will too. Are you in a hurry? I've got a new house white here. It's from Gascony. Care to try it?"

Lawrence sidled up.

"Well, if you insist."

"But what does he do here?" asked Eve, frowning at her husband as he picked up a glass.

"He told us he writes things on mystic England, ley lines, druids, Celtic legends, stone circles, stuff like that." Zeus grinned. "All a bit weird, I suppose. His books are published abroad, in Milan I think he said." Zeus winked at them. "He was a friend of the Rhine Maiden in the Pottery for a long time, too."

One of his assistants, a straw-haired girl with high cheek bones and clear blue eyes, was wrapping a bottle of North Norfolk wine for Eve and smiled at her.

"Somehow I feel we'll never find the truth about Prospero," she said and picked some fluff off Zeus's jacket. She was a classically featured girl and her hair crowned a wide brow above her warm smile.

Lawrence caught Eve studying them together.

"There's something between them, you know," she told him after they left and were walking home down the middle of the street.

"Well, how d'you know?" asked Lawrence.

She looked pityingly at him.

"I just know."

*     *     *

Ice was still around next morning despite the arrival of March. Lawrence's boots rang hard on it as he walked down the village street, crossed the main road and passed the Deli on the way to the post office. Suddenly Zeus rushed out, curly black hair waving around, and dragged him in to meet a glamorous and buxom blonde. She was standing at the counter with a saucer of cheese pieces and sipping at a glass of white wine.

"This is Marilyn. She lives in Blakeney," he said. "She's a masseuse. And a wonderful dancer, too!"

He turned to her. "They've just moved up."

She gave them a radiant smile and picked up two empty glasses.

"You deserve a drink, then – both of you," she declared. "Z, where's the bottle?"

He produced it and topped up everyone's glass. Marilyn gave him a warm kiss – a very warm one for just one glass, thought Lawrence, more than a mouthful and it lasted longer than it took her to swallow the drink afterwards. She giggled, broke off and told him that Zeus was a drummer and that she sometimes danced with a group he played with. All spice for conjecture – or was it just the local custom? In any case some more background was emerging.

Back home that afternoon Eve told him that he had to do something about their kitchen mixer taps. They had been leaking for some time and now it had all become too much for her. The taps had been Edwardian – and quarried out of solid brass like the stair rods. On top of each of them the manufacturer had engraved his name. "Barber Wilsons, Est 1905", it said in old-fashioned black type. The whole contraption ended in a long spout. It curved elegantly up and then down to the sink – like a swan drinking. That was what Lawrence liked about it. He had bought it in a Portobello Road junk shop a few years before. It had only cost forty pounds.

"Another bargain that we don't need," Eve had told him scornfully. "You know we can't use it in London."

But somehow he had known it would be just right somewhere one day. And – like the stair rods – it was. Nevertheless, while he was at the Deli that afternoon the leak at the swivel had become less than cute and more than irritating. Apparently Eve had now insisted that the water should stay in the sink and go down the plug hole, like in anybody else's sink. At first it had been only a little leak and he had told her: "Well, that's part of the charm of country living." They weren't in smart and trendy Notting Hill any more. They were in North Norfolk, where you took the wet with the wet. Then the leak had become a spray. But he had still been charmed by it. After all, the spray had formed a delightful curve. It had reminded him of the cannon fire in Leonardo da Vinci's fortification diagrams. He had recalled his algebra equations from school. What was the first one? Ah, yes: $S = UT + \frac{1}{2} A T^2$, he had said to himself and had begun to work out the velocity of the water as it spurted out. 'S' was the distance the spray went – that was the distance from the tap to where it had soaked the Delia Smith cookbook behind it. He had timed how long it took to land there. That was 'T'. As for 'A', that was the acceleration due to gravity, 32 ft per second per second, of course; everybody knew that. 'U', that was the speed of the water when it left the tap. Eventually he had worked it out at 4ft/second. Not bad for an Edwardian tap – second-hand, too.

But he had an unexpected blessing. And, despite his helicopters and so on, Leonardo hadn't worked it out before he died. The kitchen faced towards the sun and Lawrence was fascinated by the rainbow he could see in the spray as it curved towards the window. First red, then through the colours of the rainbow to violet. Newton was the one who discovered that, he remembered.

In the end the spray had reached Elizabeth David who, Eve had decided, was more serious than Delia. So when he arrived home she made him call a plumber. They hadn't met the plumber before but he was a friend of Pippa's. In fact a few days ago she had mentioned him to them over a pint in the Red Lion in Stiffkey, a village a few miles further west.

In London plumbers never arrive when they promise, charge you at least fifty pounds for crossing the threshold and demand more exorbitant fees – or else! Then they vanish half way through the job. And they usually leave bits of sawn-off piping lying about all over the place. When at last you reach them on the telephone, usually a couple of weeks later, they demand another exorbitant amount of money to come back and finish the job. Were Norfolk plumbers to be the same?

Not this one. Anton rang the door bell at the appointed time. That was a good sign for a start. He wore a white shirt, a sober tie, a neat pullover and a dark suit. His hair was cut and he wore steel-rimmed glasses. More like a bank clerk than a plumber, actually. Lawrence made him a cup of tea. He had feared that the swivel would cause problems for the plumber. He couldn't work out how to get it off and replace the washer. He had already made a few pokes at it with a knitting needle, but that didn't work. Maybe a blowlamp would do it? But Anton merely turned it smartly to the left, lifted it up – and it came away.

"Trade secret!"

He looked at Lawrence and grinned.

It took him less than a minute to fish a washer out of his pocket and replace the old one. Then Lawrence remembered who he was. He had met his wife once in Stiffkey when he had bought a lamp from a shop there and picked it up from their house after the shop had closed. He remembered seeing shelves full of books on Norfolk history. Some of them were really old.

"Yes," said Anton, "yes ... I'd picked up a few books along the way about Norfolk. There's a lot of history around here. You know the Iron

Age fort at Warham, inland, a few miles from here? Trouble is," he went on without waiting for a reply, "I've got to move the books. We've put the piano there now and I've got to build new bookshelves above it."

A historian plumber with a piano? Just the sort of thing Lawrence was beginning to expect in North Norfolk. To cool Anton's cup of tea he had put more milk than usual in it. He might have wanted to leave as soon as the job was done. It would have embarrassed him if his tea had been too hot to drink. He'd have had to wait until it cooled off. It was a natural enough problem. The kettle had taken longer to boil than he had taken to do the job.

"You see ..." Anton went on. He held the cup in both hands but made no attempt to drink from it. "It's quite long, that piano." Lawrence thought for a moment, then -

"What about ...?" he hesitated.

"Joining them to the verticals at each end? Yes, that's the thing," Anton nodded, then looked at the cup. "But then there's the problem of holding the shelves up in the middle ... it's a good six or seven feet wide."

He shook his head. Newton, let alone Leonardo, would have had trouble with that, Lawrence could feel him thinking.

There was a pause.

"Well," Lawrence hesitated again. "What about some ...?"

"Yes, horizontal strips supporting the shelves?" he agreed.

Then he pursed his lips. "Problem is, wall's not vertical," he explained. The matter was more complicated than it seemed. At last he took a sip of tea.

"Top of the wall ... it's an inch and a half further out than the bottom...." He shook his head. "You've got to allow for that."

"Then what about upright ...?" Lawrence began again.

"Vertical strips of battens? And pinned to the wall first?" he smiled again. "Ah, yes. I reckon that's the answer. Wall's pretty soft, though, you know. These old cottages aren't much better than wattle and daub. Plaster's very dry." He frowned, looked at the cup again and put it down.

"Trouble is, then you've got to think about the type of rawl plugs to use." He shook his head, picked his cup up again, looked at it and put it down.

"There's a new range just out. Could be the answer for my walls. But you never can tell." He looked at the cup again, picked it up, took a sip of tea and put it down again.

There were clearly plenty of problems. Lawrence had considered showing him the bookshelves he had just built in the dining room and their bedroom. But did they have food enough to feed him at lunch and for dinner? And where was he going to sleep?

And then Lawrence understood.

"How much do I owe you?" he asked.

Anton seemed surprised. He looked at the cup and hesitated.

"Oh, make it a fiver?"

Lawrence remembered Toad of Toad Hall, when at last they caught Toad and gave him his sentence in court.

"Six months for the theft of the washing," scowled the judge. "And twenty years for the cheek to the policeman."

Fifty pence for changing the washer. And four pounds fifty for the talk about shelves and rawl plugs. Nothing like a London plumber.

"Sometimes, it's more difficult to get them to send a bill than to come," claimed Ronald laconically at the George and Dragon next day, as he drew Lawrence and himself a pint of warm beer.

"I can't understand it. Maybe it's the cold weather." He looked at Lawrence with his crab-like eyes, raised an eyebrow, turned to the bottle of scotch on the wall and tipped a double into his glass.

By now they had realised that life in North Norfolk was clearly not on the fast track. And the way no one seemed to want to send in their invoices, they felt, was another example of the extremes they had discovered. But they didn't realise that another extreme was waiting for them. And when it came it would to add danger to the edge.

"Marilyn was a looker," commented Lawrence to Zeus about the glamorous masseuse. They had called round for two bottles of white wine, more olive oil and half a pound of Roquefort cheese.

"Too right. I've known her a long time."

"We thought so," smiled Eve. Zeus grinned and undid a shirt button.

"But she's brainy, too. She used to be part of a local philosophy group. But then she suddenly left, don't know why."

"Was Prospero involved?" Zeus wasn't sure.

"Maybe. But ask him," he said. "You've met him now."

A week or two later they discovered why she had left. But that morning, after a walk to the church and a slow wander in the vague direction of home they called into the George and Dragon and found Prospero sitting with the poet Pippa, their hostess at supper the week before.

Lawrence remembered that at her dinner party no one would tell them who that statuesque beauty was, the one with the long flowing hair and the profile of a tea-clipper's figurehead, the one he had seen walking alone down the village street. Justine, wasn't that her name? What of her? When Lawrence asked Pippa, she snapped a sharp reply and turned away to stare out of the window. Eve smiled at that and Prospero told them, yes, her name was Justine, she was a potter but a free spirit, too. She used to live with the other potters but had since left, he said. Why? He looked at Pippa's back and spread his hands. Didn't he know? Or did he?

Pippa swung round.

"I've just written a new poem and I'm going to read it," she announced. She peered into her bag, pulled out a crumpled sheet of paper, cleared her throat and glared at them.

"It's about a friend of mine."

*"In the nightwood I hear him still*
*Down the lane beyond the wall*
*Listening to his sudden call*
*My eyes peruse the ancient stars*
*Too early yet for meteor showers*
*There is no wind this summer night*
*Owl skimming between dark and light*
*Beyond the river across Home Hill*
*He utters a form of farewell*
*Then echoes curve it far away*
*Leaving me with nothing more to say*
*Leaning on the lambent window sill."*

"He died a few years ago, a very dear friend." She took out a handkerchief and dabbed her eyes with it.

"Now you can go on talking about Justine," she snapped at the three of them, "which you seem to want to do so much."

And she gathered up her shopping and swept out.

Eve smiled at Prospero. He told her that Justine had done nothing against her.

"Oh, I know," said Eve. "It's just woman talk. But, but – what more about Justine?"

"She lived with a man in the Pottery," Prospero told them.

"The Marxist?" asked Lawrence. "The Village Marxist?"

Prospero smiled. "Ah, apt! But soon she'll leave the Pottery – and will leave him too."

He made it sound as if she was acting under his instructions. He went on. "Some days past she sailed with the Dutch skipper of the Albatross."

The Albatross? Lawrence and Eve looked at each other, puzzled, and Eve made a face. He couldn't mean their mortgage? He didn't know about it. So what did he mean?

Prospero explained that this was the name of an old two-masted schooner, clinker built, about a hundred foot long.

"The ship's a beauty. She runs well upon these sharp winds that blow from the north round here." He took a sip of Chianti. "She sails to Europe and loads cargo there."

Apparently she had been built around 1900 and was the only trading sailing ship left in Britain. He told them that she had a long bowsprit with three jibs and both masts had a full fore-and-aft rig.

At Prospero's mention of the bowsprit Lawrence suddenly turned to Eve and gripped her arm excitedly.

"But we've seen it," he told her. "Remember? On our first visit? That first time we were on the beach? When there was that high wind and those three fishermen?"

"Oh, yes!" She remembered too and turned to Prospero, smiling. "It was one of the things that had decided us to come and live in North Norfolk. But you know, that name, it's also what we call our – " Lawrence had made a face at her and she stopped. He was right. They didn't want everyone to know how near they were all the time to going bust and having to leave their home. But the name was significant all the same, not just a co-incidence. But it had to be a co-incidence. Anyway it was a good omen. A beautiful old ship like that fitted into the time warp of North Norfolk. It seemed to wear the coastline like a glove. Anyway, wasn't living with that terrible weight of their mortgage the price they had to pay to live up here? And somehow she felt comforted that their Albatross was also the name of that ship.

And then, what of the great-coated pig rearer, the one Zeus had told them about with his sides of pork? Hector, wasn't that his name?

"Ah," admitted Prospero. "Yes! He's the master of a full rich hall."

"Yeah, but I've only been there once," said Ronald from behind the bar. "And he never comes in here. I hardly ever see the fellow."

It was all too much for Lawrence and Eve. They looked across at him.

"You're doing well, but you haven't even met half of them yet," he said laconically, and pulled them another pint of warm beer and a gin

65

and tonic. This time he made them pay.

They sipped slowly. Each hoped without saying so to the other that the Arab diplomat really would take their house in London. They couldn't bear to leave now.

*     *     *

The next day they went round to the pub again. They still had a lot to do in the house, what with deciding where to put their clothes (would they have to buy expensive wardrobes?), replacing a broken tile on the roof that was causing leaks (could they reach it themselves without having a builder in?), dealing with rising damp in the dining room (was there more?), curing dry rot in several joists (would they have to take the floors up?) and doing something to an unstable chimney (how can they stop it falling through the roof?). But much more important than all that, as Eve made quite clear, was whether Justine (whom she hadn't even met yet) was still with the Village Marxist (whom she hadn't spoken to yet). And if not, why not and what had Prospero to do with it anyway and was she really with that Dutch sailor she was meant to be with now (whom she hadn't even known existed before today), the skipper of that ship the Albatross (which she hadn't even seen yet either)?

But Pippa was there in the pub talking to a man with a pigtail. This, she explained as she introduced them, was Brian, the artist whose work they had seen in the village's gallery. Pippa had told them that he sometimes painted himself into his own paintings. But Eve wanted wardrobes, not a picture – at least not yet. Not until she had somewhere she could hang up her clothes in. And she had had an idea. In the sitting room there had been alcoves each side of the fireplaces. And the alcoves had old pine doors. So Eve asked Brian to make a wardrobe using those doors.

Lawrence wasn't sure about Brian's pigtail. But he was prepared to overlook that in North Norfolk. While he worked on the wardrobes he told them his life history. Art training at the Royal Academy Schools in London, then catering for a living and painting for dear life. Then twenty years ago he discovered North Norfolk and moved up; for ever, too – no doubt about that. He belonged to the group of artists on the coast all living lives of luxury on a pittance. When Lawrence and Eve had arrived they had known they would find plenty of stereotyped water-colourists – 'Burnham Overy Staithe at sunset', 'Reeds on Stiffkey marshes', the interminable studies of the village's mill and all the rich variety of birds inhabiting the marshes. But Brian ... Brian had developed a style in which he mixed together Stanley Spencer (without religion or curious sex), Lowry (without tall chimneys or swarms of gloomy stick people), Blake (but drawing better) and Beryl Cook. And that's more like it, because they soon discovered that his pictures made you laugh! He painted seals that looked like Harold Macmillan, trees that were an outrage to the Green Movement and clouds like tears. He did things with perspective that would put a car dealer in jail in ten minutes. He could paint three hundred bricks in a picture and make them all different. Lawrence didn't really know why that was interesting but it was. The bricks were compulsive – he couldn't stop looking at them. And they found he could put a whole philosophy of life into a face one centimetre wide. A man sun-bathing outside his beach hut at Wells, or a couple gazing down the throat of a seal at Blakeney Point. And his Norfolk sharpies, those racy cutters with white sails – they look like sharks and obviously can't sail but it was all funny. And there was always a little old lady being tugged along by a frantic dog. They were both always off the ground and being chased by their own shadows. Finally, that fellow with a pigtail often turned up, too. Every time he appeared he was leaning at an impossible angle as if he had glued his shoes to the ground. But he never seemed to fall over.

Once Brian had arrived, he rarely strayed far from North Norfolk. In fact, he told Lawrence, he hadn't even been to Norwich for two years. But his perception of his surroundings, of the coast and of the people, was 'deeper than a well and wider than a barn door.' And it served to nourish his imagination. And from this microscopic attention came the world in a grain of sand. Like Gilbert White or Voltaire, in fact like everyone on the North Norfolk coast, he cultivated his garden.

At midday they all went out to the George and Dragon for a few pints. It seemed he knew everybody. They certainly knew him. At the bar he handed Ronald a print of one of his small paintings – a study of the church.

"That's very nice. I'll put it in one of the rooms," said Ronald and drew him a pint. "We'll call that one five pints, OK? I'll put it on your slate."

"That was the rate last year, Ronald," said Brian. "It's gone up now. I think ten would be more like it. You'd pay twice that in London."

After a brief discussion, during which Ronald explained the price of beer in London while the first two pints vanished (one was Lawrence's – warm beer again, he noticed with pleasure), they agreed on seven pints. On the slate Ronald chalked up five to go. Nearby, the Guardian sat absorbed in a newspaper, a glassful of creamy Guinness before him. As always, he behaved as if he were in his private club. He saluted elaborately when he saw them and gave a general invitation to his fiftieth birthday party.

"Next Thursday, Eve. Ok?" He looked over his glasses at her and groaned. "Don't bother with a present and, Brian, not even one of your prints – or should I say especially?" he grinned. "Perhaps I shouldn't. Very rude. But this is definitely not a date for excessive celebration."

The George and Dragon threw them out in the late afternoon. As he stalked down to lock the door and make sure they left, Ronald said, "the police have a habit of coming in and asking if we're closing late or opening early. And I can never make up my mind which it is."

"I sometimes think you'd rather not open at all, Ronald," smiled Brian. "Just sit there and drink all by yourself."

Ronald raised his eyebrows, half-closed his eyes and leaned forward, swaying slightly.

"How did you guess?" he managed to say – then locked them out.

They stood in the empty road wondering what to do next, as one does when leaving a pub in mid-afternoon. After a few moments –

"There's someone else you must meet," said Brian. And he led Eve and Lawrence down the middle of the road to the Smoke House. By now they had visited that dilapidated lean-to and salivated at the glistening fat bloaters, hooks spiked through their heads and now swinging like rusted shackles in a high wind, the pots of grainy mackerel paté that would be the price of caviar if it was as scarce, the nuggets of pale gold shaped into potted shrimps in a cauldron of rich butter and the rows of kippers spread wide like flatfish but ribbed and smoked now to burnt umber like the bricks of their house and lined up like a Gilbert and Sullivan chorus. Lawrence hadn't seen bloaters for years. As for the potted shrimps, the last time he'd eaten them was long, long ago when he had been an untidy little boy during those innocent summer holidays by the sea. At twilight, laden with buckets and spades and shrimping nets, he had trotted home from the beach. Tired and happy, he remembered, he had been ready only for potted shrimps on toast before a quick bath, a kiss from his mother – and bed.

Eve and Lawrence had already formed an early morning habit of nipping round for a couple of kippers or, even better, bloaters for breakfast. They usually ate them with a few thick slices of well-buttered brown bread made from flour from that water mill at the valley's head.

And a few cups of hot tea made it a massive breakfast – memorable too, even clinging. It stayed with them all day.

The Smoke House's chimney was hard at work. They all squeezed past it as Brian took them to meet that Moses figure they had seen before. He was sitting with some papier-mâché models. Above his beard he gazed shyly at them with deep-set eyes. There was something very Greek about him – not ancient Greek but Greek orthodox. Lawrence half expected him to lift up two kippers and make the sign of the Cross at them. His models were all of people about 2-3ft high and doing some very odd things. Brian leaned over and picked up one of a man standing with his hands widespread, holding the ends of his overcoat out like the wings of a bat.

"He calls this one The Flasher," said Brian with a grin. He turned it round. Beneath his overcoat the man wore a Victorian-type bathing costume with red stripes and a happy but imbecilic expression. Inside the overcoat was written: "Kippers for energy."

"He usually has it in the window – facing inwards. People want to come into the shop to see whether the man really is, you know, flashing and then of course they buy something. It spruced up business no end. The trouble is he's having a battle with the council about it at the moment. Some nonsense from Brussels," he shook his head and groaned.

"Then there's another one somewhere," he went on. He turned to Moses, who stood up as if on a signal and fished around beneath the table, like a man in a porn bookshop producing something special from behind the counter. He drew out a large tableau of four figures. Crouching on the pâpier-maché floor was a man, more or less naked and looking up in fascinated horror at three huge Amazonian females bending over him. All were naked from the waist up. Their pointed breasts had bright scarlet nipples. They looked scornfully down on him. Each of them was brandishing a long whip and each was about to crack it down onto his quivering skin. At least, that was the impression. Lawrence gulped.

"Interesting," sounded somehow too inadequate a word but it was all he could raise.

"It's the cold weather up here, you know. Moses is very kind but rather reserved," commented Brian. As they left Brian handed him another small picture, and received a large parcel of something wrapped in newsprint in return.

"The place looks poverty-struck, doesn't it?" smiled Brian. "But he's doing very well – that dilapidated lean-to look ... it's presentation. It's what makes it look authentic."

But it was at least half an hour before Lawrence realised that Moses hadn't said a word.

*     *     *

At the Guardian's birthday party the following Thursday they were thrown in at the deep end of the demi-monde of North Norfolk's artistic life. At the door they had passed Prospero's assistant squatting outside with his golden retriever. Prospero himself was sitting inside – talking to a young girl with huge eyes and a mass of curls. They heard a little of what he was saying – "... he thinks you are so beautiful, you know. Well, of course he's right." She was smiling and listening intently.

They knew few other people but easily recognised Brian. Lawrence noted with relief that he had cut off his ponytail for the occasion. Now the curly hair round his forehead turned him into a Roman emperor. He was explaining something to the Rhine Maiden but broke off to introduce them to a striking-looking man with dark features, smiling but frowning too.

"Lawrence, this is Jekyll 'n' Hyde."

"He's got a nice little line running the Bookshop and the Art Gallery," explained the Rhine Maiden to Eve.

"Ha!" snapped Jekyll 'n' Hyde. "God knows why. No one in Norfolk seems to want to read. Probably can't anyway," he added.

"Well, it's one up for the village to have you here," she told him.

"Oh yes," he grinned and his eyes suddenly crinkled and he gave them a charming smile. "I suppose I'm a public benefactor."

The Rhine Maiden winked at Lawrence.

"He holds art shows there, too, Lawrence. You two should have a dekko at it, now you've fetched up here."

In a corner the Village Marxist was in earnest discussion with a tall woman with classic features and long flowing auburn hair, the one they had seen leaving the Pottery on their first day down the village street.

"D'you think that's Justine?" asked Eve as they passed them.

"I've no idea," Lawrence shrugged, but couldn't resist looking. "But no doubt we'll find out sometime."

They saw her shaking her head at something the Village Marxist was saying. It was a movement that made her hair ripple down her back. She stood up, but sat down again with a patient smile as he pulled at her sleeve.

Zeus came up to them with a twinkle and a grin, his white shirt unbuttoned and his sleeves rolled back. He had a bottle in one hand and some glasses in the other. And with his black beard and the curly hair on his chest he looked even more like the blacksmith who had once owned his Deli. He gave Eve a kiss and poured them both a drink. With him was the assistant who had been rather friendly with him.

"This is Leda, remember her at the forge – that's what we call the Deli?" he grinned.

Eve looked at him, then at her – and hesitated, mouth open.

"Is that really your name?" she asked.

"Yes, of course!" she said, as if to say 'what else?'

And she smiled at them. She had a steady clear blue gaze. Her eyes were as deep as the sky.

"But...but ..." Eve got no further.

"You didn't catch our drift before, did you, Eve?" smiled the Rhine Maiden as she passed by with a plate of curry for the Guardian.

"Go on, you two, try the red I poured you," suggested Zeus. "It's a new Cab Sav in today from New Zealand. They're making more and more red there now, and I'd like to know what you think of it." He poured himself a glass, scratched his chest and winked at them.

But in spite of Zeus's warm greeting Lawrence and Eve didn't know many other people. But they did recognise the blonde beauty Marilyn. She was the woman Lawrence had met at the Deli. Now she looked elegant and her eyes were shining.

"She seems happy," remarked Eve. "There must be a man in the background."

"Oh! I should think so, indeed," said Lawrence.

And when they both approached the Rhine Maiden, they heard her saying to someone they didn't know – "Brian and Marilyn are an item now."

Maybe that's why he had cut off his ponytail. They suddenly realised that although he had been building their bedroom cupboards for at least ten days he hadn't mentioned Marilyn to them. But why should he? They realised they had a long way to go.

Pippa was there, wobbling and giggling and chatting gaily to all sorts of people they didn't know. Often the few people they did know talked to people they didn't know about things they didn't know about either. And there were looks and gestures between people they couldn't understand.

And why did the Guardian turn his back on Prospero, asked Lawrence?

Eve sighed at him.

"That one's easy, don't you see? It's because of the Rhine Maiden. She'd been Prospero's lover, remember? Zeus said so – well, sort of. And anyway now she's with the Guardian. He's just putting a fence round her. And she loves it."

Even so, Lawrence and Eve left early. There were so many people they didn't know. They realised that village gossip was still only a smoking gun to them. They saw the results of relationships but not their causes. They had met a few local people, but it was clear that they didn't know much about even them, let alone about any of the others whom they had hardly heard of. They felt as if they were exploring in a labyrinth. They held only one or two threads in their hands. They had no idea which would break or which, if any, would lead them into the heart of village life. Could they ever manage to snare the unicorn and follow the one true thread? The uncertainty was depressing. But some people were clearly a bit of a blind alley.

"I think I know all I want to know about Marxist propaganda," remarked Lawrence.

"Well, anyway, it's a bit as if they don't want to talk to us," said Eve plaintively.

Prospero came up to them as they left. He had sensed their bewilderment.

"These folk of the coast – they're all new to you," he told them kindly. "All their chronicles saw birth years long past. The mystery of their acts won't long survive. You'll come to love them on this sea's marge here." He smiled at them. "We're all in its spell. You will join us too!"

"Thank you," she said warmly. After they had left she glanced at Lawrence, frowned and looked puzzled. "I've heard that before, part of what he said ... sea's marge ... but I can't remember where."

"Well, who knows?" said Lawrence. "But we're still marginalised. We're still really strangers."

And home they went. That night their mortgage, their private albatross, was a little more difficult to bear. And for a while she was restless and snapped at her husband before she managed to fall asleep.

\*     \*     \*

Their cat, the inscrutable jet black Sphinx, liked it better up here than in London. It wasn't the climate (she preferred the central heating), it wasn't the neighbours (she never talked to other cats), it wasn't the sunsets or the open skies (she kept her head down and anyway she was short-sighted), it wasn't the exercise on the marshes (she slept most of the time) and it wasn't the sea (she didn't like that at all). No but it certainly was the food. Blackbirds, robins, sparrows or chaffinches – in fact any sort of bird (she wasn't fussy), field mice, voles and moles ... she really did appreciate the variety. She never could get anything like that in London. And of course it was all local and all fresh. After all, your food could hardly be fresher if you ate it while it was still alive. She was generous, too. One night Lawrence took a salad to bed for a late snack. Before he turned out the light he put the empty plate on the floor. Next morning, a breakfast offering awaited him – room service of a tiny field mouse, just enough for one mouthful, neatly laid upon the plate.

The garden in their house in London hadn't been too big. The houses had only been about six yards wide. And next door had lived a large and aggressive dog. So on the whole their cat preferred indoors, especially if the central heating was on. And she ate her cat food regularly, not bothering with something a little more natural. So she had not shown her real character. In fact she was rather like a sleeper planted in the city for some foreign power. It was only after they had moved up that Lawrence, at least, discovered the true nature of their cat, indeed of any cat. Which, of course, was that she was one hundred per cent psychopath.

"That's very unfair," protested Eve, when Lawrence told her his theory. "Look, she's so loving."

At that moment the Sphinx was lying on her back on the sofa next to Eve, purring gently, eyes shut and legs in the air as Eve tickled her stomach.

"She's so lovely, she loves her mummy." Eve picked her up, held the Sphinx close to her face and shut her own eyes.

Unfortunately Lawrence's theory was very soon vindicated. It happened like this. They had been down to the church to inspect its pew-ends. The Guardian, churchwarden as well as local historian, had told them they were all carved in different shapes. It had been a wintry day, even in the church. Eve, wrapped in a thick coat and scarf, had decided she wanted to do some sketching in North Norfolk and settled down with a pad and a crayon to draw a pew end. The rector was in the church when they arrived. They soon realised it was he they had seen driving that Morris Minor on their first day. He walked up the aisle while she was sketching. He was a plump and deceptively amiable character. He had a serene expression, smiling eyes, a beaming face and a wisp of hair wafting around his head. Text by Betjeman out of P. G. Wodehouse, one might guess – or vice versa. He introduced himself.

"Hello, I'm Philip! I look after the souls in our valley here." He leaned over her shoulder to look at her drawings. "Well, I try to. I say, that's jolly good," he exclaimed enthusiastically – and then hesitated for a moment. "I say ... I wonder if you'd be interested in something. We really want to make use of all the talent we've got here ... but I thought ... these are so nice, would you be interested in doing some flower arranging for us? Just now and then? At the church here?"

Eve was thrilled. She blushed and looked over at Lawrence.

"She'd love it, "he told the rector. She nodded, still blushing.

"That's wonderful!" He beamed at her. "Well, I'll ask Millicent to get in touch – d'you know her? She's our churchwarden, you know – a formidable lady." Did he wink? But he turned to Lawrence.

"Incidentally, have you seen the carving at the top of the pillar – the capital – supporting one of the arches by the organ?" he smiled and gave him a conspiratorial twinkle. "Actually, it's rather rude. He's scratching his bum. Mind you, I don't necessarily suggest your wife draws that one!"

Lawrence wandered off to take a look. Philip began plugging in a new CD and tape recorder he needed for special services. Most of it was church music, the odd chorale from the St Matthew Passion – but every now and then The Rolling Stones or The Who broke in loudly.

"Sorry about that!" called Philip from the lectern. "The devil doesn't always have the best tunes but he tries hard. My son got hold of a tape yesterday and seems to have stuck this one into my machine just to vex his dad!"

By the time Eve had drawn all she wanted it was a good hour and a half before they returned home. As usual they walked back along the lane between the banks of wild thyme, down the alley and through the door in their garden wall. Inside the house their jet black Sphinx was sitting calmly in the middle of the hall. She was facing the door as if expecting them. How nice, they thought. How gentle, their pussy. Purring affectionately, she rubbed against their legs. She even reared up as they bent to stroke her. Her front paws were raised together. Her eyes were half-closed in innocent appreciation. How loving! They were really so touched. Finally she lay on her back and purred quietly, as if inviting further intimacies.

"What a lovely little pussy-wussy you are," said Eve as she knelt down and stroked the Sphinx's stomach. "Kissy-kissy-kissy."

She picked the cat up and, going "kissy-kissy-kissy", held it as she stood up and pushed open the dining room door, which had been left ajar. The room was full of feathers. Some were still floating around in the air. But most of them were in little heaps on the floor. She turned back to Lawrence who was taking his boots off in the hall.

"Did you burst a cushion this morning?" she asked him. Then she trod on something and stumbled. She looked down – and screamed. It was the head of a bird. Its sightless eyes stared at the ceiling. It seemed to be – or to have been – a thrush. And among the pile of feathers was one of its legs. Or rather half of one of its legs. Eve screamed and threw the cat away from her.

"Oh! That beastly cat! Take it out!" she screamed at Lawrence. He picked up the Sphinx, which by then was crouching under the sofa, and shook his head in sorrow.

"Mummy doesn't understand you," he told her. "Humans don't understand that a cat's gotta do what a cat's gotta do."

He put the Sphinx down on the kitchen floor and placed the bird's head in front of her. The Sphinx bent down, sniffed at it and looked up at him, puzzled.

"OK, it's a bird's head. So what?" she seemed to be saying.

"Where is the rest of that bird?" he asked sternly. "You ate it, didn't you – and without killing it first?" The Sphinx ignored him, half closed her eyes and stalked off, totally relaxed and no doubt thinking of lunch – in the way of a psychopath.

"As for that head, never seen it before," said her tail, sky-high. "It's ab-so-lute-ly nothing to do with me. Even if it was, the bird had to die."

And he couldn't prove a thing. The cat sauntered on, but when Eve recovered and rushed at her as she passed the dining room door, crying "shoo…" or words to that effect, she decided she had an urgent appointment elsewhere.

*　　*　　*

The weather slowly improved. The air became lighter and the after-noons longer. Sometimes Eve and Lawrence liked to stay in the pub until closing time, as if spring might appear in the saloon bar when Ronald called "Time." Thursday night was Pottery night, when the members used to assemble there like a family. They would all sit at one table and Eve and Lawrence would sometimes join them. It made the couple feel at home, even when Ronald became more and more monosyllabic towards closing time. Whether this was from drink or need of sleep, no one knew. But he was clearly irritated that anyone wanted to stay until 11pm. When in the end he threw them out Eve and Lawrence found it difficult to see their way the short distance home from the pub. There were no street lights. And they didn't want to fall into the river.

So one morning they decided to go shopping for a torch in the nearby town of Holt. They hadn't used their car for a time and it had a flat battery. So they caught a bus.

Standing on the coast road they watched it sail towards them like a galleon, swaying at the corners as it came. At the Stop the doors opened and wild jazz music greeted them – even though their fellow passengers were all of a certain age.

"D'you think they appreciate this music?" whispered Lawrence.

"What did you expect?" asked Eve. "The Last Post? You reckon they'd prefer that?"

Lawrence hadn't been in a bus for years. The seats were so high, he could see much more than from the driving seat of a car. That alone was liberating – just the type of travel for North Norfolk. The bus climbed up inland from the village, took the straight road down towards the woods, passed a gamekeeper's cottage and climbed again.

At the top of the rise, where for a moment Lawrence could see in several directions, he spotted a small brick building. It had six sides and was hardly the height of a man, only about ten foot wide and half hidden under a crop of briars behind a hedge. Horizontal slits were cut into the walls. He suddenly realised what it was.

"Look!" he told his wife, who was half asleep. "A war-time pill box.

I thought they'd all gone."

"So it is," she said and dozed off again.

Holt was a well-provisioned Georgian town favoured by those of that certain age. There were two or three bookshops, good-quality clothes shops, an up-market grocery and a few genteel teashops. To terminate the services a firm of undertakers waited at discrete premises in a side street. Buying their torch turned out to be tiring, so they had to visit Holt's chief pub, the Feathers. This was an eighteenth century inn with a deep mahogany bar counter, a well-polished brass rail and a warm fire. The afternoon gin-and-tonic set was already on parade, present and correct.

Eve left Lawrence talking to them and sought out a dry cleaner. The manager soon discovered she was a newcomer. So he greeted her with an introductory speech of welcome and praise for the joys of North Norfolk. Then he began a sequel on how much dirtier clothes became in cities than when in North Norfolk. The grime, the soot and the rubbish that came with cities – and then the wear, oh dear!

"Ah, they make good money down there," he smiled at Eve. "But we prefer the life up here."

Two little old ladies and a farmer from near Cromer joined in. Eve told them how much London's car fumes got into her woollen clothes, not to mention her hair, just by walking on the pavement. One of the little old ladies said she thought it such a shame. But the farmer pointed out that in North Norfolk the wind and the rain took its toll on clothes too. In the manner of the Speaker of the House of Commons, the manager directed a balanced discussion on modern materials. He invited views on which material best kept out the cold. The queue behind Eve began to contribute to the debate although someone behind her was getting impatient (it turned out that he had only moved up a couple of weeks before). One well-groomed lady spoke at some length about her husband's trousers. Apparently they were made of wool and had lasted for ten years. At that someone from the charity shop next door mentioned that she had a woollen jumper for sale, if anybody was interested. Then a lady with a large shopping bag smelling of pheasant said that her family always wore waterproof clothing. It was just as well that Lawrence had been sitting comfortably in the Feathers. He might have been waiting for Eve at the bus stop. It might have begun to rain and he might have got wet. As it was, by the time she returned he was on his third pint of warm beer and was taking a lesson from the gin-and-tonic set on how to cook mussels.

Before catching the bus home they had two important purchases to make. Eve wanted to buy vegetable seeds. In Notting Hill all she'd had as a garden wasn't much more than a window box – certainly nowhere to grow vegetables.

"And I'm starting from scratch," she announced, smiling. "These will be all mine."

And so she bought seeds for carrots, cabbage, leeks, parsnips and onions. They then sought out a game butcher. They found one – with a straw hat, twinkling eyes and a Van Dyck beard. His window was full of game – pheasant, partridge, hare and duck, all hanging from rails and with rainbow feathers everywhere. Next door was his fish shop, its slab piled with flatfish, mussels, mackerel, trout and crab and lobster.

"If you'd like some, I've got plenty of woodcock at the moment," he told them. "There's a lot of frost about, even though it's the middle of March ... it drives them to the estuaries round here. It's not so cold there, you see."

Lawrence and Eve bought a brace of woodcock – although she felt sad that anyone would want to kill a bird with such an elegant beak.

"Wait til you taste them," said the butcher. He put his fingers to his lips. "Anyway, they'd be pleased to have provided a bit of pleasure!" He grinned at them.

They took the bus home and stopped off at the pub before closing time. Lawrence wanted to ask Ronald how they should be cooked. By now he was beginning to give up looking at his watch when they arrived. It seemed they were in danger of becoming friends.

"You'd better ask Harry. You know – Tom's dad? He'll be in shortly," he said to them over his shoulder as he topped up his beer with a double scotch. "He'll know."

Harry arrived a few minutes later. He was wearing deep thigh boots and left a spoor of damp footprints from the door. He slung a bag on the bar opposite Ronald that rustled and began to roll to the edge.

"You got four in there. That'll be a couple of pints as usual, eh?"

"They're moving! They're still alive," protested Ronald. "Today's catch? You're only getting one pint for that, Harry. I'd have made it two if you'd boiled and dressed them."

Harry began to grumble, muttered something about "bloody inter-lopers", but finally subsided. He took his pint and sank over it, shoulders hunched. His thick black curls had begun to develop streaks of grey. It made him look quite distinguished, even though his cigarette almost dipped into his beer. Ronald told him Lawrence and Eve

wanted to know how to cook woodcock. But Harry kept his eyes on his pint, uttered some totally incomprehensible phrase and shrugged again.

"Now then, Harry," Ronald told him severely. "Stop talking Norfolk. They're locals, not visitors."

Apparently Harry became incoherent when he didn't want to talk to visitors. That way they couldn't understand him so they left him alone. Lawrence and Eve had discovered this was a typical Norfolk attitude. And one they liked – so long as they were the right side of it.

"Oh, ah," said Harry clearly, gave Lawrence a wary look and then smiled. He winked at Ronald.

"You want to roast him. Pull his feathers off and spread a bit of fat on him. Gibraltar House? Yes, you look under the beam across your fireplace there, you got some nails there where they all used to hang woodcock from to roast 'em, done that for years ever since I was a boy at least. Hang 'em from a bit of string in front of the fire. Tie it round his beak, not his neck, head'll fall off otherwise. Twist the string so that he'll go round and round. Put some bread underneath to catch the juice. Not toast – bread. Only take a few minutes and it'll get like toast by then. But you got to get 'em close up enough to the fire."

And he subsided over his pint again.

Back at home evening came early. Lawrence drew the curtains and lit the fires in both downstairs rooms. As the light faded they warmed the house. He found some lengths of string and tied them round the beaks of the woodcock – not their necks. He crouched down before the dining-room fireplace and felt behind the beam. Yes, there were the nails, just as Harry had said! He wondered when they had first been hammered in. He tied the strings to the nails and placed a dish below them. In it, and below each woodcock, he laid a couple of slices of brown bread. It was the stone-ground bread from Letheringset Mill. He twisted the string – and round went the birds. Harry was right. They didn't take long. After about ten minutes the slices were drenched with the rich juice and had become rich toast. And the woodcocks were ready.

Lawrence and Eve pulled off the heads. They laid the woodcock on the bread and added a dash of cognac. Those woodcock, they were small, only a few mouthfuls. But they were delicious. Even Eve admitted it.

Supper was so good that, maybe with the help of the cognac, they both dozed off in front of the fire. And when they awoke they got the fright of their lives. Or at least Lawrence did. The sterile winter was still holding North Norfolk in its cold fist and sea fogs still rolled across the marshes towards the village. It was long after midnight when they had woken. The television was flashing silently. The central heating was off. And the fire had gone out. Before dragging himself up to bed Lawrence staggered out to the garden for some fresh air. At that time of night he often heard the soft honking of a wavering V-line of geese. They would cross the garden high overhead on the way to the coast. And he was still fascinated by the gable of their house and its silhouette against the pale night sky.

But that night there was a grainy fog. As he stood in the garden he heard a low surge of noise. It was a rumble mixed with a slight rattling and a scraping, almost a clinking. It wasn't loud but it swelled up and then faded away. Again and again it repeated the same pattern of a rumble and than a scrape. He knew at the time that it seemed ridiculous and he was a bit dazed with sleep but he felt a sudden chill of panic. He thought ... "My God – that noise, it sounds like tanks in a war film!" Was that rattle a clank of tank treads? He couldn't be sure. But maybe there'd been a national warning on television while they had been asleep.

The North Sea, it was so open, gaping at night like an immense wound and with nothing between them and the Baltic and ... Russia.

They could be ashore before anyone knew about it. The news often reported them doing unstable acts, shooting off rockets and trying to make out they were still a major power ... quite capable of trying some insane invasion. And Weybourne, that coastal village not far away – Tom had told them that with deep water close inshore it was the easiest place to invade England. A German cable ship had been seen off the coast just before the war, he had said. "But that is in confidence, you understand. I have ... " he had lowered his voice and looked around, " ... I have certain contacts, shall we say." During the war the government had built strong defences at Weybourne beach. Some were still there – gun emplacements and pill boxes, for example. But they were sure to have needed repair. And, well, it was late at night. That was always a time when resistance was weak. Lawrence wondered whether they should hide in the wine cellar until the tanks had passed. He tried to remember how many bottles they still had. They might have to hide out for a time. Had he left a corkscrew down there? And what about sanitation? Did drinking a bottle of wine produce a bottle of pee? That way they could at least keep pace with the empties. But what about when the bottles ran out? And then – but that didn't bear thinking about. And he couldn't concentrate. Anyway perhaps he'd be able to smash down the bricked-up doorway with empty bottles and then they could escape through the underground passage to the marshes. He and Tom could organise a resistance movement behind the lines. In four seconds he had pin-pointed several safe houses (the Deli, the pub right under their noses and what about the Smoke House?), a network of couriers (plenty of little old ladies on bicycles pedalling innocently through the early morning mist) and hiding places for small arms and hand grenades (perhaps the Pottery's kilns and the boot of the rector's Morris Minor?). He knew he had to stand and fight. He wondered if he had time to get the pitchfork from the shed before the tanks smashed through the garden walls. Their treads would ruin Eve's flower beds, too.

He looked around, bent double, rushed indoors and shouted to her to come out. She threw up the bedroom's sash window and listened.

"Idiot!" she sighed. "It's the sea. The waves."

She was right. The tank tracks' scraping was the sound of the waves breaking on the shore a mile away. The fog had carried it so well that it sounded as if the sea was fifty yards from them and near the windmill.

So Dad's Army stood down and went to bed.

Next evening Harry was in the pub again, head sunk between his shoulders and gazing into a pint, his nose scarcely an inch from the beer. Beyond sat Prospero with his coat draped over his shoulders. With him sat a tall woman with a Roman nose, high cheekbones and long auburn hair rippling down her straight back. Eve pulled at Lawrence's sleeve.

"It must be Justine," she whispered.

Prospero's dark, hunch-backed assistant sat by himself at another table with a pint of beer and a bag of shopping. The golden retriever was sitting beneath the table, head up and looking around brightly but always coming back every few seconds to Prospero, who was listening carefully to something the woman was telling him. It seemed to be a report. "And then I did this ... and he said that so I went there ..." But she paused as he put his hand on her arm for a moment to introduce them. Yes, it was Justine – the free spirit, as Prospero had called her. Justine was wearing a wide Paisley shawl around her shoulders. The untidy curls of her long hair gave her the fascinating potential of a slightly untended garden.

"I've heard about you," she smiled. "You've met Zeus at the Deli, haven't you? He told me there were some new people in Gibraltar House. I love that house. It's so magical. I was at the sale. Well, we all were. I remember that it was so run down in those days."

At that moment Zeus and Leda arrived. His waves of jet-black curly hair spread over the fleece he was wearing. It all made him look twice as big as Leda.

"Hullo, you two," he called to Lawrence and Eve, as they found a seat next to Prospero and Justine. He handed over a jar of paté to Ronald in exchange for a pint and a glass of white wine for Leda. He beamed at Justine and in an undertone said to her: "You're looking lovely."

Leda grinned and gave him a playful slap. Had there been anything between him and Justine? Later Justine stood up, put down her empty glass and dipped into her bag. She fished out an earthenware mug – obviously made in the Pottery. She waved it at Ronald to catch his eye. He stalked down the bar and looked at it suspiciously. His crab eyes narrowed but at last he nodded and laconically spread out three fingers of one hand. She gave it to him and left. Over her shoulder she smiled and called to Lawrence and Eve: "I have to go now to pick up my daughter. Perhaps we'll meet again soon. You never know on this coast."

Prospero turned to Harry and asked him about the positions of some of the shifting sands offshore. Apparently one of the boats moored by the windmill was his and he didn't want to get stuck on them.

"I must know their depth. But these sands move fast," he said. And he explained that this made his lead line unreliable. Clearly he reckoned that Harry was a better source of advice than all those middle-class Sunday sailors who kept their yachts at nearby Blakeney – even if Harry did speak Norfolk, blew cigarette smoke over everyone and had never been to a public school – except to deliver fish.

"I wonder what Justine was saying to Prospero," said Eve, almost to herself. "It was as if she was reporting something to him. He was just sitting there listening."

Lawrence and Eve had earlier realised that gossip was not just a stimulant to start a conversation. It was also a form of barter, like the exchange of a mug for a drink they had just witnessed. But if you didn't have any gossip to exchange you could at least be appreciative. And that would encourage more tit-bits. Prospero had stayed behind so they bought him a glass of Chianti and asked him about the Pottery.

"Well, those people here ... they are all my friends," he told them. "In the commune here I made them all one."

"Ah," interrupted Eve. "That explains why they seem like a family. But why did you join them? And why did you leave them?" She stopped, a bit flustered – and blushed.

Prospero appeared not to notice her hesitation.

"A small group's sanctions ... how strong should they be? They must protect the freedom of each man, yet impose on him his social duty. I made the commune's group and joined with them. We shared our lives and everything we did."

"You mean ...?" asked Eve, fascinated. "You mean, besides money ... really, really everything ... I mean, each other?"

"That was my design: it was my foundation." He smiled. "Then came further shape with the Pottery. It gave them art and made them money too. I chose this coast for its magic raw touch. Life on the edge – it concentrates the mind. Have you noticed this?" Lawrence nodded at once. "I am sure you have. We're in an island by ourselves up here. Paradise or jail? Since you hold the key, you alone must choose. You're your destiny."

"Oh," exclaimed Lawrence. "Of course. Yes! That partly explains the bell-jar atmosphere we feel here. But please go on."

"My friends? They were clay in my moulding plan. I made the mould and poured them into it. Indeed I chose this village for its name. It makes my footprint and my symmetry."

"The pots, the bowls, everything, their shapes and their texture, they're like this coast. Was that deliberate?" asked Eve.

He smiled gravely.

"Of course. We all must live close to the earth, for there we find that's where the magic starts." He paused and glanced at her, but it was a statement, not a query.

"Yes, we do too." She smiled. "It's why we came here. But were you friends with any of them? I mean, close friends?"

By now Eve was like a pack of hounds after a fox and closing in. But again Prospero didn't seem to mind.

"Yes. In those young days we were all close friends." But particularly important to him, he told them, was the beautiful long-haired German girl, the Rhine Maiden.

"Well, why aren't you with her – and them – now?" Again Eve sounded rather abrupt but she knew so little.

"When it went well I left for other work, which will develop everything I've done. Sometimes I watch them, but they all do well."

"Yes, but what about the Rhine Maiden?"

"Before I left them I found her a friend."

"Was that the one we call the Guardian?" she asked. He nodded.

" Yes. And you will have seen another man."

"Oh, not the one we call the Village Marxist?" she interrupted him. Prospero smiled and explained that this other man had been skilled at all the practical things that had to be done – such as building the show-room and operating the kilns. So Prospero had made sure that the Village Marxist had an interest in staying there, which would enable him to leave to begin his other work.

"How did you do that?" asked Eve suddenly.

Prospero paused and coughed.

"Do you really wish to learn the secret?"

"Well, of course!" she replied quickly. So he explained that he had made the Village Marxist fall for Justine and vice versa. How? It was simple. Apparently he just told each of them that the other found them totally fascinating and fancied them passionately. His actual words were:

"I said he thought her beautiful and wise, and that he loved her with a great passion. And he that she found him strong and manly, irresistible."

"Oh!" cried Eve. "That's a trick. It's not fair!"

Prospero raised his eyebrows and shrugged his shoulders under his loose jacket.

"Ah! They believed it! What else does one want? And then it came true, the heart's placebo!"

After that it had all happened naturally. The Village Marxist had stayed, of course. Soon, as Prospero had planned, he took charge of all the practical work. And he and Justine had become lovers, of course. But their relationship was disrupting the rest of the group. Justine, a free spirit, was its outsider. Arguments developed and Prospero decided to release her from her fascination for the Village Marxist. Soon he introduced her to a lonely sailor – the Dutch skipper of that schooner, the Albatross. He knew the ship would draw her away. And he was right. The wild and open sea was better than dialectical materialism – especially for a romantic woman. The communal Pottery had caged her in. Now she felt liberated and more content alone.

"So in that way I freed her from my plan. They have still a bond. They share a passion. It's unsatisfied but harder to break than one that through the years has run its course. She is a loner, a classic figure in psychology. Not an easy one."

So from time to time, it seemed, she still felt close to the Village Marxist. In between those times, Prospero made sure that another newcomer to the Pottery, a girl with huge eyes and a mass of curls, would become enamoured of him.

"The Guardian's party? She was there with me."

Soon, the transfer almost complete, he moved out to another house nearby.

"And there I primed the next stage in my work."

"Your work? What's that?" At this stage Eve could almost have qualified for the Spanish Inquisition. But Prospero merely smiled again. He paused and then went on.

"Where I once lived – that island in the Med, an English writer who'd lived there for years had left his country out of sad despair for his fellow men. Today's football crowds, he said, paralleled those that once had swarmed to relish public hangings in the past. Such is the sad decay of English life."

Eve shivered. But she was still puzzled.

"Well, I agree. But what has that to do with your next project?" she asked – but Prospero rose to go.

"Perhaps another time! We'll meet again."

And before leaving he told them to go to some of the concerts held in North Norfolk's churches.

"You'll find their placards nailed upon the trees. Their churches' music, if you wish to hear, conducts the magic on our favoured coast."

And with that he was gone, coat over his shoulders, his servant behind him and his dog leaping about everywhere.

As they walked home along the empty road, their boots echoing against the walls, Lawrence said to her:

"You know, the real thing that's going to make you want to live here, not the weather, the climate, the food, the edge ... you know what it is?"

"Well, what, then?" she asked cautiously, suspecting a trap.

"It's all the gossip. You can't have enough of it, darling."

She smiled in the dark, leaned up and kissed him.

*   *   *

They were still struggling to work out what there was between the various people they had met in the village. But somehow they found it easier to recognise the different types of people living on the coast. There were the ones at the top of the heap or who reckoned they were (plenty of room for disagreement on that in North Norfolk). Time had tarnished the eminence of some from the old landed families. Long ago their ancestors had managed to grab a chunk of land for themselves, not to mention a title or two. Their money is often described (by them, at least) as old and therefore somehow superior to money acquired today, when pocket boroughs are not so common. Photographs of their descendants and hangers-on spilled over the social pages of Norfolk's glossy county magazines like a tumble of gilded sugar beet.

In the twentieth century came the shadows of the landed families, of similar outline but lacking their substance. If they had been to a public school – or even if they hadn't – they would have considered themselves educated. They would certainly have been well spoken – which would have fooled the locals. And in the pragmatic style of Walpole they too had bought property when the buying was good. Three or four estates and a manor house or two had still left change from even a modest inheritance. They spent their days in farming their land, church parade, tennis afternoons, dinner parties and good works. They hardly went anywhere else or did anything else except, of course, go to war. First the fathers, then the sons. Same families, same enemies too. Their development was limited by an education of uncertain value and their experience of life outside Norfolk to foreign travel shooting Germans rather than game. They shared these limits (but not their money) with the good-natured locals often known as Norfolk Dumplings.

This local society served them almost as a subject race. It has been around as long as the landed families, although with a rather less attractive acquaintance with sugar beet. More mud and rain than gin and tonic. In brief, they were the families who had no land. So they were forced to work for those who did. They lived close to the earth and the sea. The family of Harry and Iris was one such family. But there was never enough work to support them all, especially when machines took over more and more farming jobs. So the ambitious ones took the escape route – the one taken by Horatio Nelson, Norfolk's Hero, and by Tom today. They had left to take their chances in the world. Plenty made fortunes or even founded a country or two – sometimes both. Mostly they helped build the empire – when trade followed the flag. If they stayed at home without money or land their lives were indeed 'nasty, brutish and short.' And if they raised their heads from the plough – well, the sight of them swinging in the wind next day concentrated the minds of the survivors. And they were only saved by the parliamentary enforcement of their rights revealed to them at last not by the clergy but by the English translation of the bible – the Authorised Version of 1611.

These types of people could be found in some form throughout rural England. But in North Norfolk lived more rootless people. These were the ones who had come to live here after the war. They were not local and they had little money. But they had travelled the world and they were all seeking something – even though they were not always sure what it was. But they were all free spirits and all had been drawn to life on the edge. So they had searched for and found a way to live in North Norfolk. Many, like Pippa and Brian, were artists and writers. They were creative and independent. They had recognised the inspiration offered by this understated landscape, its coastline and its sea. These qualities all appealed to their free spirit. And they recognised, too, another quality that was scarcer – but always present. That quality was invisible, like magnetism or a secret. One knew it existed by the way people acted, but one still didn't really know what it was. So Lawrence and Eve knew it was there in North Norfolk although it was some months before they realised what it was. And other sorts of people understood the secret, too. They, too, had found their ways to live in North Norfolk. They had taken advantage of the growing tourist industry. The more conspicuous of them ran the village shops – the Deli, the Bookshop, the Pottery, the Smoke House and the George and Dragon. They were all independent, all drawn to the magic of North Norfolk – and all committed to making their living here.

But there were others more difficult to categorise. They were the odd people with underground histories, unexpected and unseen ... like Prospero – the man of mystery, Justine – the disturber of men's hearts, Anton, the historian plumber and Hector the unseen great-coated pig rearer. They were not on public display. They lived in hidden places. Now and then they flitted in and out of the village, leaving a trail of mystery behind them. They did not need to live in North Norfolk but all had fallen for its powerful compulsion. They had done strange things and were still doing strange things. Their rough edges had grown back. They had felt the rain on their faces. And they, most of all, were the people who made North Norfolk different.

So it was clear that some very independent types had moved to the coast. Writers or shopkeepers, they were all personalities and they had carved out their own styles of living. They had ignored mass culture, television and package holidays. They had even rejected ambitious careers. Lawrence and Eve had never guessed such people had existed – even though the epicurean treasure cave of the Deli had given them a clue. And they had certainly never thought they would all be so content, expressing their own personalities with different talents. But all were deep, industrious, without social vanities and involved with each other as a community. Lawrence and Eve remembered how they had dreamed their dream of an English country community. Now it was coming true, in a style they had never imagined and, according to Prospero, with the community involved in some sort of role they couldn't work out.

And yet there was another group. This was the quota of comfortably off retired professional people who can be found in most attractive English villages. Sometimes, indeed, such villages function almost as a still life (or – more appropriately, as the French have it – a nature morte), the grim reaper's waiting room for the well-mannered middle class who quietly turn the pages of Saga, Country Life and National Trust journals, as they did in active life, while awaiting their turn. This quota didn't always mix with the bedrock of local society or the artists living here. Hanging their paintings on their walls was one thing – if there was room between watercolours of the windmill or the geese at sunset. But the artist himself in their drawing rooms? Not quite what they had in mind – especially in North Norfolk, home of wildness. And they didn't visit the pubs, either. Drinking in public? Dear me, no! Nor did they mix with the shopkeepers. They might have bought some pottery or a few kippers from them but they didn't often invite them to dinner. And they didn't mix with the old working families either – nor vice versa, to be fair. After all, they spoke different languages – almost literally.

So the village was divided. And as usual it took someone detached from local society to make it plain. That was when Lawrence saw Prospero talking to the villager who had showed them the winter aconites behind the church on their first walk through the village.

"This is Freddy Blake," explained Prospero gently. "He's a friend of mine."

He told them that Freddy was proud to be the village's oldest inhabitant. For Freddy's part, he greeted them with his warm smile, remembered their first meeting and made sure to ask after their health. That he repeated this query every five minutes did not diminish its value. Lawrence never saw any of the more affluent residents discussing life, let alone the universe, with him – except Prospero, who always stopped for him and thought carefully about his comments.

He and Lawrence agreed that wisdom came easier from a simple and unadorned heart than from an expensive suit.

"Society does not acknowledge this," he smiled. "A conclusion that we must all desire! For how could we find ourselves if it did?"

Underlying it all was the dull weight of their albatross. It had become a stranglehold around their necks. Again and again returned the thought that they would never be rid of it. During the day they could forget their burden for there was so much to do in the house. They were painting, building bookshelves, framing pictures and fitting carpets. They had decided to fit their hifi music-playing equipment into one of the wood-storage alcoves next to the dining-room fire. This meant installing an elaborate framework for it. But in the early evenings, when they rested and took their first drink of the day, it reappeared and worried them badly.

"Be thankful for small mercies," they said to each other. In other words, be thankful for that Arab diplomat who would shortly be renting out their house in London. He wasn't going to help sell it. But he would be helping to stop the mortgage payments crippling them. And they might be able to hold on until the market rose again – if it was ever going to. And neither dared mention to the other what would happen to them if it didn't.

In the far distance was the mirage of the paradise of North Norfolk life. It was still not quite definite and still out of reach. But they felt it was almost beckoning to them and encouraging them not to give up – but to hold on. It was symbolised by the shimmering image that every-one had told them of, that old schooner the Albatross, with its bowsprit and its raking masts and its filled-full sails pounding past their coast and cutting through the north-east breakers as if still in an earlier age – when the day had gone well. One day they would see this ship for themselves. And the thought of it somehow seemed to lighten the pain of their own albatross.

*　　*　　*

Their social life in North Norfolk was still embryonic. So when they needed friends, London was still where they found them. And one weekend they invited up some old neighbours. They were keen to come. They suspected that Eve and Lawrence had discovered some sort of secret of living. And they wanted to sniff it out for themselves. Lawrence told them it wasn't really a secret. It was just that they had found a paradise. And he told them that if you wanted to live in it badly enough, you just did. To prove it he took them down the alleyway outside their garden and opened the faded door in their flint wall.

"Look!" he said. "From darkness into light! See what I mean? All you need do is open the door! Don't just follow your career path down that alleyway. Remember the pleasure principle – and take a risk for it! Take your chance when the door is half open and it shows you what could be waiting for you!"

He wasn't sure they were ready for it. The husband had already mentioned something about promotion. But next morning they were all crammed happily into one car and rolling westward together along the coast road. It was bleak even for late March, although yesterday they had seen the first crocuses in the garden. The sight of them meant that daffodils were on the way – and tulips soon after. Eve had been so delighted. She was convinced that the earth had made that little extra tilt towards the sun and that spring was on the way. So she was very disappointed next morning when banks of driving fog hid the marshes and even enveloped the car.

"I was too optimistic as usual," Lawrence admitted to his guests.

"But spring will come, I can guarantee you that. Yesterday was just a little premature." And he added, with the knowing air of an insider, "but this fog, it's real smugglers' weather."

They stopped for petrol at Blakeney, the sailing village Lawrence and Eve had realised was the tourist centre and ideal for family sailing holidays.

"Not much of a day for a holiday," commented the garage owner, as he filled their tank.

"Terrible," agreed Lawrence. But what was that about a holiday? Didn't he realise they lived here?

"But we've got to show our friends the sights. They've come all the way from London."

Then he noticed that the pump was still calibrated in gallons, not litres. The garage man saw him looking and smiled.

"Well, yes," he said. "I did get some sort of form from London a year or two ago, can't remember when. They wanted me to change it over into litres and some twerp from the council came round to check on it ... said it was the law from the Common Market or something. But I told him I hadn't voted for that and what was good enough for my father was good enough for me – and for him, too, I said."

"Well, what happened?" asked Eve.

"Oh, he didn't like it. But I think he decided to keep quiet about it. I told him I'd ring up the EDP," he grinned. "Didn't see him again."

"Well, I hope he wins," said their friends as they drove off. "He might ... you're in a sort of backwater here. It's not on the way to anywhere, hardly a conformist county."

"Bloody-minded is the word," agreed Lawrence. "Even better – English."

Soon they were all in a junk shop in the winding village of Stiffkey, four or five miles further west. Their friends spotted a mirror they liked. But they didn't have enough cash on them to buy it.

"Well, if you like it," said the man, "take it and send me a cheque later."

The husband actually blushed as he whispered to Eve.

"But ... but doesn't he think I might just vanish? I mean ... they, they ... " he struggled to get the unaccustomed word out, "... they trust us! It's like it's sort of ... pre-War!"

"In 1935, maybe? That's what we think, too," smiled Eve. Their friends were beginning to get the secret.

And he was right. The man did trust him, although they'd never met. Their friend took the mirror and sent a cheque later. Well, that wouldn't have happened in London, even in 1935. And Lawrence and Eve were delighted. They hadn't really expected this return to pre-war values. So they naturally felt they had to celebrate it with a drink – not at pre-War prices, Lawrence pointed out. Reality, he admitted, has to force its way through sometimes, even up in North Norfolk.

The Red Lion was a few yards down the road. Its floor was sprinkled with sawdust. The beams scarcely cleared their heads. The barman had just lit a fire. The flames were crackling at each other like chickens in a sack. It was the only sound in the place. Otherwise it was so quiet they could almost hear the woodworm. Then somewhere a clock struck noon. The pub was empty except for the village postman. He was sitting motionless before a pint of Guinness. Above the mantelpiece hung an oil painting of Horatio Nelson and Lady Hamilton. They were painted in what used to be described as a compromising position. On the opposite wall a poster announced a jumble sale at Stiffkey Church. "Come early to get the best bargains," it said. "Nothing over 6d." Irresistible. It was dated 2nd September 1935.

With a gesture symbolising their sense of belonging they threw their coats on a chair and sat back to drink their beer – warm again, Lawrence noticed happily.

"You wouldn't get this in Notting Hill," said their friends. "No music either."

By now they had begun to guess at the secret. And wasn't there a famous writer who once lived here? The Tarka-the-Otter man, wasn't it him? Before the war? Ah, yes – in 1935! Perhaps he had seen the secret too.

They cruised on westward into the fog. By the time they reached the little port of Wells-next-the-Sea, the fog had crept further inland. And now it had become rain. They had booked lunch at The Moorings, a restaurant by the quayside that Zeus had recommended.

"The place is small," he had told them. "But the menu's big."

Wells hadn't changed much over the last hundred years. There were no big hotels and hardly any four-storey houses. The grain silo at the quay was the tallest building. So the town had plenty of sky between its old houses, most of them built two or three hundred years ago. Black weatherboarding was often wrapped round them like an old tar's jacket and long grass hid them from their neighbours. Yet up from the quay lay silent and hidden squares, as silent and as hidden as they had lain since they had been built. Back from the harbour sat The Butts, the South Kensington of Wells and as elegant a square as anyone could wish for. Tall trees bordered its rectangle of green. It was embraced by Georgian residences, all served by a hotel and two pubs. Was there a church in Wells? Difficult to say, but it must have been somewhere. The main street, if that was what it was, straggled down to the harbour, or rather the waterfront. It was lined by shops and private houses. Jenkins & Co, haberdashers, had a chair by the counter and a hat-rack at the door. On the floorboards lay strips of linoleum. In a corner slept a dog. Beyond the haberdashers little Georgian houses stepped down towards the harbour. They all needed a coat of paint and one of them had lost its front steps. But they were perfectly proportioned. Any one of them would have sold for a few million in Mayfair. Nearer the harbour was a chemist's shop. Its door stood between Doric pillars of mahogany. Each window showed man-sized glass jars – round and voluptuous. The one on the left was filled with a floating deep purple liquid that reflected the mahogany. The other shone sea green. Gold lettering curved across both windows. Eve read the words: "Hartree and Plumb, Dispensing Chemists." The couple looked down through the drizzle to the harbour at the bottom of the narrow street. Tall masts were outlined against the sky. They were on the edge again.

They discovered a couple of pubs on the waterfront. One was closed for the winter and the only customer in the other was a little old lady wearing a hairnet. She was sitting quietly in a corner, hands on her lap. A glass of barley wine was on her table. A sleeping dog lay close to her boots. Further along the harbour an abandoned candyfloss counter gathered grime. Seagulls skimmed low over the water. A few fishing boats and dinghies sat on the mud. Wells' harbour was safe from the sea – a mile away. That has helped the town live off the sea all its life. Even today, although caravan parks stretch northwest, tourism has hardly crept further into the town than the candyfloss counter and a couple of amusement arcades near the grain silo. Most of its shops cater for those whose greatest need is for shackles, sails and fishing tackle.

Three trawlers arrived while the couple were still standing at the quay with their friends. The fishermen began to unload their catch of herring. The seagulls abandoned the water and wavered over to them. Beyond them, beyond the quay and a sixty-yard basin of harbour, a wide and empty landscape of sand dunes spread north into space until everything merged into the horizon's haze. Several creeks cut through the dunes. Above them masts showed, as if planted, where boats lay. The channel passed the harbourmaster's building to port and stretched away to a far-off row of beach huts that broke the horizon and announced the open sea. Lawrence glimpsed tiny flashes of spray where the channel met the waves. He remembered that Tom's fishing boat was berthed somewhere here. Tom had told him of the sand bar at the end of the channel. At low tide, he had said, there was only a foot of water. If you drew more than that you had to wait for the next tide.

Moored at the far end of the quay was a big two-masted schooner. It was tough – a hundred foot of brass, teak and tar. It had a clinker hull and a bowsprit as long as a sea-yarn. "ALBATROSS", it said, in big brass letters across the transom.

"That must be it! The ship Prospero and Zeus have been talking about," said Eve excitedly.

Three young men at the main mast were pulling on some halyards and the jibs were going up. A hatch opened in the forepeak while they stood there. A figure appeared from below, emptied a bucket over the side, then turned and saw them.

"Hi!"

It was Prospero's friend Justine. Her hair was tied in a haphazard knot above her head and she was wearing tight jeans and a navy sweater.

"We met at the pub, remember?" she called. "With Prospero?"

Of course! Her hair cascaded over her face as she leaned down the companion way and called below. After a few moments a bearded head appeared. It was Jan, the schooner's owner and skipper. A coil of rope was draped over one of his shoulders. He climbed up from the fore-peak, tightening a bolt in a shackle as he came. Justine introduced them but he merely nodded and smiled briefly as he passed along the deck towards a pile of anchor chain in the bows.

"We're leaving soon," she explained. She balanced on the gunwale, holding the rigging with one hand like a Circe, a siren in modern dress. "We'll be leaving shortly to catch the afternoon tide and if we miss it we'll have to wait another twelve hours."

She told them they were bound for Rotterdam.

"He's from Holland. He was an academic once. But he told me he became tired of that life. It didn't have enough bite, enough risk."

But why call it the Albatross? Not a good encouragement to fate.

"Yes, but that was the idea, I think." She nodded. "It was his challenge to fate, to the myth, and he wanted to live the challenge. If he went down, he went down fighting. It makes sense, especially up here. And ... ," she spread her hands helplessly, " ... well, I must be like that too; because here I am."

They smiled, wished her luck, waved good-bye and walked the remaining few yards to the restaurant.

So at last they had seen the Albatross. And slowly Lawrence and Eve were beginning to understand how this schooner could somehow symbolise the spirit of North Norfolk. But they weren't yet sure why. Nevertheless, they knew that she was giving them strength. She showed them the rich prize that went with life on the edge. And that made it easier for them to hold on – and to run the gauntlet of the other albatross of their mortgage for as long as it took. For a very brief moment Lawrence had an idea. If the worst came to the worst they could sign on as deck hands, sail away and escape from all their troubles on land. But he felt it best not to mention the idea to Eve, not yet anyway. She'd probably want to bring the cat.

"The Flying Dutchman," Eve was murmuring to herself, "doomed to sail the seas until he finds on this earth a wife who would be true to him unto death. Every seventh year he goes ashore to seek her."

She looked up at Lawrence. "That's the legend ... do you think Justine will be the one?"

"I'm sure you're right," he replied. "Come on, I'm hungry."

"But there's the Village Marxist, though," she went on, not listening to her husband. "It's safer on shore. But there's a reward to being at sea, for a life of risk."

"Yes, we know that, now that we're up here – all at sea!" he groaned. "Let's get inside. I'm cold – not to mention hungry."

The restaurant was small and its ceiling low. It was full. People were crammed together at five or six tables. Three faces at the next table seemed familiar. Hadn't they come across them at the Deli? Weren't they from their village? They caught each other's eyes and were drawn into conversation. Yes, they were indeed village neighbours. And judging by their figures, they all liked food. Victor was a genial, bald and stout party who could have doubled as Toad of Toad Hall. He delivered stiletto comments in a self-depreciating, almost protesting, manner that clearly announced total self-confidence. Sitting next to him was his wife Pat, good-natured and ample, but easily a match for him – as they quickly learned. They lived beyond their village's quay and only a few minutes from Eve and Lawrence at a big old house with a tower on the lane before it met the Cromer road. Lawrence and Eve were soon informed that it was the biggest house in the village and had been built about four hundred years ago – or was it five hundred? With them sat an imposing and magisterial figure, Millicent by name.

She was a cookery writer – Eve had heard of her. She lived just beyond the village church and was heavily involved in village life. The couple soon discovered that she was also the chairman of their parish council. And wasn't she the churchwarden the rector had mentioned to Eve, the one who was meant to be contacting her about church flower arrangements? And that was just the start. Later they discovered she had a finger in almost everything else going on in the village. They realised they were lucky to have met them all so soon. Of course, having seen them in the village was not enough. In England you don't buttonhole people and talk to them without a how d'you do. It would undermine civilisation. The lefties would take over, mob rule would only be a matter of time and their houses would be invaded by an unwashed rabble to whom they hadn't even been introduced. So Eve was not completely surprised at her reception when somewhat nervously she told Millicent that Phillip the rector had suggested she do some flower arrangements and that Millicent would get in touch. This was waved away with a charming smile, a mention of the future and a head withdrawn behind the menu. But notwithstanding that, if you put strangers together in an outside setting, like a shipwreck, an earthquake or a restaurant, something might happen ... well, of course, it's still clearly irregular. But in an emergency it might be considered an improvised introduction, if only during lunch. They were all curious of each other but they were also English and well brought up men and women to whom curiosity is like sex: if you must have these urges, it's vulgar to show it. And as for Lawrence and Eve, they were like new boys at school and could hardly take the lead. Asking questions of people you had just met? How forward! People like that probably bought their own furniture – or were foreign.

So they had to wait until they were spoken to. Luckily their tables were next to each other. At first the conversation was conducted in snatches, thrown out in free moments because it distracted the senior residents from their scrutiny of the menu. That was more important than talking to newcomers, who had to learn their place – which for these senior residents came far below the salt. During this important stage Eve overheard some remarks from Millicent about the quality of one or two dishes. They surprised her, remembering that she was the impartial chairman of the parish council – until she remembered too that this chairman was also a cookery writer, so imperious was probably a better word than impartial. The restaurant was evidently on trial, as it were – if not under fire. Well, not yet, anyway. Lawrence noticed that it took the three of them even longer to choose the wine. It was clear that Victor had firm views on vintage burgundy and had already sent back a bottle of Pommard '82. "Corked," he had laconically announced. It turned out that he was a merchant banker. Lawrence was relieved to see that Norfolk's wine trade was being exposed to critical standards painfully and selflessly acquired during decades of merciless City lunches. Their conversation together began at last with impersonal comments on the region, the coastline and of course the weather. After a decent interval it graduated to gentle but probing questions as to where Lawrence and Eve lived and when had they bought their house? More important – was it their holiday home or their permanent residence and did they intend to stay? But in return, when they did venture a few tentative queries, the replies were briefer and more off-hand than informative, as if everyone knew where the residents lived and what they did and as for those who didn't – well, they would just have to guess.

"It's the middle class mafia," whispered Eve to Lawrence as she hid her face behind the menu and looked sideways at him.

"What's that?" he asked loudly.

"Shhhh," she whispered. "Don't shout. You know what I mean. Confident, well lined – well padded too. The mainstay of the village."

"Yes," agreed Lawrence. "And no harm in that, either. We need people like that to run our paradise for us. Good company, too."

"And I bet they're connected with the church," she said thoughtfully.

As for the menu, no wonder they took their time. It had nineteen opening courses. There was goats' cheese marinated in olive oil, several breeds of oyster, baked trout and salmon – and everything fresh. Then thick mushroom soups, patés by the dozen and all different. But the main course was where the serious eating began – jugged hare, pheasant, partridge, snipe, rabbit and game pie.

And that wasn't all. The owners, Jocelyn and Gerald, were another ample couple who obviously loved food. You could tell that at first sight. Lawrence remembered that old French saying: "Never dine at a restaurant where a thin cook cooks." Double assurance here. And these two obviously liked friends as well, characteristics that often went together. A table was kept free near the bar for local friends who might drop in now and then for a chat, a drink or just to read the paper. The four of them noticed how Gerald sat with them and poured them a drink – when he wasn't presenting a bill, acting as wine waiter, struggling with the cash register, opening bottles or gossiping. Jocelyn could be seen beyond the kitchen door. It seemed to be always open. She was ample-girthed enough to nearly fill it. But she was constantly moving, chopping, stirring and tasting. Yet now and then she had time enough to steer past pots and pans and find a chair at the table. Once there she pulled out a red handkerchief, wiped her brow, gave her friends a kiss and disappeared again.

Everything was fresh and nothing frozen or – horrors – micro-waved. That went for the vegetables of course, but also the fish and the game. The place was in shotgun range of Norfolk's larder – the open fields and woods around Wells – and so near the waterfront that you could chuck a herring back if you felt like it. It was all on their doorstep.

Lawrence, Eve and their London guests padded gently through lunch. It was the only way to make the most of every taste. And after a couple of hours, when the time came to pay, it happened again. The restaurant didn't take credit cards and no one had a chequebook.

"Send us a cheque later," said Jocelyn. Their friends were speech-less. At last they said –

"The trust. It's like before the war again."

Next day they left for London. It was mid-afternoon on Sunday and the only thing their visitors had done that day was to have breakfast.

"We don't want to leave," he told Eve. "But I want that promotion. Mustn't annoy the boss!" He smiled feebly.

"Yes, but that's only because he wants a new car," laughed his wife.

As for Lawrence and Eve, they ambled again along the coast road to the restaurant in Wells, this time carrying their friends' cheque. They had hoped to have lunch there. But it was early afternoon by the time they arrived. Jocelyn and Gerald's customers had all departed. All that remained were a few oyster shells and a half-empty bottle – the scattered leavings of earlier feasting.

But they were welcomed and ushered to the locals' favoured table. On it lay that day's newspaper, an opened bottle and two glasses. The newspaper was quickly cleared away, the four of them sat down together and two more glasses were conjured up. Soon arrived an impromptu mushroom vol-au-vent. Another bottle or two was opened and ... and, well, perhaps a veil should be drawn over the rest of that afternoon. But Lawrence and Eve felt they hadn't just discovered the secret of this coast. They were beginning to live it, too.

Next morning, when they were still thinking about that lunch and when they might meet their new acquaintances again, Lawrence saw a notice in the window of the post office. 'Scooter for sale', it said –

with a telephone number.

"It would be easier than cycling and cheaper than a car. We don't really need a car up here anyway," he told his wife. "After all, we don't go anywhere. We don't need to."

The scooter's owner lived in a flint cottage by the church. When the door opened Lawrence found himself two hundred years back and below decks on HMS Victory. Before him stood a Jack Tar in a navy sweater, dungarees and waders. Framing his face was a ring of mutton-chop whiskers and curly black hair. 1935? – more like 1735.

"You're too late, my beauty," he beamed at them. "I sold it. And I got a horse instead, now. I bought Jill's off her. She's buying another one."

But he invited Lawrence in and gave him a mug of tea. Lawrence couldn't believe it when he told him his name – Horace Nelson. Lawrence didn't like to ask him how long his family had been living up in North Norfolk.

A few days later Lawrence saw him hoeing the flowerbed outside the church door.

"Aye," he acknowledged, straightening up and rubbing his back. "They said it needed doing so I thought I'd pop round and give it a going over. These weeds needed rooting out." It seemed a very thoughtful gesture.

"Ah, well." He leaned on his rake. "They wanted me to come to their church lunch, all free, to make up for my time." He smiled and shook his head. Church lunch?

"Yes." He grinned. "They go to Millicent's house other side of the church and have a good lunch all gossiping away and then they pay something towards getting the roof done. But I told them it wouldn't suit me. I'd fall asleep. So rector bought me a month's feed of hay for my horse instead."

And he shoved his rake into a clump of nettles as if he was ramming a wad of gunpowder down the mouth of a cannon. Praise the Lord and pass the ammunition or, rather, hay. In North Norfolk the church moves in a mysterious way.

\*       \*       \*

Their train compartment was small and the seats slightly uncomfortable. They were covered in leather even if a little worn. But they seemed narrower than usual. The windows only opened halfway down and were fixed in position by a leather strap.

A notice overhead said: "Please do not spit out of the window." The compartment was panelled in mahogany. There was a lot of well-polished chunky brass. Above their heads were brass-framed advertisements for Bovril (a dog wagging its tail), Horlicks (a family ready for prayers before bed) and Budleigh Salterton (a gay beach scene, in the days when gay meant gay). Thick brass angles supported a luggage rack of strong netting.

They were on the branch line from Sheringham to Norwich, there to change for London to make the inventory for their new tenant, the Arab diplomat. The two carriages ambled along behind the engine as if enjoying the sea view from the cliffs. From time to time smoke spiralled past the windows. Just before Cromer the coastal line joined the Norwich line where the engine driver leaned out and handed a 12-inch key to a signalman so that he could change the points to allow the train to head for Norwich after leaving Cromer. It was a steam age device to prevent the train returning to Sheringham a little too early. After this ritual the train backed out from Cromer like an embarrassed guest and reversed all the way to Norwich.

A couple of months of taking root in a North Norfolk village had given them a sedentary life. The house had needed much work, they had friends to make in the village and gossip had to be exchanged. The furthest they had travelled so far was to Holt – three miles inland. So they weren't used to movement and it seemed now that the countryside it was that travelled, not them. It appeared like an Edwardian toy theatre, the one where you pulled tabs at each end and the characters on the stage moved to left or right while you stayed still. So the trees near the track in the foreground slid quickly backwards. In the middle distance they moved a little more sedately but still backwards. But behind them, all the way up to the horizon, trees were moving in their direction and trying to chase them – but never quite managing to catch up.

Now and then a thatched cottage or a Georgian vicarage took the stage, perhaps on the banks of a willow-bordered stream. The house sped towards them, sliding more and more quickly over its lawn until it crossed the stream and vanished again while the stream itself rushed backwards and out of sight behind the last carriage. At a water trough three immobile cows approached the train, watching it closely as they advanced. They grew bigger and bigger and their heads turned to follow it as they receded and shrank. Two tractors drove at them while waiting in line at a level crossing. After they slid away sideways

Lawrence and Eve watched them shrivel up and vanish round the bend behind the train. A church squared up to them, playing hide-and-seek with the trees surrounding it, while the tombstones rotated around its tower. Travel was clearly a foreign country in North Norfolk. The landscape might move but the people didn't, rather like the papal conviction that the sun moved round the earth. But then Lawrence and Eve were learning that North Norfolk was indeed the centre of the universe.

Norwich Station – people and loudspeakers – horror, horror! Then a train as long and as quick as a snake and they were at Liverpool Street Station in no time. So many people rushing around and bumping into each other. And as for the tube ... it was rush hour and the crowd nearly pushed them onto the line. Although Eve managed to find a seat Lawrence had to stand because one end of their carriage had been taken over by a yob culture gang of lager louts with shaven heads and brass rings on their ears and noses. One of them was naked to the waist, revealing two or three tattoos and a huge potbelly – which he kept slapping. They were all shouting at each other, crushing their cans of lager and throwing them around at the other passengers, all of whom pretended they didn't exist.

"This is what we escaped from," whispered Lawrence to his wife out of the corner of his mouth. But she kept her eyes firmly shut.

At last they left the tube and were back in their house in Notting Hill and working hard. The sooner done, the sooner back, they said to each other as they paced through the rooms making lists of cutlery and pictures. Next morning the agents checked the inventory with them. By lunchtime they were back at Liverpool Street and climbing into the Norwich train. And suddenly they felt back on holiday. It was the Inter-City line and bang up-to-date, with chilled Australian Chardonnay and prawns at the buffet. Even when they sat in their crowded compartment the wine did its work and prepared them for re-entry to their time warp. And now, as the long express snaked swiftly through the pastureland of East Anglia, their money worries made them appreciate all the more the landscapes they passed on their journey home. And the landscapes were of course all English – the rural market town of Stowmarket, a few yachts anchored near the edge of Ipswich's Deben estuary, the thatched cottages or Tudor farmhouses hidden in the woods and the occasional glimpse of a gabled mansion with spacious lawns. At last they entered the outskirts of Norwich and glided into the terminus.

By that time the journey through East Anglia had lost them forty years. Somehow they were back in the 1960's. At the station buffet the sandwiches were dry, the bar was full of cigarette smoke, the service was slow but the waiter was English. Lawrence ordered a warm beer and a large gin and tonic to toast their return to Norfolk. They raised their glasses, smiled over them into each other's eyes and clicked the rims gently together. Eve reminded Lawrence to look out for the Sheringham connection.

"But if we miss it, there'll be another one in an hour," she said happily.

The two-coach steam puffer was empty except for a family with three boys, two weary parents and five rucksacks and duffle coats. It clickety-clacked again along the branch line. No rush, no worries. They saw how the countryside north of Norwich was so different from that of south Norfolk. It was as if they had somehow reached another country, maybe an island. The train ambled gently home through the rough and empty North Norfolk fields. The war years fell away. Smoke curled past their compartment windows. Again the trees retreated backwards and the tractors slid slowly sideways. They watched the cows carefully. Were those three the ones they had seen on their way to London? Lawrence was fairly certain that they were. Past their window flowed empty cornfields, bare now and cut close to the hard and stony ground. Then came wild woodland and tiny churches, their flint walls and round towers standing in the long and forgotten grass. They held their breath at the deafening silences at the wayside halts: Wroxham, where the family of five tumbled out for the Broads; Gunton, Norfolk's Best Kept Wayside Halt, told in crocuses; North Walsham, cattle stalls by the line and a whiff of manure; Cromer, pier shows and pubs; West Runton, caravans, cliffs and at last the first hint of ozone. Finally, as it had done for so many years, the train crawled to within a foot of the rusting buffers at Sheringham, sighed gently and fell asleep.

By then they were safely back in 1935. The telephone boxes were red. There was candyfloss for sale. And there were no war clouds in sight. They were already floating in the bell-jar isolation of the pre-war years. Their car skirted the marshes and sailed home to the valley of the two mills. It was early evening when they drew near the first houses of their village. The smell of wood-smoke blew away the last anxieties of London. Warm and welcoming, it opened the door again to what was swiftly becoming their timeless paradise. And, as if to underline their growing conviction that all was well, daffodils were swaying in the garden and there was freshness in the twilight air. The earth had rolled its face towards the sun and spring was on the way.

The contrasts in North Norfolk jolted them again with a couple of new experiences. One was really dangerous – and that came later. But the first was harmless and it took place when they made their second visit to Holt.

Catering as always for well-lined, well-dressed and well-preserved citizens, it wasn't exactly what Lawrence and Eve had wanted from North Norfolk. But they soon discovered the Railway Tavern. This was a low-ceilinged dive that stayed open all day. The patrons arrived early and were usually still there about seven hours later. They were even still sitting in the same chairs, if perhaps a little nearer the floor. By then they were considering whether they should have a sixth Guinness (or was it a sixteenth?) or switch to scotch on the grounds that it was getting dark outside. In tea rooms at the other end of town, the senior citizens of Holt were no doubt seated in drowsy comfort, blazer and tie ready and correct. As they slowly stirred a cup of China tea, they were no doubt absently popping a thin cucumber sandwich into their mouths.

But an even greater contrast lay a few hundred yards away – beyond the by-pass to Cromer and hidden behind a pair of gates. At its entrance stood some sort of giant Alsatian in a seven-foot cage. As soon as it saw them this monster began slavering with rage, leaping up and down, shaking its bars at them and rattling a huge chain shackled to its collar. It probably thought they were lunch.

Behind the gates were mountains of scrap steel. A path had been cleared between them. It made the place look like wartime Hamburg after a week of heavy bombing. Buried inside the mountains were rusted motorcycles, winches, corroded hawsers, rope as thick as a man's thigh and coiled into huge piles like fossilised pythons, tubs of solid tar shining like a moonlit sea, heaps of splintered wood, guillotines rusted as if with a face rash and even two or three ancient lorries almost totally embedded in scrap. Only their cabs showed – like giants' diving helmets. Under a mound of wire netting was a thirty-foot piano accordion on wheels. Thick spikes stuck out of a barrel the size of a train's boiler. Embossed on its engine were the words: "Fodder Beet Rotovator, Woods of Stowmarket, 1935."

But perhaps the oddest surprise was the owner's home, a modern bungalow with close-cut lawn and well-tended flowerbed. Its gleaming mahogany-stained front door was neatly fitted with highly polished brass fittings and a sign saying "Mon Repos". It sat directly behind the dog's cage and next to a 30-ft pile of old tyres. The balance of habit and mind, so often absent in homo sapiens, was alive and well in North Norfolk – at least at the scrap yard.

*     *     *

The approach of spring had clearly given the Sphinx a good appetite. In the mornings Lawrence and Eve quickly became used to dead mice on the kitchen floor. Sometimes, if she had been hungry one night, their cat had actually eaten what she had killed. By morning only a neat pile of intestines and perhaps a kidney would remain. One rainy day Lawrence caught the Sphinx toying with a tiny field mouse. She had already bitten off part of one leg. Now she curled her paw like a slow bowler about to deliver a googly. She gave the mouse a playful bash ... and then another ... and then another. There were long pauses between the bashes. And all the time the mouse cowered paralysed by fear in the corner. Without stopping to consider that raw nature must have its way he pulled the Sphinx off (who scratched him), picked up the mouse (which bit him) and put it out of doors (which drenched him with rain). Dragging what was left of one leg behind it, the mouse crawled away to a crack in the flint wall and lay there, huddled and motionless. Next day it was gone, eaten alive or escaped, he never discovered. In the garden they often found dead mice or birds, some-times both. "Murder in the Flower Bed" was but a flimsy hint of the Sphinx's gardening skirmishing, and "She Kills by Night" a soupcon of her intentions in the dark. And all the time she's such a soft and cuddly little thing.

*     *     *

Just before lunch that month something unusual happened. Their doorbell rang. So far they hadn't had many visitors. So they weren't used to hearing it – apart from the postman's arrival. And they usually dreaded that because he often brought unreasonable letters from their bank.

But now on their doorstep stood the formidable figure of Millicent – cookery writer, chairman of the parish council, churchwarden, organiser of church flower arranging and today, it soon became appar-ent, also chairman of the Church Restoration Fund Committee and organiser of its lunches and no nonsense about being chairperson or even chairwoman – let alone 'chair'. She swept in, reminded them they had met at The Moorings restaurant in Wells and brought with her an invitation to the next Church Restoration Fund Lunch at her home. Since she could have so easily posted it, her visit was clearly a reconnaissance. Millicent was one of the first villagers to visit them and she clearly needed to do some fine tuning. What of their interior décor? No doubt it had to be noted and reported back to the parish council, if not necessarily used in evidence. As they guided her to the conservatory for a drink, Eve saw her sneak a glance around the room. Were these incomers Colefax and Fowler or stripped pine and painted floorboard hippies? They had seemed reasonably acceptable at The Moorings, she no doubt mused secretly to herself. But since then they had been seen leaving the George and Dragon after closing time several times in a row and, what's more, talking to Prospero. And how much had they paid for those curtains? She had long ago learned what they had paid for the house. As if dealing with brigands she handed over the invitation card with one hand and received a gin and tonic with the other.

"I shall be doing the catering, of course. Everyone seems to like it," she told Eve and smiled faintly, with a nominal attempt at modesty. "Usually only certain people are invited to this lunch. You seem to have passed the test of ... "

She didn't finish her sentence but sniffed and looked down her nose. The church's selection committee was obviously taking a risk in inviting them. Then followed a polite period of warming-up gossip. It would be too rude to describe it as probing. But the questions were like an interview for an appointment. She seemed surprised, even rather piqued, to learn that they had already met the owner of The Cedars, a large Victorian pile on the way to the church. The owner was a young man who had been left the house by his mother. Zeus had introduced them over the wine-tasting bellows at the Deli. They were clearly jumping the gun. No doubt they should have waited twenty years to meet him.

"Give us time," they thought to themselves.

"His mother was such a supporter of the church," said Millicent. "She was Chief Guide for Norfolk, you know. She used to bring the Lord Lieutenant along to open our annual fête. He was a personal friend, of course."

Of course. Millicent's survey of the room caught their large Modigliani nude on the wall, the one they had found in a London skip.

She swallowed for a moment, looked quickly away, snatched another furtive glimpse at it and then continued in somewhat of a hurry. "Yes, well, yes, she'd been here for years after her husband died during the war. It's so nice that one of her family is still in the house."

She kept her eyes firmly away from the nude. Eve and Lawrence exchanged glances. The son in question had told them that the place was a white elephant round his neck. He wasn't enjoying his legacy. Still, they were incomers. It wasn't their business. She left with a promise to contact Eve about flower arrangements in the church.

How nice to be invited to the church lunch, thought Lawrence. How gratifying that they were accepted by the church establishment so soon. He sat back, pleased that their quality had been noted. But, of course, as he reminded himself, this was only proper.

Eve snatched the card from him and turned it over.

"Charge: £5.50, it says," she told him. "It's a fund, a charity lunch. And that's what it's going to cost us to get in."

She looked at it again.

"Goodness! £5.50 each, too!"

Ah, well, he thought. There always was a serpent in paradise.

But a week later they reported for lunch. Their route to Millicent's house lay past the village green, the Three Swallows and the church behind it. Horace was standing outside his front door trimming grass from around the roots of a rosemary bush. They stopped to talk to him.

"I know where you're going," he said. "Better make sure you get enough to drink."

And he waved them on with a laugh and a flourish of his shears.

"You know something?" said Lawrence. "He's a happy man."

Eve looked at her husband.

"I bet he hasn't got a mortgage either."

"Well, it's no good," said Lawrence. "I know what you're thinking. But we couldn't even buy a cottage like his, much as I'd love to. It's all we need, after all. But by the time we'd have paid the mortgage off there wouldn't be enough left over even for something small like that."

She put a hand on his knee.

"Don't think about it, darling." She looked at him. "I know it's very worrying. And I know I was so against it at the beginning. But there's something so magical here ..." She paused for a moment. "Anyway, we're still alive and at the moment there's nothing we can do about it. So let's just enjoy lunch."

Then she added brightly –

"And did you see that rosemary bush? It's flowering. Spring really is on the way!"

"Yes," said Lawrence absent-mindedly. He had just noticed a half-built part of the church. "I'm sure you're right. But look at that south transept. I was just wondering how long it's been without a roof."

At Millicent's house they parked their car next to a pale blue Morris Minor, the one they had seen on their first walk down the village street.

"Look," announced Eve. "The rector's car! I hope he's here. Maybe we might meet him again."

"I wouldn't be at all surprised," replied Lawrence.

Over lunch they learned that the money to build the south transept had run out at the end of the fifteenth century. And the church has been trying ever since to raise enough to complete it. Its parish documents were stored in some mildewed vault beneath Norwich Cathedral. Apparently one of them showed that the dean of the time had written that the cost would be £7 13s 6¼d and the job would require thirty masons, who would take about five years to finish it. But that was in 1525. Henry VIII had been more interested in demolishing churches – after robbing them, of course – than building them. So nothing happened. And a hundred and twenty years later, less time than it took the Lord to blink, Cromwell wasn't interested either. Then inflation had devalued the currency. So the cost had always kept several strides ahead of whatever money was available. A balding man across the table, who had joined in the discussion, calculated that now it would cost around £75,000, even though three men could do it in less than a month – "which would mean inflation of nearly one million percent," he said with a smile and poured himself a glass of wine.

Their fellow luncheon guests all came into a single category – the senior one. And all were clearly determined to live as long as possible. Millicent stood near the kitchen door. She was not actually moving – or doing anything physical at all. But she was supervising cohorts of wives in serving lunch. Eve noted that somehow they were all smaller than her, rather like those Egyptian paintings of pharaohs with their retinue. Soon Victor and Pat arrived – the stocky couple they had met at The Moorings restaurant in Wells. They recognised Eve and Lawrence and came over to sit at the same table.

"Millicent cooks well," Victor informed them. "But I'm not too sure of her palate when it comes to wine." He frowned suspiciously at the label on the bottle served them by one of the wives, poured for everyone and sipped his glass.

"Drinkable, I suppose," he conceded and took a mouthful.

"You say that about every wine," retorted Pat, chin cupped in her hands and elbows on the table. "And you drink too much anyway. You always forget you can't drink as much as you did twenty years ago."

"Oh, that's unfair," said Lawrence, "everyone seems to do that here!"

"The one thing that annoys me about this government," he said, taking no notice of his wife and looking around for another bottle, "is that they won't cut the duty on wine."

"Well, why should they?" she asked, looking over her shoulder at him.

"We're in the European Community, or don't they call it Union nowadays? It used to be called the Common Market, too, long ago." He shrugged. "The government will have to harmonise its duty on wine when we have the euro. And they didn't go into that when they should have."

"Spoken like a banker," said Lawrence. "But it's a political decision."

"Anyone for a raffle ticket?" cried Millicent to the diners, waving a booklet of tickets high in the air. "Buy a ticket and get your name on a Stop!"

"A stop?" asked Eve.

"Yes, it's for a new organ," Pat told her. "The old one collapsed ten years ago. But in the last few years enough people have come to live up here and we can afford to help buy another one now."

"I'll have a dozen tickets!" The same bald man waved his hand in the air.

"There you are," said Victor. "He used to work in the City."

"And he plays jazz music on the church organ," put in Pat, smiling.

They paused to eat the trout prepared on the instructions of Millicent.

"Zeus donated this for our lunch," said Pat. "Have you met him yet?"

"Oh, yes! One of the first people we met, actually. The Deli, it's a wonderful place," said Eve.

Victor turned to her.

"You know, he's quite popular with his staff – the girls, I mean."

"Yes, I've noticed that," laughed Eve.

"Well, I've been taking bets on who's going to ensnare him first. Would you be interested in buying a – "

"Victor!" reprimanded Pat. "You shouldn't go on soliciting bets like that. You've been doing it all week."

"Well, darling," he laughed. "Eve seems interested!"

"Well, she's married. Anyway bets is one thing," said Lawrence. "But do you want us to harmonise our interest rates as they do in Europe?"

"Not at the moment," said Victor. "But we'll have to, one day. Still, up here we're trying to ward it all off. We're quite self-sufficient in North Norfolk as you probably know by now ... smoked salmon and kippers at the Smoke House, fish off the coast thanks to Tom and then there's some decent wine and beautiful local food at the Deli, books at the Bookshop and crockery at the Pottery, quite apart from all the game around inland."

"Pottery at the Pottery, not crockery, if you don't mind," corrected his wife.

He didn't listen and leaned out and neatly grabbed a fresh bottle of wine from a Restoration Fund wife who had been carrying it to another table – and then called for a corkscrew from Millicent, who frowned at him. He continued without pausing. "Of course there's that stone-ground bread from the mill at the top of the valley and even Norfolk wine not far away, although it's only white and a bit thin. Have another glass?"

"Of course," said Lawrence at once.

"You know," Pat turned to them. "You must have realised by now that we live in a valley with a mill at the head and another mill at the foot?"

"Yes, we've discovered that," smiled Eve. "And..." but she was cut short by Philip as he passed their table.

"And don't forget the five churches," he beamed as he sailed along, hair floating around the top of his head like a halo, hand upraised and fingers outstretched, as if to demonstrate the number of churches and bestow a benediction at the same time.

"Do you know," Victor told them, "that Philip – our rector, he's just passed us – he's got a Morris Minor? It's pale blue. It's so English. Well, of course they've got millions of them in India, but they haven't got any rectors. It's just the car for a rector here."

"By the way, Eve," said his wife, taking no notice of him. "That reminds me. Millicent told me Philip thought you'd be interested in helping with flower arranging – yes? Oh, good! That would be lovely. Can you drop in for coffee sometime? What about Tuesday morning, elevenish? We'll go on to the church. There's a christening next Saturday and we'll need some help."

Eve glowed. This time it was Victor's turn.

"D'you know who's the highest paid man in Holt?" he asked them. "Give up? Well, it's the barber."

"All right," Lawrence smiled. "Why?"

"Well, look at everyone here. Nearly all of them are bald – "

"No to mention yourself," put in his wife.

" – and surely it only takes three minutes to cut their hair," he went on as if he hadn't heard her. "Well, that's about £4 a go – which is £80 an hour. Not bad for cutting hair eh!" he laughed. "Even the solicitors here don't quite charge that much, even if they do scalp us in other ways. Yes, they charge for an hour even if they take ten minutes." He looked pained – as if to say that bankers would never do that.

Later Lawrence managed to buttonhole Philip and ask him about the south transept. He smiled and shook his head sadly. His wisps of white hair broke free for a few moments.

"Ah, yes," he sighed. "The trouble was that all that time we've had so many wars with Europe – the French, the Germans, the Dutch, the Spaniards – not to mention the Pope." He paused at that, beamed mischievously and shook his head again, this time in mock sadness. "It all cost so much that the government minted more money to pay for them."

He paused and looked at Lawrence.

"Good value for independence, though, wouldn't you say? But then everything began to cost so much more. We could have done with Mrs Thatcher in those days."

He smiled at Eve and said to them both: "do come round to the church again soon and I'll show you some more brass rubbings. What about this time tomorrow?"

He turned to her. "Any good? Right! And I promise that none of them'll be rude either!" This time he winked at Lawrence.

Lunch continued. Millicent in her churchwarden hat, rather than in her Church-Restoration-Fund-Lunch hat, made a speech. And another churchwarden made another speech and then came round with a real hat.

Eve put in a £10 note.

"Well, it's a good cause," she told her husband, who was frowning at her. "And anyway I like them all."

"Well, so do I," said Lawrence. "But does our bank manager?"

Looking over the lunch tables, Lawrence couldn't see a real North Norfolk local anywhere. Not someone who had been born and brought up in the area, like Harry. He was beginning to suspect something.

"I have a feeling," he whispered to his wife, "... what you were saying at The Moorings. It's the middle class mafia again. It seems as if they all treat this restoration fund and the Church Fête and the local parishes like their own middle-class playground, what with this jazz organist from the City of London and the banker and the cookery writer, played out regularly like a soap called ... I know, Congregation Street ... and with a pub called, say, the Mitre."

"But at least it keeps the church going – and the village, too," she pointed out.

"Well, there aren't many locals in this cast, either."

"Yes, more like a ghetto ... yes, "she agreed. "Where's Harry or Freddy Blake? Not even Iris. They've been here longer than any of them."

"Maybe they weren't invited? Look at Horace. No, this has to be a middle-class soap."

"I wouldn't be at all surprised if they weren't. But they wouldn't have come if they had been. Anyway," she hugged herself and smiled at him. "I'm so looking forward to the flower arranging."

# Spring

It was early April when one Sunday morning Lawrence woke up, looked out of the window and saw their guests, a couple up from London, sitting in the garden.

Nothing odd about that, one might think. Except that the earth's slight roll towards the sun last month had been a false alarm and the day before they had all been on the marshes in a cold northerly wind and had nearly frozen. On the way home log fires had been demanded in all downstairs rooms. In fact the husband had insisted on lighting them – just to be sure, as he put it. And his wife had asked for an electric blanket for their bed that night.

Inviting people up from London was Eve and Lawrence's way of taking their minds off the albatross of their mortgage. If they had also been neighbours, their guests could offer first-hand clues on how the market was going in their street. And Lawrence was always delighted to notice that even the most fastidious and civilised Londoner will behave like a cave man when he reckons he can get away with it. And a weekend in the country was the place for that, especially in North Norfolk. It nearly beat abroad.

This cave man was a sophisticated and urbane City banker. In London he had not thought country life of much interest. His weekends were spent in Paris rather than the Yorkshire moors. And he didn't have open fires although he did have the sort of gas fire that looks like one. You turn on the gas tap. You light it with a match. And it roars away. The pieces of coal (if that's what they are) never wear out. No smoke or unsuitable smells. No ashes to clear up. One night someone had thrown a ball of paper on it. He had leaped forward with a howl of anxiety and scooped it clear. But now, up in North Norfolk, he had been striding around the marshes in green wellies (bought for the weekend) and shouting into the wind. He leaped over the ditches – and ended up in two of them. Then he began making up names for the birds he saw, which all turned out to have some sort of sexual link (gull was a 'girl', for example, and 'tit' and 'goose' went without saying; none of it very original, especially for a banker). And when he got tired of that he spent half-an-hour throwing stones into the sea. He was on the job of getting the house warm as soon as everyone reached home.

"I'll light some fires," he announced, arms akimbo in the hall, green wellies still on and looked around him for wood.

"Ah, thanks! You'll need to fetch in firing," said Lawrence. He had for some time realised how their guests loved country living, even with little encouragement. It gave him time for other things, like sitting back and watching them work.

And he sat back and watched the banker bring in wood and lay fires in both the sitting room and the dining room. He chatted to him now and then to let him know he was being appreciated. His guest prepared the fire the way he'd been taught as a fag at public school. No nonsense with firelighters for a start. "That's pansy," as he put it. First, he found a page of newspaper (preferably The Financial Times). Then he tore it up and compressed it into small balls. He laid them carefully over the grate and covered them with little sticks of kindling that he'd previously chopped. But the kindling wasn't just thrown on. Oh, no! They were neatly laid like a crossword puzzle. Then he added the coup de grace with small lumps of coal nestling in the spaces between the kindling. No recusant priest ever had a better fire prepared for his soul's attention.

A few more al fresco additions … and both structures began to look like something on show at the Tate Modern. They were flimsy enough to resemble get-rich-quick schemes sometimes advertised in the Press – if there was a difference.

Finally, lighted matches were proffered diffidently at the centre of each pile in the manner of a sacrifice at the altar of a Vestal Virgin or, more likely, the proposal of a glass or two of vintage port to round off a City lunch.

Wuthering Heights soon took over. Thuds and crashes were now heard outside as he swung the axe at a pile of logs with an implacable ruthlessness usually only employed when foreclosing on a customer. A few moments later it was as Heathcliffe that he re-entered the house, arms full of logs. His normally impeccable hair fell in loose strands over his forehead. Beads of sweat sprang out on his skin.

Determination gleamed from his eyes. By now the fires in both rooms were just catching. He dashed out to the coal hopper to fill Lawrence's two buckets.

"Feeding the accounts," he explained over his shoulder. And all performed at a speed normally reached only when sprinting from his bank's seat at Covent Garden to the Crush Bar. Nor was that the end. He filled the buckets again and placed them in readiness by the fires. This was, apparently, a stand-by credit. He sprang from room to room and back again as if desperately seeking Catherine on the moor. Each time he inspected his handiwork as carefully as if putting the finishing touches to a take-over bid. Inflation was ready to take on a new meaning.

"I think they'll go well now," he told Lawrence, sank onto the sofa and picked up The News of The World. In London he only read the city pages. But that's what North Norfolk does to you. Lawrence had been working, too. He had opened a couple of bottles of champagne. It's called division of labour. Lawrence brought him a glass. He deserved it.

After supper that evening Lawrence gave their guests a special version of Irish cream liqueur. It was something for which Tom at the village grocers had provided the recipe.

"You need coffee beans and a special sort of cream. Hang on, I'll ring a mate in Norwich to get the recipe." And he did. He spent ten minutes on the telephone and then wrote it all down for Lawrence. They felt really touched. They already knew one or two people in the village who wouldn't have done that, however long they had lived here. And Tom hadn't been asked to the Church Restoration Fund Lunch either.

But there in the garden next morning were their guests. They were sitting in the sun and drinking their coffee as if spring had arrived. Didn't they know there had been at least two false starts this year? Lawrence and Eve had been told that it always arrived later than in the south – and so it did. However much they might have relished its raw nature at the time, they had found that winter in North Norfolk could go on for much too long. Their hearts had soared whenever clear blue sky had appeared – especially after a particularly savage week of frost and hail. And a day or two later the shivering weather had returned.

But their guests were right. And as if to prove it came a twittering in their bedroom chimney. They bent down and looked up. Yes, a couple of birds were building a nest right at the top. And several more were chattering outside in brisk courtship. They all sang with slightly different tunes and their voices were light. And they all sounded excited. So it must be true – spring had at last emerged from the chrysalis of winter!

Eve and Lawrence came out to sit with their guests. The sky was washed clean. The air was so fresh and still they almost held their breath. An enormous weight had been lifted from them. They breathed easily and lightly. They expanded! They smiled and laughed – impossible not to.

And suddenly they all noticed that the garden was full of miracles. What else could they have called it? Someone had scattered the trees with pale green specks as if from a shotgun. Take the apple tree – buds like green jewels were sitting in clusters, torn like little flecks of fabric to make furry parasols and all open to the sun. Eve and Lawrence couldn't stop wheeling around. Behind them, on the flowering cherry by the wall, the one Eve had planted shortly after moving in, a few petals were beginning to open, just a little – as if shy. They were the colour of shrimps but edged with fresh blood – as delicate as a baby's fingernail. The tree next to it was beginning to blush deep pink, and –

"Look!" shrieked Eve. "Look! At the wall!" By now they were almost running. "There's a flower on the jasmine!"

Sure enough, a single yellow flower sat like a star in the middle of the dark leaves, the growth from the shoot that she had planted.

Lawrence couldn't resist saying: "Well, you don't get spring quite like this in London, darling, do you?"

She gave him a warm smile.

"And can't you see?" cried the banker's wife, laughing. "Your pear tree?"

It was so big no one had noticed it. It was full of fronds of buds so small you could hardly catch them. Each was like a teaspoon of avocado topped with a dab of cream.

Everyone sank back with amazement. And then they heard the sound. From the wood beyond the barn, through that still air it came.

"Cuckoo, cuckoo!"

That settled it. There was only one thing Lawrence could do. He knew it wasn't even mid-day but he went inside and brought out a bottle of champagne. And half an hour later he went inside again and brought out another bottle of champagne.

Late that afternoon their guests left for London. They had to be in good time for Monday morning and the bank. Weekends were all very well, but the bank was real life – oh yes!

"Oh, dear!" said the wife. "It's so wonderful here. Such a pity we have to leave so early. It's been on my mind all day."

Lawrence and Eve smiled at each other. But after their guests had left they again felt so delighted about the coming of spring that they each felt a surge of energy. They bounced about as if they had no weight and were on the surface of the moon and needed to share it with someone. It was like saying "Christ is risen!" – perhaps even the same. But in any case they called round to the pub to share their pleasure with Ronald. After all they were locals. They were staying, not going back home to London.

As usual he was stalking up and down behind the bar with a glass in one hand and a cloth in the other. But this time the way he flicked his cloth at the bar had an unusually savage swipe to it.

"You look grumpy," said Eve, smiling at him and looking puzzled as she ordered a large gin and tonic.

"Well, wouldn't you," he snapped, jerking his head back. After a few minutes of generalised grumble it all came out. Apparently two months ago he'd applied for it.

"For what?" asked Lawrence.

"It's St George's Day next week." Ronald looked at Lawrence, rolled his eyes and jerked his head upwards. "If you're going to live up here, you've got to know that."

"Well, OK, but what did you apply for?"

"I wanted to extend drinking time," he said. "But they won't let me. But they gave the pub in Blakeney an extension for St Patricks's Day. I ask you! For the Irish!" He jerked his head back.

And to show how much he felt about it he said: "Have another pint on me."

*    *    *

Prospero had told them that North Norfolk's church concerts were advertised by notices nailed to trees. And once when Lawrence was following a car with a dinghy on its trailer on the way to Blakeney quay, he saw something nailed to a tree. It was a notice of a Good Friday concert at the nearby church. There was only one work to be performed. But what a work! It was the inspired English oratorio, Handel's "Messiah." But who were the performers? On the notice it said: "The Kelling Orchestra and The Kelling Choir." Kelling? That was a little place on the coast road to Cromer. You could easily miss it if you didn't slow down to take the bend in the road. There were about ten houses and a school. No shops. How could enough people live there to make up a choir and an orchestra as well? Let alone to find the soloists? And how good were they going to be?

So they were rather apprehensive that Good Friday evening. But they needn't have worried. Later they learned that the Kelling Orchestra and Choir meant all good fiddlers and singers twenty miles inland, if not further. The singing was full throated, accurate and lively – and a real joy to hear. It all went with a swing, in fact – just as Handel intended. Everyone must have known it was going to be a good performance because the church was packed. There must have been at least five hundred people. Where on earth did they all come from? And can they all have heard about it from notices tacked to trees? Lawrence and Eve were beginning to realise that in North Norfolk people still got in touch with each other as they had done long before the telephone. People living as far apart from Blakeney Church as the fifteen miles to Gresham seemed to learn about what was going on without actually moving. It was all a bit puzzling for a newcomer who wasn't yet wired up to the local internet.

But then in one of the pews they recognised Justine and the Village Marxist from the Pottery. Their heads were together and he seemed to be explaining something to her.

"Isn't she with Jan?" whispered Eve. "You know, the skipper of the Albatross? We saw her with him – remember?"

"Yes, I do know who you mean, darling. We did meet him, you know. But I don't know," he said. "We've only been here five minutes. Maybe Jan is away to the continent with his ship ... and another woman." He looked at her and shrugged. "Well, you know what sailors are."

Eve gave him a stern look and pursed her lips at him before she waved to the Village Marxist and Justine, who beckoned and made room for them. They caught the end of his comments: " ... that's why Jesus' apostles were the only true communists, the only ones who really shared. The system has been corrupted by materialistic societies ever since." He got up and shifted along holding his cushion. No sharing of that, evidently.

And there the audience sat, all equally entranced by Handel's miracle, most of all by the tunes, then by the enriching harmonies formed by the combination of soloists, orchestra and chorus. But it was cold. And the cold became more and more distracting. Lawrence and Eve each wore gloves and heavy overcoats. But they increasingly felt the hard pew beneath them. As the performance wore on they exchanged one pain for another – the church got warmer but the pew got harder. A new way to suffer for the Lord, perhaps. But it didn't matter and they were pleased that they found themselves warm at least when, aching just a little, they tried to straighten up at the end. And they were so pleased to have discovered for themselves something that all country people knew. And that was how to entertain themselves without having to be entertained, let alone having to visit fashionable centres of excellence such as Covent Garden or The Wigmore Hall. What they might lack in skill – if they did – they made up for in enthusiasm. And stuff the critics!

Their stiffness soon went as together with their new friends they walked down the hill to their village. The full moon hung over the marshes and the sea beyond.

And then Eve had an idea. "Next year we'll bring our own cushions."

"But will we be here next year?" asked Lawrence, grinning. She pinched his hand gently and leaned against his shoulder in the dark.

*     *     *

By now they had unpacked nearly all the smaller objects that had been carefully wrapped up for their move. It was exciting to unfold tissue paper to reveal a Japanese bowl – it had been a wedding present from Eve's mother – or a clay lamp they had bought together on a visit to Egypt. The objects set the couple on a journey rediscovering their lives. And there were a few really curious things they'd completely forgotten about. Some had been lying under a spare bed for years. For example, there was a large wooden board bearing the words "Love One Another" in elaborate gothic letters and decorated with branches of entwined vines, ivy and roses. And other weird objects had been mouldering away in a cellar throughout their time in Notting Hill. One was a three-foot wide church clock face. Two concentric cast-iron circles enclosed large Roman numbers as they went around from I to XII. Every now and then in London Lawrence had wondered what to do with it. He couldn't really bolt it to the front wall of their house and set it working. Some council official would have told him to take it down. The odd thing was that up in North Norfolk he felt he could actually do something like that – because he no longer felt oppressed. So, free from snooping officialdom, he was able to think of all sorts of uses for this clock face. There was something about the coast that encouraged him to try almost anything. It was the feeling he sometimes had when he was abroad and off the leash.

It was as he was gazing out of their kitchen window into the back yard that he realised how he could use this clock face. That yard was an eyesore – not just concrete, but cracked and stained concrete. But looking at it he knew he had found the place to lay out a herb garden. And the clock face would be at its centre. He painted its two circles with gold enamel and the Roman numbers between them with olive green. He bought a few dozen bricks – the sort with hollow centres – and laid them out on the concrete as a big rectangle. Eve put the clock face in the middle of this and, from each number on the clock (I to XII) Lawrence radiated twelve lines of bricks out to the sides of the brick rectangle – like the Japanese flag.

"We'll put flints in the hollows of these bricks. It'll match them up with the flint walls. Oh yes!"

He smiled at his wife; and they broke off work for lunch at the pub. They were finding it difficult to avoid the pub at mid-day, especially now they had discovered its wonderful sandwiches – smoked salmon, chicken and coleslaw, crab, Hector's ham, prawns – and all between slices of Letheringset wholemeal bread. The Rhine Maiden was right about that bread. And the pub was even more becoming a second home now that they were friends with Ronald. All he needed to add were racks of newspapers, thought Lawrence, and they'd be there for hours. Perhaps that was why he didn't add them. Eve and Lawrence were getting on with him but he never bothered to conceal his view that customers were still a pest and not on any account to be encouraged. As for friendship, perhaps he might make an exception – or perhaps not.

After lunch they drove up to a gravel pit they had found on a hill track that led out one of the valley's fords. Lawrence needed gravel and flints for the herb garden. He wanted to spread the gravel between alternate lines of the bricks. Then Eve would fill the spaces between the gravel with soil before planting the herbs. That way they could step from one gravel segment to the next without treading on the herb bed between them.

Flint certainly matched how Lawrence and Eve felt about living in North Norfolk. As the stones cascaded into the back of the car he was dazzled by the sunlight flickering off them. It was the hardest of stones and it suited the climate and the atmosphere. It was prehistorically hard, hard before man developed one of the world's first trades and began to split it for spearheads, hard long before homo became sapiens, Cambrian hard, hard before microbes had begun to stir in the primal swamp, hard before anything had moved upon the face of the earth, hard before carbon and amino acids had begun to build the blocks of life, hard before millions of millennia when volcanoes and earthquakes had set the earth on fire and cracked it open, hard before the earth's gravity had lassoed the moon, hard before all the elements had begun to exist, hard perhaps before the stars' hydrogen fusions had created helium, hard almost before the big bang.

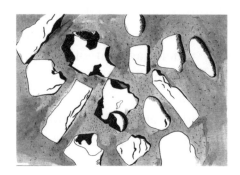

Lawrence shook himself awake. He was getting carried away again, like the time he had been gazing over the marshes. But still, he had discovered that flint had that basic quality that characterised North Norfolk. He watched fascinated as their colours changed when they lost the sunlight. Mirror black to a dull bruise, streaked rose or coral to dried blood – always from clear to opaque. But Lawrence saw that flint in North Norfolk was different from flint found in, say, genteel Sussex, the dormitory county with as many estate agents as old folks' homes. Flint in Sussex becomes gentler when the sun reflects off it. It changes from coral not to dried blood but to the colour of a pale salmon sandwich, from dull blue not to dense black but to the colour of a delicate grey blouse.

It hadn't taken long for them to appreciate flints. They knew, of course, that they were all more or less elliptical, roughly similar to an emu's egg, and also that each one's shape and colour differed a little from that of its neighbour. And they knew that their surfaces looked a dulled blue-grey. But they soon discovered that when the flints were chipped and split, perhaps for an axe-head in the old days or just for use in building, the edge became as sharp as a sacrificial knife. They found that the split surface became black-glassed obsidian and it flickered with reflections like a precious stone. And sometimes it turned into ochre, sand-flecked like rhino hide, warmer and more alive. And they had realised that if it had been scarce its value would have surpassed that of diamonds.

They had long since noticed that cottages were built with round flints, usually in random layers, not in rows – and uncut. Then they saw that important buildings were built of flints cut into squares. They saw that the flints were laid in line, vertically as well as horizontally. In such buildings the walls were faded chequer-boards of aquamarine, cobalt and gun-barrel.

"But haven't you noticed that whether chopped square or not, each one is still a little different from its neighbour?" Lawrence asked Eve.

"Yes, like people of one nationality," she smiled at him.

"Well, you wouldn't much say that of the Japanese," he sniffed. "More like England, don't you think?"

She nodded thoughtfully.

"Mind you, they wouldn't agree. But I think so. Lots of different types but all English flints! Vive la difference! It's what makes the English character."

Having abandoned the idea of finding a scooter, they had bought a couple of bicycles. Late one April morning they cycled up to the Nursery outside the village. Eve needed herbs and more vegetable seeds for her vegetable garden.

At the Nursery were four greenhouses, each about two hundred feet long. They were heated by yards and yards of ancient 4-inch pipes snaking around the walls or between rows of teetering tables. Heaped on the tables were piles of tomatoes, chrysanthemums, begonia and other assorted plants. Every now and then the heating pipes shuddered in uncontrollable spasms, like a dog shaking water off itself, and shed large flakes of rust everywhere. The ground outside was laid with samples of shrubs, hedges and saplings, piles of peat and compost, a privet hedge, a miscellaneous dump of trellises and all sorts of earthenware pots. Nearby was an army of small statues. They were cordoned off by ropes, presumably in case any of them might come to life and make a dash for it. Venus de Milo? No problem, just name the colour. Cherubs? What's your preference – boy/girl, wings with/without arrow, frontal/rear? Wishing wells, rustic/medieval, with/without hobgoblin? Micky Mouse/Donald Duck? Plenty of choice. Gnomes? Grimm, with/without fishing rod and/or pond? Nudes? Female/male, robed/bare, with/without figleaf? Toadstools? Coloured/spotted/plain? Grouped/single?

Between the Nursery and the village church a shallow field had just been ploughed. Crevasses of damp brown furrows pointed towards the church. Down the slope beyond it stretched the marshes and beyond the marshes lay the thin strip of sea, a blue ribbon binding up the coastline.

Lawrence had never forgotten the time years ago when he had first tasted fresh coriander. It had been as if he had tasted a jewel rather than just looked at it – not the actual taste of the jewel but the way it might have tasted judging by how it looked. Such a taste was something almost indescribable – by him, anyway. But Eve had wanted to build a herb garden even before they had unpacked the clock face. And the plan had become a real need when she first saw the huge bush of rosemary growing near Horace Nelson's cottage by the church. It had looked so tempting. Lawrence imagined how it might have been in medieval times. Suppose back inside the church you'd just confessed your sins and had been given absolution. You'd have left with a heart all pure again. Your step would have bounced with righteous virtue because your soul had been newly washed of sin. But temptation gives no pause. There it was in your path – someone else's rosemary bush. Dare you pluck a stalk or two? The priest is just behind you. If he catches you, it will be back to the church and a dozen Hail Marys – or something worse. Well, he reflected, it wasn't the church's interest to make anyone permanently virtuous.

Lawrence never got to find out who owned that bush of rosemary on the edge of the village green between church and pub. Horace had told him it must be 'rector' – as he put it. Hundreds of years later it was still an easy matter to snap off a few stalks. But nowadays Eve had decided to go to a Sunday service now and again and it was especially tempting after church to snap off a twig or two, knowing that they were going to roast a leg of lamb for Sunday lunch. But guilt had its effect. After all, that's why the church makes use of it. So now they found themselves at the Nursery.

Its herb department was efficiency itself – in fact overflowing. By comparison herbs in supermarkets seemed manicured and anaemic. As well as a root of rosemary they bought mint, thyme, basil, sage, dill, fennel, oregano, coriander, chives, hyssop, marjoram and parsley – all with their own roots and fresh and juicy.

"What the hell!" said Lawrence – and threw in some lemon verbena. "Looks good, smells good – even if you can't eat it."

They bought more vegetable seeds as well as the herbs. Then they added a dozen bags of compost. By now they realised they should have brought the car.

"Gibraltar House? I'll bring them down for you in half an hour," called out the owner. "And you can pay when I turn up."

So they left him and sailed on the bikes down the hill, past the church with its rosemary bush, past the green, past the Three Swallows and on to the heart of the village through a spatter of rain that, as usual in North Norfolk, had begun without warning. By the time they reached the Deli, they were definitely wet. And that, of course, gave them a good excuse to take refuge inside. Zeus was long now a friend whom they saw nearly every day. And they had discovered that sometimes he kept an opened bottle of wine and a few glasses on the bellows in the wine department.

Despite the rain the top half of the stable door was open. And there he was – at the bellows behind his great forge. He was surrounded by picnic hampers and bottles of Norfolk cider.

By one of those amazing co-incidences of life that happen in North Norfolk he had just opened a bottle for a customer to taste and was filling one of the glasses.

"Just in time! I might have known it." He grinned and scooped up more glasses in his fist. Eve was half surprised but also admiring that he didn't break them, his fist looked so strong. The wine was an interesting Chilean Cabernet Sauvignon – very interesting, actually. Even the customer got a glass.

After fifteen minutes the rain stopped. But by then Zeus had insisted they compare it with another Cabernet Sauvignon – from McLaren Vale in South Australia, he told them. They bought some asparagus. Like the pork hanging from the beams it came from Hector Hall nearby, he said ("Hector, you've met him yet? Large greatcoat?"). All their shopping under one roof, they thought. After an hour – another drink and a wander round the Deli – they headed home. It was only at the last minute that they decided to pop into the pub for a chat with Ronald. And by another lucky chance – still puzzling to Lawrence even though he was increasingly recognising that was how things happened on the North Norfolk coast – they found the Nursery owner.

"I left the herbs in your garden, seeing that you weren't there," he said, getting off his stool. "You can pay me next time you're up at the Nursery."

His Norfolk accent was typically gentle, sort of caressing. And he had a twinkle in his eye.

"Suddenly we had lots of people in after the rain stopped. Here, I brought you a little something to make up." And he held out a shoot of a rose, its yellow bud still tightly closed.

"Ah!" said Lawrence. "That rose looks thirsty. Care for a pint?"

After two pints and a large gin-and-tonic for Eve, they managed to return home. They decided it would be safer to walk rather than ride. And they brought the Nursery owner with them.

"Come and see our herb garden," they had said. And once there he looked at the clock face and grinned.

"Best thing you could do with that thing. Not many of us go to church now. And I'm always late anyway. Would be even if I had a watch that size."

But he liked the idea and warmed to what they were doing.

"A couple of weeks after you've planted out all these herbs they'll all be spreading out and coming on nicely. And why don't you put a big vase in the middle of the clock with some forsythia in it. It'll trail over it all really well and it's yellow so it'll go nicely with that rusty paint you've got there. You'll want to get that rose in, but there's no hurry," he told them. "Just make sure it gets plenty of water."

Eve made them tea and the three of them strolled around the garden. First stop was her vegetable patch. Most of them were almost ready for planting out. They both squatted down and he told her which ones were going to give the biggest vegetables. By the time he had finished they realised they would have to treble the size of her patch.

"Give us some more rain and they'll soon be on your plate!"

He straightened up and looked round the garden.

"You'll need to cut this ceanothus back ... it's hiding that shrub behind it ... that jasmine needs more water, it's delicate this time of year and you must keep it up."

He caught hold of a loop of twine nailed to the flint wall behind the jasmine.

"Look, hang it on this line here. Someone else had the same idea," he said. "It'll do the trick. And you'd better cut those shoots that are rising up off the weeping laburnum here."

He grinned at them. "They're growing the wrong way. Some flashy garden centre in London must have grafted the shoots on and sold them to you. Typical!"

Half an hour and another cup of tea later he left. He had sketched out a sort of prognosis on every plant in the garden, helped Eve to put in the vegetable seeds and told her how she should plant them out later. They were literally nourishing their roots in North Norfolk.

And the amazing thing was that Lawrence was fascinated by it all and by the slightly different needs of each plant. After all, when they had lived in Notting Hill, he remembered, a plant was a lump of cannabis that the police slipped into your pocket.

Before lunch a few days later they laid flints in the hollows of the bricks radiating in lines out from the clock. Then they filled the spaces between these rows of bricks with compost alternating with gravel. Then thyme, the first herb, went in the space between XII and I on the clock face. The next space – between I and II, that would be filled with gravel. And so on, with sectors round the clock alternating between gravel and herbs – gravel, mint, gravel, basil, gravel, chives, gravel, sage.

"You realise there's not enough room?" grumbled Lawrence. "I'll have to plant the parsley in with the sage."

"Don't worry," remarked Eve, as she poured him a glass of Chablis. "There are worse things in this life."

"Like the bank manager, I suppose," he grunted, as he took it and looked at her over the rim. "And do I understand that you feel we might have done the right thing after all?"

But all she did was to look closely at her glass and say:

"I think I'm going to have to make my vegetable patch a bit bigger. I hadn't allowed for planting out."

A few days after it was all completed Eve, who had been hanging pictures upstairs, rushed down to Lawrence in excitement. She found him sand-papering the corners of the dining room's bookshelves. It was the final touch before putting in their books. At that moment they were still piled in a heap under the windows. He was thinking he might call it the library. He had never had room for one in London. The idea of a library gave him a relaxed sort of feeling. And he'd hardly ever had that feeling in London either. Eve interrupted him.

"Come up and smell it! Top room!" she cried. So Lawrence followed her upstairs. And leaning out of the window above the herb garden he too caught the heady scent of sage rising up to them.

"Sage and onion stuffing! As good as roast chicken." They shook their heads and laughed at each other at the sheer pleasure of it. And then they paused and looked out again, past their garden's flint walls at the view of rectory, stables, elms and hillside. And they smiled at each other again, as they had done that first day.

\*       \*       \*

There was something else about North Norfolk, especially on its coast. It was something they hadn't really known about before they arrived. It hadn't featured in their memories of those weekends years ago. In those days the climate, the sea, the weather, the fields ... they had been the main attractions.

But now Lawrence was older. He had come to appreciate quality rather than quantity. And so something else had become important – the food. And fresh food, too. They had discovered that North Norfolk had the richest larder in England. Most of it was wandering around the fields waiting to be shot, chased, snared or generally apprehended in order to have its throat cut, be skinned, plucked or otherwise prepared for the human stomach. They found it difficult to drive along Norfolk's lanes, even its main roads, without threatening the life of some scatty pheasant or partridge that always seemed to wait for a car to approach before beginning to cross over. They all seemed to think that because Norfolk was a dead end they could use the roads without a care. But Lawrence often passed a heap of fluttering feathers and a dark lump on the tarmac. The other day, when they had been driving to the Dun Cow at Salthouse, one of them had quite inconsiderately flown at their car, smashed their right-hand headlight and hadn't done itself much good either. An expensive pheasant. He could have bought sixty or seventy of them for the price of the new headlight. Some days earlier, Lawrence had come across a dozen deer standing motionless at the edge of a wood near Holt. He stopped a hundred yards from them. They were caught in their stride and stopped dead too – all looking at him. Their coats were the same light tan as the trees and the undergrowth behind them, so they were difficult to see. They were frozen there for so long that it was as if time had stood still and they had become part of a medieval tapestry. For weeks afterwards venison caught his eye on the menus of local restaurants. And one day Lawrence had seen four hares rushing around in circles in a field near Langham – mad as hatters. Another sign of spring. Another item for a marinade.

Fish? From Kings Lynn round past Lowestoft Norfolk bulges into the North Sea like an overfed stomach. Its coastline gives it more seafood that most English counties. Crab, lobster and skate all await the cage or the hook. On the marshes mussels and whelks pulsate gently to the flow of the tides – waiting for anybody with a basket and a pair of gumboots. Enriched by cattle droppings, mushrooms spring up at dawn. And samphire, too, this rich man's asparagus, lies among the creeks like Ophelia's hair – damp, limp and abandoned. Round the coast to Great Yarmouth, herring and bloaters are stacked on the tide and waiting for a net. You can fish for sea bass and even squid a few miles off the coast if you can get Tom to take you out in his boat.

"If you want trout," he told Lawrence, "you and Eve should drag a net along the coast – one with thigh boots, the other on the beach. They come to the shallows to rub the lice off them. It's illegal, though." He looked sternly at Lawrence. "The SAS does not do that sort of thing."

John Hurlingham, the Laughing Cavalier with the Van Dyck beard who had become their favourite butcher in all England, had a window display that was a still life of teal and mallard, pheasant, widgeon and partridge, rabbit and hare, pigeon, snipe and woodcock – and every one of them local. They were all mixed up together, feathers tumbled everywhere. Mallard and teal lay in a heap of cobalt and emerald. Death had dulled their colours but their heads were tucked beneath their wings as if asleep. Three or four cock pheasants – glittering Prussian blue, jade and scarlet – were strewn limply as if unconscious. They lay beside a lanky tawny-flecked and sand-speckled hare that had been thrown down like a discarded silk stocking. Nearby was a clutch of three woodcock, their neat umber feathers streaked like rain-wetted bark. They were trim and tiny with tapering beaks, long and dainty. Their eyes were hooded and they lay huddled together like stillborn kittens. At the window lay a child's pet, a grey fluffy rabbit with white floppy ears. It seemed asleep but its eyes stared and a pink fleck of blood pricked its mouth. John usually had a half-carcase of pork hooked up in his window together with five or six strings of sausages – Norfolk, Cumberland, Lincolnshire and the Hurlingham Special (the most blood-stained and swollen of the lot). Once he strung a large carcase across his shop window – head, carcase, legs, tail and all. Lawrence never got to find out what it was – wild cat, probably. It was like some Stone Age feast. And late in March he had stuck the heads of six hogs on sharpened pikes and put them in his window. Coarse bristles and mean little eyes, traitors, recusants or protestants ... Tudor England was not far off that day.

In the next-door shop he spread out his flood of sea food – fog-grey yet salmon-flecked red mullet, an epic pyramid of flint-blue mussels coruscated with winkles as if shipwrecked, scattered deep-sea pearls of priceless rose-seeped shrimps and scrap-yards of armour-plated shell-fish, crab and lobster, their colour ebbing away from pink to grey. They were all lumped together like a pile of bodies on Bosworth Field.

It wasn't long before John began to give Lawrence and Eve hints on how to cook a dish, maybe a side of gammon or a leg of lamb. As for pork, he once even told them how to kill a pig.

"I learned the trade on a farm behind Wells," he told them. "We used to go round all the farms north of Norwich in those days. But now I only kill Hector's pigs for him. You know Hector?" he asked. "At Hector Hall?"

"Greatcoat?" asked Lawrence.

"Greatcoat!" He grinned. The Laughing Cavalier came alive and licked his lips.

"The best way to carve it is to start like this and keep close to the bone." He held the side of pork with his left hand, moved his left shoulder forward, raised his carving knife in his other hand, looked along it and carefully lined it up towards the pork like a matador's sword after it is raised up from beneath the muleta cape.

"You've got to get the point in the right place. It's a bit like bullfighting, yes. And when you're cooking it, don't forget the marmalade."

Marmalade? For cooking pork? They found out later, like a lot of things in North Norfolk. But that afternoon they were there to buy a leg of English lamb for some old friends coming for the weekend. As John cut it, he said:

"I've got a lovely bit of Albanian lamb for you, if you'd like that as well."

Albanian lamb? He grinned.

"Yes, it's not like this – this English lamb. But it's on the bone ... feel like some? Or a joint? Or maybe a nice bit of ox-tail?"

Ox-tail lamb?

"Yeees, you know what I mean," he grinned again. "The government has been buggering us around again. All that nonsense about banning beef on the bone. Making out it was dangerous!" He snorted. "Not so dangerous as crossing the road outside here after midnight on Sunday. And d'you know why they did it?"

They were beginning to understand.

"That's right! Just to suck up to those faceless buggers in Brussels, not to mention the French. They got us into the mess and they haven't got the guts to stand up for us so they try to tell us what to eat instead. So I call it Albanian lamb."

"That's right," said Lawrence. "And it gets much worse. Did you know that even when we decided to stop banning it the Welsh and Scotch Parliaments were able to stop us eating it?"

"I certainly did!" answered John. "I sometimes think that lot in Brussels wants to really get the English. God knows why."

He winked.

"Maybe because we'd been beating the lot of them for centuries."

\*    \*    \*

Next day it was at a mid-afternoon Sunday lunch with their friends and well into the weekend when Lawrence was just about to carve John Hurlingham's leg of Albanian lamb and the doorbell rang.

Justine, the Albatross's figurehead – as they had come to think of her – was at the door and would they like to come round that evening to her daughter's birthday party? Of course! And that was their third village invitation. Lawrence and Eve smiled at each other.

"It's slowly happening," she said. "And perhaps the Village Marxist or the Albatross' skipper will be there."

"Can't you think of anything else?" grumbled Lawrence. "Anyway, probably both."

But meantime – Sunday lunch. Lawrence had cooked red peppers for their London friends. He had stuffed the peppers with fennel he had bleached in boiling water and sliced across the root. Then he lined the peppers with crushed tomato. When he and Eve moved up they had brought with them a big old mortar and pestle, one of the items that had been well wrapped for the journey. It had belonged to Eve's great grandmother. During their years in Notting Hill Eve had kept hairpins in it. But now she crushed coriander, pepper and fennel seeds with its pestle, sprinkled the mix on top of the peppers, slid them into the Aga and baked them for an hour. After that she squeezed lemon over them and threw on some leaves of parsley at the last minute.

Earlier Lawrence had brushed the leg of Albanian lamb with olive oil, spiked it with plenty of rosemary from their herb garden, slipped big chunks of smoked garlic deep under the skin and sunk it in a bottle or two of red wine in a cast-iron pot on the coolest plate on the Aga. There it would cook slowly for a few hours while they walked over the marshes to the sea. He suggested to their guests that they might consider a pint, or maybe two pints, at the pub in Stiffkey. Yes, it would delay them. But half an hour more or less for lamb was as important as what was showing that afternoon on television.

By the time they returned they'd be able to spoon the meat off the bone. But before they sat down Lawrence would spread mustard and breadcrumbs over it all, together with a few other things he would think of later, before putting it under the grill for maybe fifteen minutes. Then the skin would be crisp and sizzling with garlic.

On Stiffkey marshes the path to the sea crosses a creek at a bridge. There they came across a fisherman harvesting mussels. He introduced himself – Jimmy Blake, brother of Freddy. And they knew Freddy. Freddy was that friend of Prospero (and, they hoped, perhaps of theirs too), the oldest inhabitant and the one who had shown then the winter aconites near the church. Like his mussels Jimmy was dripping with seaweed and smelled of seawater. They watched him at work. He had a highly specialised style. He scraped up several dozen mussels from the bed of the creek and threw them into a big porous bag. Then he bashed them up and down on the bottom of the stream.

"That'll keep 'em honest," he told Eve. "Nasty little buggers, these fresh-brook mussels. My mum got food poisoning off one of them ten years back."

And he gave the bag another bash on the stones followed by a fierce sieving. Obviously this concentrated the minds of any rebels who might be thinking of having another go at his mum. Then he packed them in an old sack with some red twine and began to scrape the next lot from the bed of the creek. He said he'd go on until there were no more mussels or until The Red Lion was open, whichever was sooner. So they ordered some mussels from him to eat before the Albanian lamb and went to the Red Lion, which was open.

When they reached home Lawrence planned to crush one small clove of garlic, finely chop one medium-sized onion and carefully soften them both in a clean saucepan over a low heat on the Aga with 2 1/2oz of butter, adding half a small glass of white wine. He would take time to thoroughly scrape every little piece of barnacle and seaweed off the mussels so that they were completely clean, and then place them in a deep pan of cold water and throw away any that floated. After that he would dry them carefully and gently heat them in the pan for three minutes, a few at a time. He would make sure that any that didn't open in the pan were thrown away. Then, once all were opened, he would carefully remove them, keep them warm at 45°C in the oven while straining the onion, the garlic and the white wine in the pan through a muslin sieve to produce a pure liquid which he would then gently pour over the mussels, on which he would neatly sprinkle a little carefully cut parsley. To accompany the mussels he would open a bottle of Sancerre 1995 and keep it chilled in the conservatory before bringing it into the dining room.

But once home and with appetites cut sharp from a pint or two and the smell of sea-water on them after a couple of hours on the cold marshes, everyone crammed themselves into the warm kitchen opening bottles, gossiping loudly, laughing at their own jokes, losing the corkscrew, treading on the cat, hacking up a few onions, telling jokes to Eve as she threw the mussels around in a big pan on the hot Aga, topping up her glass, finding the corkscrew, opening another bottle, helping her pour it into the pan and throw in a big lump of butter, treading on the cat again, getting cigarette ash in the pan, cutting up half a dozen cloves of garlic, waiting poised with a tub of cream to pour on with a couple of handfuls of torn parsley they'd just picked from her herb garden. And then they all ate it with plenty of baked garlic bread and a few more bottles – some white, some red – in record time sitting around a blazing fire. And that's how Sunday lunch goes in North Norfolk. Not to mention the Albanian lamb.

By now they had begun to make friends in the village and their London guests were becoming rarer and rarer. Their friends this weekend had been next-door neighbours in Notting Hill for many years. They had both converted their houses from bed-sitter warrens. They had both seen their children grow up together. They had often played tennis together. They had gossiped and given dinner parties together. Over the last twenty years they were one of the group of neighbours who had become good friends.

They had arrived that Saturday morning – just in time for a late breakfast of kippers and potted shrimps from the village's smoke-house, with slices of that stone-ground brown wholemeal bread. Living in the country had given Eve and Lawrence time to eat a good break-fast. And breakfast like that provided them with the energy for a slow wander to one of the village's pubs – or to both. And that was where they took their weekend guests – to both.

Late in the afternoon Eve and Lawrence took them to the sea on the Salthouse marshes. The wind had got up and the air was full of spray. On the beach a competition was going on. Each one hidden behind windbreaks, a dozen fishermen sat fifty yards from each other all the way down the beach. Their rods were bent tight and the lines vanished into the surf. One of the fishermen picked up his rod, reeled in the line, ran forward and hurled it further out.

Their friends turned towards them, the spray on their faces and their eyes shining at the sight of that line flying. Lawrence told them that he and Eve had seen something like it on the beach when they had first visited the village. They nodded, looked at him closely and nodded again, smiling. Now they understood and now they knew how Lawrence and Eve had felt. Now they knew why these two had come up to North Norfolk.

As they walked back in the early evening the light drained away, darkness sank over the sky and one by one the lights of Salthouse flickered on. High on the hill behind the village the church slowly vanished into the deepening night.

That evening Eve and Lawrence gave their guests some of Zeus's sparkling wine, a couple of crabs caught and dressed by Tom and a widgeon each from their butcher, John. Lawrence had marinated the widgeon for a couple of days. He had added some of their plums that Eve had bottled in Norfolk wine with a dash of cognac. He had left it all to simmer for an hour or so on the Aga. The casserole hardly bubbled, just thumped slowly like a trawler's diesel engine creeping up to its berth at Wells Harbour after a fishing trip. By the time they came to sit down no one could tell widgeon from plum. Later, amid the wood smoke from the fire, they talked late over their wine by candlelight, empty bottles gleaming all around. And they talked in the way one always talks with friends just up from London for the weekend. They gossiped about neighbours they had left behind, they proudly exchanged stories about their children, they grumbled about the government and they shared anxiety over Europe ... until all were sleepy and content by the time they slowly climbed the stairs and sank into their beds.

Early next evening, their late lunch of mussels and lamb finished at last, the time came for their friends to leave for London. They said they'd loved the weekend. They said they'd been upset all day at the thought of having to go home. And they said they didn't want to leave.

But now they had to say goodbye. It was the old story of the office on Monday morning. Yes, Lawrence and Eve were sad that their friends had to go. They were glad to have seen them although relieved it was they who were staying. But they were the ones who were committed. And that made them feel again that they truly belonged to their little community in North Norfolk. And this made their life here all the richer, all the more miraculous – particularly because it was only a simple decision that had led to such a change in their lives. They felt settled, warm and comfortable. And fond as they had been of all their London friends, those two weekenders were indeed to be the last regular visitors from their past. It was something they did not realise for many months, so self-sufficient had their life become.

As they strolled the hundred yards down the street that separated them from Justine's home and the birthday party, they knew by now that they lived and belonged in this village. Justine and her children were people they liked well. And they valued her invitation.

Crammed up in the little front room were some of their neighbours – the Village Marxist and the serene and beautiful Rhine Maiden, not to mention lots of children, most of whom were desperate to see Justine's daughter's presents. Also present was Jan, skipper of that fabulous schooner, the Albatross. Here he stood, huge with beard, strong and impassive. He was talking quietly to a Dutch lad, one of his crew. Eve turned to Lawrence.

"They're both here," she whispered.

"Who?" he asked loudly.

"Shhh ... Jan and the VM, of course," she said impatiently.

"Oh, well, why not indeed?"

"Look, they're both ignoring each other," she whispered.

That was true enough. Justine and the Village Marxist were busy carrying coffee cups to the kitchen together and had disappeared for several minutes. Jan was talking to his deckhand as if she had never existed.

"I bet Jan is going to win!" she whispered.

"What?" asked Lawrence. But she was smiling to herself.

"It's the Flying Dutchman," she said dreamily. And with an air of smug finality she said firmly. "He's found his woman."

Lawrence groaned.

"Well, it must be, anyway," she told him. "The Albatross has been tied up for three months. Prospero told me so yesterday. And that's because of Justine."

He groaned again. She frowned at him, pursed her lips and rolled her eyes.

Soon freshly brewed coffee was handed round by the Village Marxist. Eve presented their gift – a little jug with a grainy brown surface they had bought in the Pottery the day before. Seeing it, the Rhine Maiden put her hand to her mouth and blushed.

"What is it? It's one of yours, remember?" asked Eve.

The Rhine Maiden dipped into her bag and held up an identical jug.

"Oh dear! Eve! We're birds of a feather." They both laughed. She turned to Justine's daughter. "Don't worry darling. Come into the Pottery tomorrow and you can choose something else to replace it!"

The birthday cake was brought in and admired. Justine's daughter blew out the seventeen candles. Everyone clapped and sang "Happy Birthday." And general conversation broke out.

Eve and Lawrence heard that she had been offered a university place.

"Well, that's a wonderful start! What's she going to study?" asked Lawrence.

"Medicine," answered Justine. "But at the moment I'm not sure I can afford it. I mean, I can't at the moment, anyway." She shrugged. "But something will happen."

Lawrence noticed how her hair rippled down her straight back.

She smiled at him. "It always does."

Jan left his deck hand and came over to them. He turned to Eve and Lawrence.

"I'm sorry I was in a hurry when we first met." He spread his hands open and smiled. "Time and tide, you must know …"

"Oh yes, of course! Did you have a good trip to the continent?"

"Well, there were some heavy seas, Lawrence, you know. And we had a near-miss one night with a big tanker bound for Stavangar. We're a sailing boat so we have priority. But it doesn't always work out like that. And with a big tanker that size, ah, it was a VLCC and low in the water so it must have had a full cargo, about a quarter of a million tonnes you know, they take so long to turn anyway. You don't argue!" And soon they both embarked on an ideal conversation – where someone's desire to talk about his favourite subject is matched by the other's desire to listen to him. Meanwhile Eve overheard the Village Marxist earnestly explaining something to Jan's young Dutch sailor.

"This country has been going downhill for years, since the war in fact," he was saying. "Look at all those skinheads at football matches, but what do you expect with the sort of television we have nowadays? It's worse than American! There's been two generations of trendy nonsense in education, so no wonder there are so many petty criminals around. The latest generation are grown-up children and that's dangerous."

He snorted and looked around for Justine to approve. But she and Jan seemed to have vanished. By now, though, he was in full swing.

"And then this government did nothing about the beef scare for years. The whole country has been rotten with corruption for decades."

"The first thing to do," he continued, not noticing the boy's confusion, "is to get this government out. Then we will be able to organise a large-scale redistribution of wealth."

He sat back with a sense of achievement. "Don't bother me with details," you could almost hear him saying. Eve looked back at Lawrence and shook her head sadly, as if to say the VM didn't have a chance.

The Dutch boy looked into his mug of coffee. Perhaps he was wondering how much of this wealth would be coming his way.

There was a knock at the door and in came a stocky man with tousled hair. He was wearing thigh boots and he smelled of seaweed and salt water. He gave Justine's daughter a big hug and handed over his present, a lobster in a shopping bag.

"It jumped into my boat this morning," he grinned, with a broad voice. "Got the boat moored at the quay here. Threw a rope round the windmill – well, a bit of it. Much easier than getting here by car – that's dangerous, that is!"

"This is Derek." Justine's daughter introduced him to them. "He's a fisherman in Blakeney."

They shook hands. His were wet.

"So you've got Gibraltar House?" he asked with a cheerful grin. "Ah, it's a lovely place. Tell you what. If you need a gardener, give me a ring. I've got a son who'll do for you and it'll keep him out of the pub."

He paused.

"Well, give him something to pay his round, anyway – instead of me all the time."

Soon he was talking shipping with Jan, who had returned to the room with Justine. Eve noticed immediately that she was looking suspiciously pink. Derek had seen a new type of drogue anchor on the Albatross' fore-deck last week in Wells. He was asking if it dragged – for if it didn't his little fishing boat would be safe using it. That carried only a few tons compared with the hundred tons of the Albatross when she was fully loaded.

By now Eve was deep in conversation also, this time with the Rhine Maiden. Another potter had just adopted a baby and, of course, it was adorable. And what about Hector, that great-coated pig-rearer whom they hadn't yet met?

Eventually they said their good-byes to everyone and left. Arm in arm, they wandered slowly home in the night air. With their torch to guide their path they walked in the middle of the empty road under the high and starry sky. And the sound of their footsteps echoed against the houses on either side.

"They'll be reaching the motorway in about an hour," they said to each other. "Not more than another three hours before they'll be home. Maybe after midnight."

"That's right," they said to each other. Lawrence yawned.

Back home they opened a bottle of wine and took it to bed. Tomorrow was Monday and it didn't mean a thing.

*     *     *

At last came the social ordeal. They were to give their first dinner party. The guests were not locals. For that they would have to have been invited first – maybe after a couple of generations. Tonight their guests were incomers, even if well established, and stout parties all – Victor, the merchant banker, his wife Pat and the magisterial Millicent. Eve had recently learned that, besides being cookery writer, chairman of the parish council, churchwarden, organiser of church flower arranging and chairman of the Church Restoration Fund Committee and its lunches, Millicent was also the eminence grise behind the Saturday morning bring-and-buy meetings on the church green.

Congregation Street was coming to dinner and the hosts were nervous.

But a heavy fall of snow, unexpected for April even in North Norfolk, took their mind off worrying about Millicent. It was still snowing as night fell. But with torches waving through the flakes their guests came stomping down the drive and shook snow off their overcoats in the hall. Everyone was cheerful. In fact they considered it an achievement to have reached Gibraltar House at all. They warmed their hands before the fire and Lawrence filled their glasses with mulled wine.

"I must say the bricks of this fireplace are quite impressive," commented Victor. "What is it? Victorian?" he asked blandly.

Lawrence looked pained.

"Victorian? Really, this isn't a pre-fab, Victor," he protested. "Much earlier than that. Seventeenth century if it's a day. Dutch, you know."

He produced a bottle and Victor held up his glass.

"Oh, Dutch? Really? Hmmm, is it in Pevsner, then? You know … who wrote about all the houses in England? He had two volumes on Norfolk, you know. I'm in it, of course."

"Not you, Victor," His wife Pat turned round from a chat with Eve about Philip's sermon last week. "The house. You're not that old." She shook her head at him. "Yet."

"Didn't you have a stove in that fireplace?" asked Victor, unperturbed. "I remember seeing it before you moved in."

"Yes, but we sold it because we wanted an open fire," explained Eve. Lawrence told them he had advertised it for sale in the Eastern Daily Press and a couple running a newsagent's near Cromer had bought it.

"She was about six foot tall with cropped hair, thick glasses, electric blue trousers with sandals and a tight red sweater. Her husband came up to her armpits."

"Armpits? That doesn't sound like round here," said Victor. He thought for a moment. "Maybe it's the sort you'd get if you advertised for wife-swapping in Sheringham."

"And how would you know?" demanded Pat, looking suspiciously at him.

"Only if you're lucky," contributed Eve, as a form of distraction.

Millicent was gazing around cautiously, perhaps looking for the Modigliani nude or costing out the armchairs.

Eventually, glasses having been refilled once or twice or more, they sat down to some fresh crab. Tom had caught them in the early tide before dawn from his boat off Wells and Eve had bought them from him a couple of hours ago. Lawrence had picked some mushrooms before breakfast on the Salthouse marshes and grilled them in red wine to serve them with the crab on a few leaves of crisp lettuce. After that – a casserole of local partridge with Brussels sprouts sprinkled with ground nutmeg and almonds (á la Pippa) and parsnips from Eve's own patch. He had hung the birds in the conservatory but he wasn't used to game. He was afraid they would still taste too tough, especially when roasted. And when you're cooking for a cookery writer you don't take any risks. He didn't want to get served up in her next article under the heading: "How Not To Cook Game." So that morning he had telephoned John Hurlingham at his butcher's shop in Holt.

"They've been hanging for at least a week," Lawrence told him. "Is that too long? I mean, they smell a bit. And Eve won't go near them."

"Well," he said, "put it this way, Lawrence. Are they crawling along the table yet?"

Was he serious? Just to be safe Lawrence had put them to bubble on top of the Aga as a very slow casserole with a few braised carrots and onions. He'd know when they were done when he could pull the meat off the bones. After that – in fact at the last minute – he mixed in plenty of cognac and cream. That should be popular, he thought. Then he sprinkled on a little sugar. He thought it might offset the dryness of the cognac. He didn't tell them what he had added but Victor loved it and asked for more. Millicent merely caught his eye for a moment. A flicker played across her face like a spatter of winter rain – more like indigestion than a smile, in fact. Was it that bad – and had she guessed? Victor took his second helping and looked at his wife, who frowned at him.

"Well, no one would trust a banker if he was thin," he protested. "They'd think he wasn't any good."

"OK, so now you're eating to keep yourself in business, I suppose?" she remarked, but contradicted herself by putting more on her own plate, and turned to Eve.

"Your flower arranging is very popular, Eve," she remarked. "I heard someone in the pub talking about it to Ronald last week."

Eve blushed and smiled at Lawrence. Pat continued. "Well, it's such a big church. We do need to fill it out with flowers. But how is your sketching getting on, anyway?"

"Oh!" said Eve, a little flustered. "Well, actually, I've started doing water colours now, Pat. But it's difficult … I mean, if I don't get it right first time I can't rub it out, like a sketch. But I do love the colours."

Still blushing, she scurried off to the kitchen to fetch more of her vegetables.

All village dinner parties have one extra course – a well-stewed helping of some strong and meaty gossip. They all chewed it like a hard root vegetable or a cheekfull of quat. Eve was sure that Leda was getting serious with Zeus at the Deli. She had seen them together at the Guardian's birthday party. Everyone agreed that he had amazing charm.

"So you've noticed her?" said Victor. "Remember what I was saying?"

"I must say you've been sharp-eyed," complimented Pat.

"Well, he's rather dishy," admitted Eve. "The girls who work there should take out an insurance policy against falling for him."

"Yes, but I'd load the premium, you know. Anyway as I'm already taking bets. I'll get it both ways. And if you tell me she's coming up on the rails I'd better shorten the odds," said Victor the banker. "Yes, he is quite striking, I suppose. Perhaps a bit overweight."

His wife went "Ha!" but he ignored her, "not like me, of course."

But the Deli, if not Zeus, is clearly a rival to cookery writer Millicent. She firmly changed the subject.

"You obviously haven't heard that The Cedars has been sold?" she announced – as if playing an ace. "It's near the church. You must have passed it, Eve."

Everyone turned and stared at her. Eve and Lawrence remembered meeting its owner once, when they were in the Deli.

"He's sold it? But when his mother died and left it to him, she said she wanted him to settle in it," protested Pat.

"Well, yes, indeed," said Millicent slowly, her voice rising slightly. "And she had been such a help to the village, what with bringing the Lord Lieutenant to the fête each year." She shook her head in puzzled sorrow.

"But that's not the worst of it," she added, "he's sold it to a property developer."

She couldn't have caused more alarm if she'd thrown a snake on the table. A shudder ran round the room. Victor scraped his chair back. Pat snorted. Everyone went white. This property developer might turn the place into a health farm. The thought made them feel ill immediately. Nothing could be worse. Except perhaps a conference centre. Think of all those suits and BMW's in the village.

"Well, Victor, you're a banker, I know," commented Millicent to him, "but I'm sure you don't want any businessmen here. I mean, we might as well all be living in Surrey – somewhere like Dorking, for example."

She slowly shook her head from side to side.

"Philip was horrified, of course," she added. "But he did say something about shelter for the poor and needy, though."

"City yuppies? Do they come into that category?" asked Lawrence.

"Oh, that's Philip!" laughed Pat. "I suspect he was being ironic."

"Well, there's a lot of land that goes with The Cedars," said Victor. "Infilling is pretty popular with the council and this developer will have plenty of scope for it."

He paused. "But Pat and I are all right where we are. Everything round us has been developed already."

He paused again. "By me, actually."

He poured himself another glass of wine as if to celebrate his safety. "When it's your development, it's all right," he said firmly.

Millicent sniffed.

"But," he continued, ignoring the sniff. "Sooner or later someone was bound to let in a developer." He continued in placatory tone. "Millicent, you're the chairman of our council. Can't you hold this man back? Isn't there some bye-law you can dredge up?"

"Not really," she said, shaking her head. "I mean, we can refuse planning permission, of course, but he'll be bound to appeal. They all do. And Cromer Council will most likely overrule us. They like infilling. They don't live here."

"It's happening all over the country," said Lawrence. "If it's not infilling it's housing developments everywhere, hedges vanishing, motorways all over the place, well, they may be needed by some people, but we don't need them, we didn't want to go anywhere when we moved up here."

"Well, Lawrence, that's one reason why we came here too," Pat told him.

"What about the birds?" interjected her husband. "It beats banking nowadays. I saw a bittern the other day, you know."

His wife seemed not to hear. "Every year the country loses hundreds of acres to roads or supermarkets. We wanted a place where that wouldn't happen. And no one's going to build a motorway to North Norfolk!"

"Well, it certainly hasn't happened yet. And anyway one mess of pottage doesn't make much difference," Millicent pointed out.

"Yes, that's true," admitted Eve. "There's a lot of space. And we are on the edge here. There's no gentrification or prettying up. Even though we get tourists, no one seems to cater for them much. I mean, you can't count bed-and-breakfast."

"Well," said Victor. "Since the war every government's idea of saving the countryside has been to manicure it. One day someone will try to pedestrianise our village street on the grounds that it will be better than being jammed with cars. I hope you'll fight that, Millicent, in the parish council?"

"I certainly will," she said stoutly. "The very idea!"

"Well, thank heavens," said Eve. "But look at all those ridiculous toy farms or model mines that have sprung up in England. Working models they call them, all sanitised and sterile and they give no idea of how terrible something like a coal mine was in those days. They're as bad as Disneyland – well, almost. And then there are the theme parks..."

"Ah, yes," interrupted Lawrence. "Before we came up here we felt that the whole country was turning into a theme park."

"Yes, but not up here," said Pat.

"Yes! That's what I mean. But not here!"

"It's just about the one place that isn't. But don't you see," Victor leaned forward, "the theme parks are like the jar of strawberry jam you take to your picnic. You put it on the ground a few feet away and all the wasps go there instead of swarming round you." He leaned back.

"In fact," he added as if he had just thought of it, "Sandringham is our jam-jar up here. All the tourists go there to goggle at the royal family so they leave us in peace. They've even got a tour in Holt taking people to see them."

He winked at Lawrence.

"1pm sharp every Friday, young man, if you're interested."

"Not quite," said Lawrence. "But does the driver hand out buns?"

"I must say, though," Millicent hurriedly pointed out. "Factory farming takes up a lot of space, too. And what they produce doesn't taste of much, either. Thank heavens we have a lot of free-range local food. And I don't just mean free-range pheasants."

Everyone sighed – ah yes! And comfort food was the only remedy. And luckily Eve had it – a good warming pudding of sweet apple tart using Cox's Orange Pippins from the tree in their garden, the one that had caught her gaze when they first saw the house. She had caramelised it with nearly twice as much sugar that she should have used. Victor loved it. Back to boarding school. All gone – good boys!

The evening ended with coffee and the rest of the cognac. And then, torches waving perhaps a little more unsteadily than when they arrived, Congregation Street braved the snow to make their separate journeys home.

*     *     *

"Quick!" Eve's voice sounded anxious as she called up the stairs.

"What is it?" mumbled her husband out of the side of his mouth. He was balanced up a ladder hanging pictures in the top room and his mouth was full of nails.

"The cat's being sick but I can't see her. I don't know where she is."

"Well, let her be sick," he replied testily, dropping several nails on the carpet as he spoke. "Now you've made me drop my nails."

"Yes, but don't you remember last time?" Eve was impatient. "She had that bone stuck in her throat?"

"Yes – and it was me who got it out. Of course I remember."

"Well, come and help again then. Can't you hear her?"

Lawrence stood still on the ladder and listened. Sure enough a harsh retching sound was coming from the garden.

"All right, then."

He sighed, put the nails at the top of the stepladder, stepped down quickly and stumbled on the last step. This knocked the ladder over, which fell onto another picture, breaking the glass. And the nails scattered around him on the floor.

"Bugger!"

He climbed down to the hall where she was standing holding a pot of flowers. And then he saw the cat.

"Look!" he said. "Behind you. The cat's here. Behind you. Not in the damn garden."

"What?" shrieked Eve. She swung round and the pot of flowers slipped out of her hands and broke into pieces on the floor. Water leaked everywhere. The cat was sitting on the dining room table watching her.

"Oh! What are you doing there?" she asked the cat, who didn't reply. "Why aren't you being sick?"

"She's not being sick because she's not being sick. It can't be the cat. Can I go back upstairs now? I've upset the ladder, broken a picture's glass, split a lot of nails and nearly swallowed some and you've broken a pot of flowers and the cat isn't being sick. OK?"

"Well, what is it?"

"I don't know. Maybe another cat. But we're not adopting it."

Then he relented.

145

"OK, I suppose we'd better go and see, then."

She picked up the cat, held her close ("Gootchie, gootchie, Sphinxie-winxie, you're not being sick after all," she said, stroking it gently) and followed him out to the garden. And there it was – a pheasant stalking around making cat-being-sick noises.

"What's it doing that for?" she asked him.

"Well, it's not being sick, is it?" Lawrence adopted an air of country knowledge. Tom had told him all about it the other day. "Actually, it's the time of the year. They're trying to find the eggs they've laid. Before they get shot, presumably."

"Well, I didn't know. I thought it was the cat being sick. How d'you know all that, anyway?"

"Ah, well, you get to learn a thing or two up here," he told her. "And now you've just got to stop your cat getting at it. Keep her in the dining room for a bit and shoo the bird away."

And he went back upstairs, spitting out a nail.

*     *     *

It had been in March that they had met Jekyll 'n' Hyde, owner of the Bookshop. That was at the Guardian's birthday party. They had been thrown in at the deep end that night but they wanted to see him under his own roof. He had seemed a bloody-minded cuss who spoke his own mind. And, after all, being independent and bloody-minded were English qualities. By now they were suspecting that the most independent and bloody-minded Englishmen came from North Norfolk.

"He's also rather handsome," added Eve. Lawrence sighed.

"Don't you think of anything else?"

So now, a month later, they decided to visit his bookshop. It was the Easter weekend and the village was busy. Visitors were wandering everywhere and the shops were full. The Guardian gave them a grin and a 'thumbs-up' through the Pottery windows as they saw him wrapping a bulky order. The Smoke House was jammed to the doors and passersby were smiling at The Flasher in the window. Over their heads Moses gave them a quick wave as he wrapped a dozen kippers. Clearly, business was good. The Bookshop's window was shared between a first edition of "East Anglian Privies" and a privately printed copy of "The Official History of Fakenham Football Club."

Lawrence smiled at Eve. She pursed her lips at him, still annoyed at being teased about the pheasant not being sick.

"Well, what did you expect?" she asked. "Ezra Pound?"

On the door was a notice that said: "PLEASE WIPE SHOES OR REMOVE SAME." Four or five people were browsing quietly at the shelves. Beyond them, an open door led to the art gallery where some bird paintings were on show. A Mozart quartet was playing softly in the background. How cultural, they thought.

Suddenly the culture was shattered by a bellow.

"Are you going to buy that book or are you not?"

Purple with rage, Jekyll 'n' Hyde was bending over a little old lady holding a copy of Pride and Prejudice.

"Well … well, I …" she stuttered. At her feet a shopping bag held three earthenware dishes and a small vase that she had just bought at the Pottery. She had been standing in one corner, well out of everyone's way and obviously quite happily browsing until Jekyll 'n' Hyde accosted her.

"You've been in here every day since Friday morning looking at that book," he snapped. "You're reading it, aren't you? In my shop!"

The other customers looked embarrassed and kept their heads in the books they were looking at.

"Well … I suppose … well, I was trying to make up my mind," she admitted nervously. It wasn't like this in Tunbridge Wells.

"This isn't the British Museum Reading Room, you know," Jekyll 'n' Hyde barked. And then he saw her shoes.

"And you've brought mud in here all over your feet. Can't you read that notice?" He flung his arm in the direction of the door.

"Do you know how much it costs to clean this floor?" He bent down to her. His face was almost black by now.

"Well, no actually, not really … but I'm … I'm sure it costs a lot."

"It bloody does. And I've a good mind to send you a bill for that, too."

Worse was to come, for he suddenly saw what she had in her bag.

"My God! You've been buying plates from across the road too, haven't you?"

"Well, they did look rather nice …"

He interrupted her.

"I've got to pay my rates as well as that lot, you know. And reading my books without paying for them doesn't help. You wouldn't eat off their plates without buying them, would you, eh? And I suppose you'll be going to the Deli next."

She realised that browsing over Pride and Prejudice wasn't really going to be possible while he was glowering at her. So she paid for it, dropped it into her bag with the plates from the Pottery and scurried out – to the Deli.

He caught sight of Lawrence and Eve, beamed charmingly and beckoned them into his office.

"But how nice to see you both. But what a village, eh? And you, my new friends, have come to live here!"

He smiled and his eyes crinkled. "I've got an idea. Doing anything at the moment? Fancy a quick one at the pub? On me? Good! You go on and I'll see you there in five minutes, right? I know how to stop these buggers reading my books. I'll close the shop!"

Yes, Jekyll 'n' Hyde may have been a volcano that alternated every few minutes with a charmer. But he came into the same category as Chris the plumber, who had given Lawrence a treatise on local history and rawl plugs, and the Log Lady, who walked and talked like a queen. It was the category of individuals who lived and worked in North Norfolk. So, after having one on Jekyll 'n' Hyde at the pub and for no other reason than that their chat with him had helped them merge into their community, they decided to buy a pound of scallops from Tom at his shop. They knew they'd be as fresh as ever they could be – still smelling of seawater, in fact. So they knew they'd be so light that they'd only need a bit of butter in the pan, maybe with some chopped garlic and parsley, swish them all around over a low heat for a few seconds – no longer – and finally sprinkle over them some of their own herb garden's parsley. On a slice of stone-ground bread they would start dinner off well. And do Tom good, too, for they cost a fortune considering their size.

In fact Lawrence and Eve were doing their bit for the village store. "USE IT OR LOSE IT" said the sign Tom had put up on the shop window. They used it.

White-haired Iris, his mother, was in the shop with them. She seemed irritated by something and it didn't take long to come out. New people had just moved into the village on the coast road. Iris had a tiny physique but she made up for it with her force of mind. She disapproved vigorously.

"Interlopers," she snorted scornfully with rural contempt for city slickers. "They're everywhere nowadays. It gets worse every year!"

Naturally Lawrence agreed with her, even though – or perhaps because – this was apparently how she had once described him and Eve. After all she was now saying it about someone else – and to him and Eve, what's more! Naturally they agreed. You couldn't have people

148

just coming to live in the village like that. Where would it all end?

By now it was late afternoon and she was looking tired. They knew she had had treatment for cancer two years before and had been afraid that it might return. Lawrence carried her shopping bag. It gave her the chance for another grumble about those interlopers. It seemed that he and Eve were more or less accepted. Still, they didn't want to count on it. After all, they had only been living here for three or four months – no time at all in the generations of North Norfolk man. Perhaps the locals had all given up thinking they would ever leave and felt they might as well put up with them. They might even buy them a pint in the pub one day. Well, perhaps not that. That would be a pint too far, considering they would have to pay for it.

A new notice was on the shop window next to Tom's sign. It announced a meeting of the N.N.C.A. to be held that evening at someone's house a short distance across the road. The local conservation association, of course. Well, they believed in conservation, especially in North Norfolk – and Millicent was doing the catering, it seemed. So later on they walked over. It was only about a hundred yards away and it only took a few moments to be there.

As they left their drive they remembered how exhausting it had been to get to such a meeting in London. The problems always started as soon as they shut their door and reached the pavement. Where had they parked the car? Was it near the house? Was it three streets off? Or had it even been towed away already? Then driving ... finding the best route, other cars too close, bikes ducking in and out, traffic jams, pedestrians, traffic lights, parking. Ah, parking! In London you can't think of parking without thinking of traffic wardens. And they had definitely been "The Enemy." There weren't many drivers in London who didn't regard parking attendants as fascist dictators, usually teenage fascist dictators. And, of course, nearly always female teenage fascist dictators – the worst of the lot. All, no doubt (since most drivers were men) exacting revenge for millennia of male domination. And when in London they left for home, the same thing usually happened all over again but in reverse. Sometimes it was impossible to find anywhere to park less than two hundred yards from home. You've paid for a parking permit? Big deal! That doesn't guarantee you a parking space. No wonder living in London was exhausting and expensive. But here they were at this meeting after only a brief and genial stroll down the lane. No parking attendants, no car, no worries. And Jill's horse was tethered to a hook by the front door.

"Look!" said Eve. "Parking."

Inside they were surprised to see so many well-heeled senior citizens. There they were, chatting together, sipping glasses of wine and daintily eating slim slices of Millicent's cake. They recognised most of them from the Church Restoration Fund Lunch the month before. Eve and Lawrence were gratified that they were so interested in conservation.

"Congregation Street's doing its bit for conservation," whispered Eve into Lawrence's ear. "Isn't that nice!"

Then they came up to Jill and Tom, who had definitely not been to that lunch.

"What are you two doing here?" cried Jill.

"What d'you mean?"

"This is a fund-raising party for the North Norfolk Conservative Association!" And she laughed. She knew Lawrence and Eve weren't conservatives.

Conservatives, not conservationists – and collapse of everyone within earshot. But such was their common bond of North Norfolk that they stayed for a drink or two, made friends with some conservatives and left without even putting rat poison in the wine.

*    *    *

There was another extreme in North Norfolk. This one was different from the scrap yard and the senior citizens sipping china tea. And this one really was dangerous. North Norfolk is a land of extremes of people and food. But the biggest extremes are in its climate. Lawrence and Eve had already experienced the bitter winters colder than anywhere else. Later they were to experience golden summers more idyllic than anywhere else. And they all suited Lawrence. He had often sought extremes in his life and each of them gave edge to the others.

But soon after he and Eve had arrived they became aware of a real weather extreme. It was a shattering local event, in fact. To be fair, Lawrence had been warned, He had overheard some chance remarks in the pub, for example. He hadn't followed them up because everyone else seemed to know about them. He didn't want to feel more of an ignorant interloper than he had to. Then they had of course noticed the knee-high patches on an inside wall of their house. The previous owner had said it was salt, not rising damp. They had seen the grooved vertical bars each side of the doorways on the coast road. And they had looked at the cracked and faded photographs in the post office.

Up here on the edge of the coast they learned that everyone knew the extremes of the weather and what it did to the sea. The sea was stronger than Napoleon, more merciless than Hitler, even more meddlesome than Brussels – the worst interloper of all. And the most extreme of the sea's quite unreasonable behaviour was the flood. But even that had its good point. They both needed something like a flood to take the albatross of their debts off their minds. For despite a recent drop in interest rates the market was still sinking. A few people had come round to look at their house in Notting Hill. But Lawrence and Eve had long since lost any optimism. Real buyers, buyers putting their money down – they were non-existent. Thank God, or perhaps Allah, that their Arab tenants were still there.

And the flood certainly took their minds off it all, at least for the moment. Only a sea wall and a mile or so of marshes lay between them and the North Pole. If that wall failed the waves would be into the village and flooding their ground floor within the hour. It had been sometime in February when Ronald had told them that the dangerous times were the Spring Tides.

"If we get a Force Ten gale from the north east when there's a high Spring tide, then we've had it," he had announced dryly. "And that tide's in a week or two." He looked at them, raised his eyebrows and leaned unsteadily over the bar. He narrowed his eyes. "So watch out. We're OK here. I've got everything battened down already. But you'll be in trouble – like your house was in 1953. You'll begin to wish you'd stayed in London."

And late in April the white horses had begun to drive straight at the shore from the north-east horizon, each one rider-less and out of control. And each one heading for their village. Eve had already been telephoned by Millicent. Now she had not merely achieved the roles of cookery writer, chairman of the parish council, churchwarden, organiser of church flower arranging, chairman of the Church Restoration Fund Committee, caterer for its lunches and organiser of the Saturday morning bring-and-buy stalls on the church green. Another role had been thrust upon her.

"The Parish Council have given me the job of Flood Warning Officer," she announced in a voice that again rose to the occasion and managed to combine authority with mock modesty. "It was very kind of them, really, but I suppose I have been living here for some few years now. We turn on the siren when we think a flood is inevitable. You'll remember the noise if you'd heard them during the War."

How old did she think they were?

"Everybody should meet at the Village Hall when they hear it. It's well above the flood danger level. You shouldn't bring more than a small suitcase. I shall be providing tea and biscuits from a special parish emergency fund."

A week or two after Ronald's warning Lawrence had driven Zeus and Leda to Sheringham to catch the train to Norwich. They were dressed in fleeces to keep out the cold. He was taking her to the ballet ("Swan Lake, actually," he had winked to Lawrence as he lit a small cheroot). The northeast wind was brisk. Now and then they could see the flickers of white waves above the sea wall. They smiled to each other as they noticed how the duck-pond at Salthouse had risen and was nearer the road than usual. How quaint, they all thought. Lawrence drove round it easily.

He dropped them at Sheringham Station, turned back and passed Kelling to began the winding descent into Salthouse. Here he could see for miles up to Blakeney Point in the west.

The sea had smashed away the beach wall. A wide front of white waves was surging through half a dozen gaps. Each gap was hundreds of yards wide. And the marshes were already flooded up to the coast road. It had taken less than twenty minutes – not an hour.

Lawrence took the road down to Salthouse and drove past a field where he and Eve had been picking mushrooms the week before. It was now a saltwater lake three foot deep. The wind had got up by now and was blowing half a gale. Overhead five or six Brent Geese and two avocets were being buffeted around amongst flying reed heads and chaff.

At the duck pond the water had risen and was now covering the road. The car's exhaust pipe was dangerously close to the surface. He had to keep the revs up and take it at speed. The water sprayed up from the wheels each side of the car. Past the pond and someone was taking sandbags up to a house. Lawrence stopped and reversed quickly but the man said: "sorry, can't spare any." At least Lawrence thought that was what he said. It might easily have been "bugger off and get your own." At moments of stress the Norfolk accent communicates more by expression than by words.

He was soon through Salthouse but now the sea covered more and more of the road ahead. At the last bend before their village the wind had risen even more and the waves were racing in. The air was full of flying spray now, not just chaff. The sea had flooded the bird watchers' hides and only the roofs showed. Broken slats from their path were floating amongst a tangle of reeds tossed around by the gale.

Lawrence was two hundred yards from the village and closing. By now his wheel hubs were underwater. He changed down to bottom gear and put his foot down to keep the revs up as near the danger mark as he dared go. It was only a short way and he had to do it. He'd lose the car if he didn't, even if it blew a gasket in the process. He switched his windscreen wipers onto double speed but could hardly see much even then. At the entrance to the village he took the right fork to reach the windmill. Here the road rose at a hump two or three feet above flood level. On its left were the walls and tower of Victor and Pat's home. Beyond the hump the village was dry – so far. But now spray was jumping it.

Before he reached the hump Lawrence had to drive over someone's garden fence. It had been smashed and hurled onto the road as if by some giant fist. Now it lay broken and half-submerged. The wild waves hissed at him and the spray lashed his windscreen. He drove over the fence and heard a rough grinding noise under the car. But he kept his speed up, reached the hump and coasted down into the village. His was the last car in for the duration of the flood.

He turned into their drive and stopped near the front door. By then the gale had increased. His eyes streamed and he was hardly able to stand. Even for those last few yards he had to lean forward and shut his eyes.

Once safely indoors, he lit a fire. It was only early afternoon but the air was cold and clammy. He remembered that during the previous two days the wind had been building up to something like Force 10, maybe Force 12. Even their walled garden gave little protection. He saw two trees were down. He went out for some more coal and had to struggle to keep upright. Only by walking sideways could he keep the coal in the scuttle. But he loved it. This was why he came to live in North Norfolk. Still, once inside he did enjoy the warmth.

And then it began to snow. Big soft flakes were jetted around in the sky like powered feathers. He would have appreciated it more if it hadn't been so worrying. Then the gale strengthened. It took the snow and blew it horizontally across the garden. Lawrence stood watching through the conservatory windows. The wind was spraying snow over the lawn as if it was coming out of a hose. That was when he realised it was blowing from the north east. That was it – the high spring tides and the north-east wind! It was what had caused those floods in 1953. Things suddenly looked dangerous. North Norfolk or not, he didn't want to get flooded out. And was that hump in the road going to save the village? If not, the village and their house would be flooded. No doubt about it. He looked out their local community newsletter. The Tide Tables were printed next to the times of church services. High tide was at 6pm. It was now 4pm so there were two hours to go. When Lawrence had driven over the hump the water was about a foot below it. If the tide rose more than that the village would be flooded. The hump in the road wasn't going to be enough to save it. It had two hours to rise above the hump and with that wind it could do it easily.

"Look!" cried Eve suddenly, and thrust the newsletter at him. "You missed the most important bit. The highest tide this month is 28 foot it says – and that's today. It's 4pm now and look it says it'll be 25 foot now. How far down was it below the hump when you got over? What? A foot? Oh my God, then there's going to be two foot of water in the village by 6 o'clock!" He snatched it back from her. "That's the time the tide will start to go down." she said. She was right.

At such moments, history teaches, there is only one course of action: go round the pub.

With half a pint of warm beer inside him and the rest on the counter before him, Lawrence learned that Harry had already pronounced upon the crisis.

"There's nothing to worry about." He had apparently reassured Ronald when he had dropped in for a pint of mild the night before.

"How does he know?" asked Lawrence. "It's so cold that no one would blame him if he'd been lying on the sofa all day in front of the telly. After all, he usually does. So how can he tell?"

"Well," shrugged Ronald and flapped at the counter with his cloth. "He's been here several generations so far. Even before television. Before radio too, for that matter. Anyway, he said he wasn't moving outside. And," he concluded decisively, "did he not forecast last month's snow when he saw all those molehills coming up?"

No answer to that, acknowledged the saloon bar. So the customers held an eve-of-flood conference. Present were Prospero, coat over his shoulders, and Derek, the Blakeney fisherman. Prospero's golden retriever lay asleep beneath the next table. His hunch-backed servant was sitting there with a pint of beer. Every now and again he leaned over and growled something to the dog – which took no notice. But Lawrence noticed that whenever Prospero looked in its direction it immediately opened one eye. He was puzzled – how did it know? Derek wore a sou' wester and a pair of thigh boots. You could almost see a crust of salt on him. For some reason he seemed to smell of iodine.

The door opened and in blew Zeus. He threw his fleece onto a chair and shook the snow out of his hair.

"The ballet was cancelled." He shook hands all round, undoing a couple of shirt buttons as he went. "Half the corps de ballet couldn't get into Norwich with all this storm. The train got stuck in a snow drift at North Walsham and we managed to share a car back to the village through Holt. Leda's closing up the forge for the day."

He eased himself onto a bar stool, rolled his sleeves up, put his elbows on the bar and ordered a pint of warm beer.

"Well, Lawrence," he said. "I remember how your house got flooded out in '53," he grinned. "Better get your larder up to the first floor, I reckon. And don't forget the drains."

"What d'you mean, drains?"

"Ah, no matter how many sandbags you've got, the water comes up the downstairs lavatories. You got to get outside and take the inspection covers off and stuff something up the drains to stop the water. A big rubber ball'll do it, house side of the opening. Can't use them, either, of course, if the flood lasts any time."

Derek grinned.

"I'll bring my boat round to the window if you give me a ring, Lawrence." He grinned again. "Water taxi!"

Lawrence swallowed hard.

"But upstairs bathrooms won't be a bother," contributed Ronald. "Unless we're in for the mother of all floods, of course," he added laconically.

"Well, I've got some food if we're cut off anyway," promised Zeus. "I can supply everyone with lots of different reds and whites to drink plus Belgian chocolates, Roquefort cheese, Bayonne ham, foie gras from south-west France, some Parma ham too for Prospero – depends how long we'd be stuck here, of course … don't want to eat the same thing every meal. And at least half-a-dozen sorts of olives (marinated or stoned). But I'm worried about bread."

"Yeah, and I suppose I've got plenty of beer," agreed Ronald. "So long as you sign chits," he added quickly.

Prospero had been quiet for some time, merely watching them. Now he told them that the flood would isolate the village from outside influences. He explained that Jung had a theory about a group's isolation. The sea's flooding could be a new experience for everyone, a collective unconscious conversion into something rich and strange whereby everybody would resonate together. It could even give them a valuable chance to redistribute partners with consequences that may lead to a greater awareness of life.

"Partners? D'you mean women?" asked Ronald. "More like a fight, I'd say," he laughed and flicked again with his cloth at the counter.

Derek scratched his head and said he didn't know about all that but he was glad he managed to pull his boat out of the water that morning.

"I can't trust being at anchor when there's this wind with a big flood, even if I rigged Jan's drogue." He shook his head. "That reminds me, Prospero. I had a look at your boat and you've put a long enough mooring on it to rise with the flood." He looked closely at him. "That was pretty smart of you."

"Ah," Prospero smiled at him. "What particular accidents have happened since I'm at this coast!"

Suddenly his assistant rose up and said.

"You need a south-westerly to blow on you."

"Yes, that's right," Zeus agreed in surprise. He turned to Lawrence. "That's our prevailing wind. And it usually keeps the sea off the wall beyond the mill. But today it's north east, opposite direction."

Without turning his head Prospero called out, "I did not call forth these mutinous winds, my tortoise. The elements commanded this loud north-east wind," he snapped. "He expects it of me," he said to the others as if in explanation.

Derek was frowning a little, looking puzzled.

"Last time," he said, "the boats got took all the way up Blakeney High Street to the White Horse and the toilets didn't work there either. But I didn't get home until four in the morning. Well, it took all that time for them to run out of beer. Wife thought I'd been drowned and I got a right scold."

Ronald listened from behind the bar and stalked impassively up and down. It separated him from his customers as they talked amongst themselves. Now and then he threw in philosophical advice. The bar lent him the anonymity of Henry V when he wandered incognito amongst his troops the night before Agincourt. In those days the French united them. Today it was the flood.

Heads bowed in thought. During one silent period the lights flickered. The silences lengthened.

During one such silence the door burst open and a visitor appeared. The snow outside had soaked his overcoat and without waiting for the door to close he began to take it off. Ronald looked at him and scowled.

"Can I help you, sir?" he asked. Lawrence had already learned that when Ronald said "sir ...," he expressed definite dislike, especially when he lingered over the word.

"Good afternoon! I'd like a nice pint of bitter, please," said the man with a cheerful grin and went on taking off his overcoat. "Goodness, it's wet outside! You lucky fellows, sitting all warm here in front of that fire! I'm glad I got here in one piece."

"Sorry; we're closed," said Ronald. And slapped the bar with his cloth.

"But ... but ...?" The man paused and looked puzzled at him, then longingly at the fire and at them all sitting comfortably at the bar.

"But ... I mean … aren't you …, I mean, you're…?" He asked again. He looked crestfallen. He stood there with one arm in a sleeve and his overcoat trailing on the ground. Wisps of snow began to swirl around him and into the bar.

"There's a pub in the next village. It might be open," said Ronald. "Please close the door after you. The snow's getting in … sir." He turned his back on the visitor and topped his beer up from the bottle of Scotch behind the bar.

"Good God!" he muttered after the door was shut. "The man actually wanted a drink!" He shrugged, shook his head wearily and took a deep draught of beer to wipe out the experience.

"Anyway," he went on, recovering quickly from that unsavoury interruption, "we've got til 6pm to know if we're in trouble. If the worst happens, don't go to the Village Hall. You'll just get Millicent and biscuits. I'll keep the pub open. Come upstairs to the sitting room. We'll have a few jars."

And there it was. The grand strategy, complete with philosophy and contingency tactics; Plan 'A' and Plan 'B', in fact. Or rather Jar 'A' and Jar 'B'. And all accomplished with masterly insight and decisiveness.

But none of that made the tide go down or the wind drop. The rain on his face – that was one thing. Quite different from the sea in her kitchen, as Eve pointed out tartly when Lawrence returned home. She added that while he was out the Log Lady had just delivered another load of wood.

"She asked after you. Too bad you were in the pub," she added sarcastically. "Incidentally, the boys rang again."

"Where are they now?"

"Tangiers. They want to know if we'd like them to bring us back a hooker."

"A hooker?" Lawrence looked up, startled.

"No, darling. Not that sort of hooker – bad luck. Something you smoke out of. I told them not to bother, 'your Dad's got enough bad habits as it is,' I said. "

But now it was just before 5pm and there was only an hour before high tide. The wind and the snow were getting worse by the minute, another tree was down at the end of the garden and Lawrence glanced again at the salt marks two feet up the wall by the front door. That was the level reached by the floods forty years ago. What if Harry was wrong?

"Can't we get some sandbags from the council?" asked Eve, suddenly anxious.

Of course! But Lawrence remembered they went home at 5pm – on the dot. They were on high ground. He reached for the phone.

"Sandbags?" they replied, and put him through at once. But he was only allowed 20 bags.

"Not enough!" he yelled. "I'm on the main road and I've got six doors." They realised the danger Lawrence and Eve could be in and he managed to order 30 bags. They said they'd send them. Right away!

Half an hour later a lorry arrived in the driving snow. It was so thick now that he couldn't see across the road. Apparently they were the last sandbags to be had. The wind was howling and the lorry couldn't get down to the house. Lawrence rev'd the car, backed it quickly up to the road, lugged the bags into the back and drove down to the front door. He and Eve laid them there and outside the kitchen door, outside the French windows of the sitting room and by the conservatory door.

As he stood in the garden piling them up into a high wall, she said:

"Chump! D'you want to stand outside all night? Do it from the inside."

Soon it was 5.30pm – fifteen minutes to go. Inside at last, and it was time to throw a few more logs on the fire and pour a drink. And there's only one drink for a crisis like this. Boiling water, brown sugar, a few cloves, some cinnamon, half a lemon and plenty of whisky – Irish or even Canadian, it didn't matter. And that was a hot toddy. In fact it was two hot toddies.

It all began to feel exciting, like a war without the guns. Just before the 6pm high tide Lawrence drained his last hot toddy and dragged on gumboots, his 35-year-old sheepskin coat, two scarves, his motorcycle gauntlets and his Russian hat. From the hall table he collected their torch. It was the one they had bought to help them home from the pub. Once on the road the wind bent him almost double. He slowly made his way past the windmill to the edge of the marsh and the hump in the road by the tower of Pat and Victor's house. Two or three people were standing there. The north-east gale was screaming. The air was full of straw and reeds. A floating pile of sea wrack and broken reeds was lurching up the road. Each surge of the waves rammed it further and further up to the hump. A few minutes before 6pm the water had reached it and a few streaks dribbled over. They swelled and turned into a wave that trickled down towards the village. Lawrence began to feel cold. The next wave had much more water than reeds. It flowed easily over the hump and gushed down the road towards him. He could do nothing to stop it and had to jump out of the way.

Then the next wave reached the top and overflowed but slowed to a trickle again. The sea had stopped pushing forward and had drawn back a little. It was the ebb! The earth had rolled their village away from the moon and it was safe.

A light came on in the tower and a window opened above his head.

"I don't know what you're worried about, young man!" called a friendly voice. It was Victor.

"Harry told me a week ago that it would be all right!" The light behind him glinted on a champagne glass.

"Care for a quick one?" he asked. "I brought the wine cellar up to our bedroom and the champagne's cooling in the bath. Didn't want to rely totally on Harry, you know. Coming up? Is Eve with you? At home? Shall I ring her? She might like a glass too."

Typical banker – a belt and braces job! Thank heaven for him. And how could Lawrence refuse? But before he walked to Victor's door he turned to the group near him and asked: "What about the next tide? Will that bring it over?"

"No chance," they replied. "The wind will have dropped by then."

Lawence somehow felt a little disappointed. Then as he opened Victor's door he remembered that they hadn't had enough money to pay their house insurance premium. He shook his head to himself and grinned. Something had turned up. The champagne tasted all the better after that.

\*     \*     \*

159

There's nothing like a flood to begin feeling really basic – biblical, in fact. Lawrence had looked up at the moon and had seen it swing away. He had seen the tide ebb and fall. And he had watched the waters move upon the face of the earth. He had seen that they had receded and that the flood was a threat no more to the people of the village. So when he walked home he knew that they had been saved. But it all had concentrated his mind.

He and Eve both knew the flood could have been cold, wet, miserable and destructive. Dangerous, too – several people had drowned in that last flood. If high tide had come earlier his excitement would have changed to dismay. He would have felt himself an idiot. They might have been marooned upstairs. They would have watched the sea destroy their possessions. They would have worried about food. They might even have begun to wonder why they hadn't stayed in London. They later learned that the ground floor of someone's house at the end of the village had been flooded out and that in Salthouse an old lady had been taken to hospital with pneumonia. But it was the danger itself that made it so exciting, even satisfying. Well, afterwards, anyway.

That was life on the North Norfolk coast – living on the edge. And you're not really living unless you take risks. And that was why they had come up here.

Lawrence stood before the dining room fire. He rested his hand on the rough-hewn oak mantelpiece and gazed into the blaze. He reached over and threw on another log from the stack in the right-hand alcove. To his left was their expensive hi-fi stereo equipment and their collection of classical CD's. Behind him the walls were lined with books and paintings.

The flood danger had reminded him of the value of what they had and could easily have lost if they had been forced to return to London – their house of course, but also the people, the food, the landscape, the edge. Every morning when he awoke they all made his heart leap. For, like layers of rich cream on a cake, they all contributed to the cake – to life in North Norfolk. But the albatross of their mortgage was still dragging at their enthusiasm like a ball and chain. They had recently suffered a short-lived bout of optimism. This time it was because people thought that the market was bottoming out. Various estate agents had explained elaborately why a price rise was imminent – so everyone should start buying, of course. But the optimism, or wishful thinking, hadn't lasted. The market went on bumping uncomfortably along the bottom. Or was it the bottom? They were still desperately uncertain. Luckily the tenants in their London house were still there and still paying the rent, although it was never enough to pay all the interest charges. But in those anxious hours when they both awoke before dawn they still tried to reassure each other. Things could still be worse, they said – although Eve wasn't quite so sure as her husband. But they were grateful that they had good health. In fact they were lucky and they knew it.

Next morning brought another sudden change in North Norfolk's weather. The gale had blown itself out overnight. The air was motionless and there was almost complete silence. Eve said she could hear a dog barking somewhere near Wiveton, half a mile or more up the valley. A wisp of smoke rose from a neighbour's chimney. The cloudless sky had no end and the sun looked silently down.

They couldn't believe it. Only yesterday the flood had threatened to drown them and they'd had a snowstorm, too. Yet now it seemed as if it had never happened. And although a crisply laundered eiderdown lay over everything, 'a rich white scarf on the chastened earth,' a few tulips were poking through. The flood danger had gone. And spring was returning.

But the village was still cut off. The floodwater still stopped people driving in from Cromer and at the west by the cross roads a large sign said: "No Through Road." So, even more than usual, England was cut off from North Norfolk. And, like a time machine, the silence seemed to have pushed everyone back by a hundred years. The village street was like a Victorian postcard. The houses looked old and worn out against the fresh snow. He almost expected a pony and trap to wheel round the corner. One or two people trudged noiselessly along to the Deli. They seemed to be wearing several layers of dark clothes – the way tramps wear their entire wardrobe. Lawrence saw a couple standing immobile outside the pub. Footsteps made no sound and nothing moved to make a noise. Even the birds seem to have stayed indoors. Like that earlier time, when they had thought spring had arrived, he and Eve both felt as if they'd gone deaf overnight.

But they roused themselves to drive to Holt. They had to collect a brace of pheasants from John, their butcher. The snow unrolled before them like a VIP's carpet. Lawrence drove carefully so as not to waken the road. The landscape lay quiet and still to left and right. It was a view they could never have seen in London. The snow would quickly have become streaked with dirt and by now would have begun to melt into slush. The car slipped a little climbing the hill past the gamekeeper's cottage. The woods had kept the sun away and the surface was icy. Twice they nearly slid into the ditch. Theirs was the only car on the road. People clearly knew better than to drive in such weather. After all, if you've got any sense you'll know that this is the season to stay at home and contemplate incest.

\*      \*      \*

After it had melted the snow, the sun smiled warmly on everyone. Lawrence and Eve realised that in spite of the false alarms they had been struggling along at the bottom of the sea for the last three months. It seemed that North Norfolk might have turned the corner and left winter behind. The birdsong was light and lively, too. Courtship had begun again and their singing was completely different from the weak and forlorn chirping in the autumn and winter. Lawrence hadn't realised that you could tell the season just from the quality of the birdcalls. Now they were chattering happily together: a triplet of thirds – A down to F and back to A three times, followed by a couple of quick plucks of F sharp – and then a wait. He could hear them two hundred yards or more away. But those were the mornings. And when he and Eve walked on the marshes at sunset and before the sky had darkened, often the only sound was the barking of a dog half a mile away and perhaps the call of some lone curlew at a far-off creek.

During the first few months in their new home on the North Norfolk coast Lawrence and Eve hardly stirred beyond the village street. They still had plenty of work to do in the house. The dining room bookshelves were finished, but more were needed elsewhere. A couple of floor boards still had to be replaced, the top landing needed sanding and they were redecorating two bedrooms. No time to do more than sprint round to the pub before closing time. Then early in May their new friends Zeus and Leda offered to show them some old pubs deep in the country.

"We won't bother with the ones on the coast road, Eve," said Zeus. "They get too full at weekends."

"With trippers," added Leda. She was happy not to drink so they voted her driver.

Once outside the village Lawrence and Eve discovered that the North Norfolk landscape lay around them like a sprawling body. They noticed a hillock in a nearby field, hard and irregular like a kneecap. Far off on the low skyline was the ridge of a collarbone. In the meadow, laid to pasture above the hillock, a breast rose and gently fell towards the ridge. Elsewhere the land stretched first for a hundred yards and swelled like a thigh. Then came a little mound to meet a rounded copse. Its head was topped by a straggle of trees, tangled hair uncombed by man. Not very flat, Norfolk.

They also realised that the North Norfolk landscape seemed hardly to have changed for the last hundred years or more – since Victorian times, in fact. The isolation, the long stretches of ragged fields, the battered haystacks and the absence of new buildings all struck them hard – like a shock. They turned inland and drove south past bleak and empty pastures along bleak and empty roads. Near woods they saw hints of a house or two. But more often than not they could see only a chimney and the line of a roof, maybe a window – but no more. Trees hid everything else. Now and then they passed isolated cottages. They were usually planted at the edges of bare fields, often hidden behind an overgrown hedge half concealing an untended garden. Lawrence thought involuntarily of Justine and wondered where she was, at sea – or in the Pottery with the Village Marxist?

Lawrence wound his window down – and then quickly up. A revolting stink had flooded into the car.

"What the hell's that?"

"Oh," said Leda easily. "They must be muck spreading somewhere round here."

She looked round and smiled at him.

"You've got to get used to that now you live in North Norfolk!"

The inland village they soon reached was Aldeborough. It sat round the edge of a cricket field and the pub only had one bar. It was quiet and almost empty. The clientele was a group of three locals drinking cider and playing cards in a fog of cigarette smoke. From time to time the barman edged round the counter, ducked into the fog, threw down a card and edged back behind the pumps. The atmosphere was what would be expected at an international chess tournament – not at a half-empty pub deep in North Norfolk. Apart from an occasional bid and now and then a muttered oath, the crackling of the fire was all that broke the silence. Two wet dogs lay steaming by the fire. Over the centuries that fire had stained the ceiling to the colour of an over-cooked omelette. The visitors threw their coats over a couple of chairs, ordered a few pints and warmed themselves at the fire. Lawrence and Eve glanced at each other and smiled. Nothing had changed since their visits up here long ago. Indeed the whole place confirmed not just that North Norfolk had stopped at around 1935, but that no one had noticed.

Later they rolled further inland to a pub at Gresham. Its only bar was more or less like anyone else's living room. Two or three small tables were crammed with family groups togged up with scarves, coats and children. Lawrence sat in an empty chair by the fire – and received a fierce glare from a regular with a long white beard when he returned with his glass from the bar. He'd obviously been sitting in it for thirty years. Lawrence got up and found another one.

"Don't worry," said the landlady. "He's a regular but he's younger than me. I'm nearly ninety, so he's got to do what I tell him. And I've never touched a drop, either – not like him!"

This logic was of course inescapable. And no nonsense about serving meals here. It took long enough to get a shandy. After that visit Eve and Lawrence got to know her well. If the pub was closed she opened an upstairs window and climbed slowly down to let them in. Her daughter was an international rifle champion and the walls were covered with trophies. That sort of thing helped keep order.

Their visit over, they stood together for a moment outside the pub to put their coats back on and their friends showed them a dense copse across the road.

"Inside it's a big mound that's all that's left of the castle belonging to a family called the Pastons. It must have been over six hundred years ago," Zeus told Lawrence. "They were farmers … had been very successful round here for generations. Then one of them was knighted and they got ambitious and began to spend time at court and that was when they got into deep water. They had trouble with the heavy boys like the Duke of Norfolk. Very nasty."

"Oh, yes!" interrupted Leda. "He concocted some sort of quarrel with them and hired a couple of thousand men to try to take their place when Paston was away in London. There was only his wife at home with just a few men and they forced her out. But she and the family got it back later. They were a tough lot. A bit like the old girl back there in the pub."

A nod to history and a tough woman. Then into the car for a drive through the empty landscape to Heydon. Here a strange pub lay in a forest hamlet that seemed almost abandoned centuries ago. Beyond it wrought-iron gates opened to the grounds of a Jacobean mansion. In the distance its three Dutch gables could be traced behind the park's bare-branched trees like a richly patterned embroidery in a filigree scarf. Between mansion and pub stood a dignified old church. In the days when they had week-ended in the country Lawrence used to alternate between pub and church. Liquid history, he used to call it. So they made a small detour. And, as always, they found within the church the rich and sombre fabric of English history. London's churches were full of it too, of course. But somehow this testimony was always more significant in England's simple country churches. High on the walls drooped half-a-dozen torn and faded regimental flags. They hung neglected and their insignia were obscured by dust. Together with brass plaques on the walls, they testified to desperate battles for the British Empire. The battles had been fought in distant lands, not against Europeans but against dusky armies and savage hordes. The flags stood for the memory of those who fell at Quebec, at sea off Trafalgar, to the French at Waterloo, in the Afghan Wars, the Crimea, that savage Indian Mutiny, the African Wars, Omdurman against the Mahdi, the Boer War, the First World War, the Second World War. And, throughout the generations, always the same family names.

All over England young men of good family had been bred with pride in deep tradition. Theirs had been the best of educations. They had been trained to fulfil their roles with honour. By these means they became the flower of England. Then they were sent off to war to fight and, likely, die. It happened again and again. It was the tradition, you see. Their story is the price of empire and the price of freedom, too. It can be read upon the walls of every church in England.

Lawrence gazed around him and shuddered – as much with respect as with horror at the loss of so many lives so often. Time for a drink.

There was no bar inside the pub next door, just a hatch and an atmosphere they had never felt before. There was nothing like it in London. About twenty people sat at the six or seven tables. A few little children ran from one to another. A bare-footed young woman with long flowing hair seemed to be friendly with all the young men lounging about. Half a dozen aged pensioners sat hunched over their beer, sticks cradled in their arms. Now and again they picked up a child for a cuddle before it ran on. They seemed a big happy family. Indeed, they all almost looked alike. As Lawrence said to their friends:

"They're enjoying themselves so much, they can't be English."

"Ah!" grinned Zeus. "But that's how it is up here."

As they sat by the fire in the pub Leda told them of her past. She had been married before. Her husband had been a sculptor who had died several years before. Eve talked quietly with her about it all while

165

Zeus explained to Lawrence the difference between pheasant and partridge. Later Eve told him that she felt there was a vacancy and that a new incumbent was being considered.

And so to their last port of call. Zeus told them to expect something special. Once across the Norwich road they actually saw another car for the first time that afternoon. It was heading in their direction.

"Now look," said Zeus. "See what we do round here."

As so often in North Norfolk the lanes were too narrow for both cars to pass but there was a lay-by ahead.

"Look, see that lay-by. There are lots of them round here. It's on our right so he'll pull in to it and let us drive past and Leda will give him a wave. OK, Leda? Watch and see what he does!"

The oncoming car pulled into the lay-by, Leda waved in acknowledgement and the oncoming car driver gave a little wave back to her with one finger on his steering wheel.

"See? He's saying thanks to her for saying thanks!"

"I suppose it could go on for ever," remarked Lawrence.

"Well, I suppose so. But d'you know – the police do it too!" Now that really was something.

"Mind you," Leda put in. "If they don't wave they're probably tourists." She smiled over her shoulder to Eve – "or interlopers."

Gently they headed east down a straight stretch towards Wolterton Hall and Erpingham. The lanes were empty, the fields were again enacting their role of a sprawling body and darkness was crushing the light out of the sky. Dozens of Brent geese rose from a nearby field. They slowly beat their black wings as they climbed, circled together in a flowing cloud and headed southwest. Their rusty croaking faded in the late afternoon air. For several minutes after the sound had faded the birds remained silhouetted across the last light of an April sky. Now it was leached with thunderous black-red streaks of cloud and dying sun. Nearby a copse of elms sheltered two rusted corrugated huts. They were at the edge of a flat stretch of land. An old concrete roadway led to it, cracked along its length now and with weeds everywhere.

"One of the old airfields around here," Zeus nodded his head sideways as he lit a small cheroot. "North Norfolk is full of them."

In the distance a sign swung gently outside a Georgian pub. "The Saracen's Head", it said above a picture of a bearded warrior. A warm glow shone from its windows.

"He calls himself the Humble Innkeeper, this one," said Zeus. "We don't think he means it. But we're fond of him. And he cooks well."

A large sign said "CAMEL PARK AND HELICOPTERS AT REAR".

"Don't worry about that. He's just been on a package tour to Tunisia," Zeus reassured them, shrugging. "Some of it obviously stuck to him."

Inside the bar an old chesterfield sofa lay before a crackling fire. A few strands of stuffing dangled from a hole in one arm. Everywhere the walls were painted a faded maroon. A couple of rusted 6-ft saws hung next to a poster advertising an auction of cattle, horses and agricultural implements at Aylsham, the nearby market town. The auction was to take place on the 12th of November 1935. Next to an old pine cupboard of glasses an enormous wine rack hung near a fireplace. Above the fire a tall and encrusted Georgian mirror bore a royal crest. Glued to its silvering, now faded and curling away, were dozens of banknotes from far-away countries, such as Nepal and Ecuador, of which Lawrence knew little. Everywhere the maroon walls were covered with stags' heads and ducal emblems. This, he thought, could be some cranky royalist's drawing room. But between the faded symbols of imperial grandeur a few tables were laid for dinner – candles lighting each one. And no music intruded upon the fire's peaceful crackling.

As they walked in, an ample figure wrapped around by a red apron appeared from the kitchen. He was carrying an immense leg of pork on a silver serving dish. Dozens of cloves were stuck all over it and the skin was glazed with burnt brown sugar. Zeus and Leda introduced Lawrence and Eve to Reginald.

The Humble Innkeeper put the dish on the counter, gave them a broad smile and a wink, raised his hand in greeting, swung a large carving knife in their direction and cried:

"Care for a slice of the Rabbi, dear friends? Good to see you again Zeus. Hope you're feeding the troops well in your Deli, eh?"

He turned to Leda.

"I say, darling, your boy friend's looking rather dashing nowadays. What have you been doing to him?" Without pausing he went on. "And d'you know the latest nonsense our government has thought up?" he asked, shaking his head. "Well, I bought myself a flag-pole the other day. I've put it at the entrance to my Camel Park and I wanted to fly the St George's flag from it. Well, they let me do it on St George's Day but they won't let me keep it up permanently! Some crap about upsetting minority groups ... I suppose that means not wanting to offend the Irish ... or the Asians ... or the Scotch ... or the Welsh ... I can't remember which. They're all the same anyway. I think it's about time we had a flag for Norfolk, actually. They wouldn't be able to do anything then, no doubt about that. Not to mention independence while we're on the subject. Staying for dinner?"

No doubt about that, either.

Next morning they found that the weather had improved overnight, as it does in North Norfolk. Lawrence paused from loading some garden rubbish into the car. He was about to take it to a dump a few miles away. Resting on his rake he looked up for a moment and saw the new moon was still visible and high above him. It was just a mint-fresh splinter. And the splinter was so delicate you'd think it would swing loose or pirouette away at any moment. It hung in a sky so clear that you could see to infinity – no haze, no atmosphere, no urban pollution.

"You know ... " He stopped loading and turned to Eve. She was on her knees planting out carrots in her vegetable patch at the time. She looked up.

"Yes, darling. What do I know?"

"I'm glad we left London."

That day they began work on the garden. Voltaire's passion of culti-vating your garden was all very well. But it required a lot of cultivation before summer. One serious problem was what to do with a ten-foot wide mound of earth at one corner. Mark, son of Derek the fisherman, had been enlisted as gardener. And he'd thought up a solution. He was a twinkling-eyed lad of twenty-one – and as quick as an eel. He had a wide grin, a bright wit and a crew-cut head of glistening black hair. He was full of confidence, of course, as any self-respecting young man should be. His solution was to turn the mound into a wide earth wall. He had tried to plant a few roots in it. It was a good effort. The only problem was that it looked worse than before.

But it was on another job in the garden, when Lawrence and Eve were away in Holt, that he really overdid things. He'd been deputised to clear up the garden and had decided to have a bonfire of some garden rubbish – branches, leaves and roots. Nothing wrong with that, except that he'd piled it up beneath their Irish yew tree. The result was a severely burnt Irish yew tree. Eve wasn't too pleased when they returned home.

"It'll grow back," was Mark's confident reply. Very much later, when Lawrence had cooled down, he rather respected Mark's attitude although it didn't help the tree. And they wondered how on earth he could find anything interesting to do in North Norfolk, let alone find a job that paid money. Maybe there were jobs around – of a sort. But they would not only damage his joie de vivre. They were the ones that didn't have much future. Cleaner? Builder's mate? Deck-chair attendant on the beach in the summer? What a laugh! And he wouldn't be long satisfied working as a deck hand on his dad's fishing boat either – coiling ropes, swilling out the bilge and being polite to the clients. And there wasn't much else for him to do. But this problem of finding work wasn't just in North Norfolk. It was much worse in Bangladesh, for example. A young man there had to spend a lot of time just keeping his head above water – sometimes literally. And the best chance he could ever have would be to hijack a plane to England. So Mark had a lot to be thankful for.

He had been banned from the garden after the Episode of the Burning Bush. Eve had said she wanted to cover the lump of earth with turf. So for the second time Lawrence looked through the Eastern Daily Press. He was amazed how cheap turf was – only a pound or two for a square metre. He rang a number near Norwich and ordered about 40 square metres. He had told them that he wanted it delivered. But he said he might not be there. He and Eve were going to The Moorings in Wells for lunch. And they couldn't miss that for a few sods of turf.

"No problem," said the fellow over the phone. Well, that was unusual. Surely they weren't going to lay it without being sure of getting paid right away?

"Just leave a note to tell us where you want it and we'll do it, even if you aren't there," they told him patiently. Amazing!

Before they left Lawrence fixed a water spray to rotate steadily backwards and forwards on the earth so it would be well watered before the turf was laid. He and Eve returned home later that afternoon. She had been driving, since Lawrence had finished off a bottle of Cahors wine over lunch. She drove slowly and at ease. A game pie at Jocelyn's restaurant left little room for discontent.

In the garden at home the spray was still on, rotating from left to right and back again as if it had never been moved. But beneath it, where that morning had been a mound of dry and dusty grey earth, was now an idyllic bank of emerald green turf, all beautifully laid and hardly a trace of lines to show that it hadn't been growing there for the last hundred years.

Two or three days later a fellow appeared at the door, a young and cheerful-looking lad like Mark. He said he had laid the turf. Lawrence gave him the cash and they shook hands. He didn't even think of asking for a receipt. It would never have happened in London, even in 1935.

They had already discovered that they lived in a paradise. But they were soon to discover that paradise is never without its serpent. And nowadays the serpent doesn't always appear with scales and a tail. For Eve and Lawrence the serpent that threatened their North Norfolk bliss reared its head or rather spread its wings at a moment when Lawrence was leaning out of the top floor window and gazing in placid adoration at their lawn. He looked at their ivy-clad flint walls, the nearby rectory and its stables. Beyond the elms, the low hills climbed gently half a mile away. He wondered if Philip was at home or scooting around the valley in his Morris Minor. He remembered how they had looked out of that window when first they had come to the house. And he was still full of that same soaring contentment. It was May and the sun was shining with generous charm. A wisp or two of pure white cloud was drifting gently along and all was right with the world. Moreover, lunch was nearly ready. He had already poured himself a glass of Chablis and was about to join Eve in the conservatory for a plate of fennel and mayonnaise mixed into some of Tom's crab, caught before dawn and brought in on that morning's tide.

Then an ear-splitting roar filled everything – the air, his ears, the house, the garden. This thunderous grinding was directly overhead and sent him diving into a low crouch to the floor. More serious, he spilled his wine.

It was of course, a jet fighter, obviously convinced that some terrorist was hiding out in the windmill and shooting it up a hundred yards from their roof at zero feet – well, almost. It nearly gave him indigestion and he had to refill his glass. This was certainly not England in 1935.

Arriving downstairs for lunch and a refill, he discovered his wife stretched full-length on the floor with her head and arms under the sofa and going: "come on, lovely-wuvely, mummy loves you, no more of those nasty airplanes, then, mummy promises … hoozie-woozie-hoozie … little poppett. Oh, COME on …"

Clearly the Sphinx was also worried about these low-flying jets. But, deplorable as this was, Lawrence knew very well that complaining to the Ministry of Defence about it would only produce the usual platitudes. But he was annoyed. He felt this style of flying was not necessary – and even out of date. So he wanted to do something. And he thought he might as well at least start his campaign. For by co-incidence the local council had just sent him some forms. He had asked for them to complain about "The Production or Emission of Excessive Noise or Noxious Fumes" from the stove of a villager near their house. The forms had just arrived but he hadn't really wanted to make life difficult for his neighbour. So he thought he might use them to have a go at the Ministry of Defence instead. That evening in the pub he discovered that a lot of people in the village were fed up with aircraft noise.

"It's been going on a long time," Ronald shrugged. "They gave me a number to ring to complain to. It didn't do any good. The bloke on the other end kept on asking me what the number of the plane was. Damn stupid. How can I do that when it's over and passed in half a second and I'm under the table with my eyes shut and my hands clapped to my ears? They probably knew that. I remember seeing a little old lady crouching and quivering with terror in Holt when one of those planes came over. It's a disgrace."

Next day Lawrence wrote his first letter of complaint to the Minister of Defence. He used the council forms to record when the planes flew over the village. Three or four of them always seemed to turn up from somewhere inland every morning at exactly 10.50am. They always screamed over the windmill at low level, turned left and headed out to sea. Then they climbed until they were lost in the haze. Sometimes in the afternoons they flew high up and out of sight above the sky. Their roaring still seemed to come from all directions. It filled the whole world with noise. It used to go on like that for a good half minute. Which is a very long time when Eve is trying to count the butterflies flitting around her sweet peas.

Lawrence would have been quite charmed if every now and again a Tiger Moth had delicately weaved its way between their chimneys like one of those butterflies. But a monstrous and thrusting black weapon blasting the air a few feet above him was not the same. So he became all the more stubborn and wanted to do something about it. This low flying almost made it hardly worth living in the village.

His first letter to the Ministry of Defence was polite. His other mistake was to make an attempt at humour and philosophy. The ministry replied with its standard bland brush-off. And the war was on.

*     *     *

After the omen of the stair-rods a few weeks back Lawrence and Eve had been sure that fate had guided them to Gibraltar House in the valley of the two mills. And they thought they had learned quite a lot about where they lived. So it came as a shock to discover there were some things they would never have known they hadn't been told. They had been living in North Norfolk some months before they discovered that a secret society existed up here. Lawrence felt they were lucky to have discovered it at all. For one thing the membership was more or less secret too. None of the locals who had lived in North Norfolk for generations – top or bottom of the heap – would have known about it. North Norfolk District Council couldn't have given him details. He was sure they wouldn't have known about it themselves. It didn't come under 'Environment,' for example, or 'Cleansing,' for that matter. And it wasn't in the telephone book. Lawrence had only discovered it when Prospero came to dinner for the first time. He arrived by himself, shrugging his coat off his shoulders onto the hall sofa and in almost the same movement taking a glass of Coonawarra red wine offered him by Lawrence.

"Ah, yes," he turned to Eve in response to her query and smiled. "My thing of darkness? At home with my dog. There are those times when they are best left home."

Eve and Lawrence had cooked a leg of Norfolk lamb for him. Before it went into the oven they had spiked it with rosemary from their new herb garden, pushed olives and whole lumps of garlic from Zeus's Deli beneath its skin and rubbed it all over with mustard. Ten minutes before they sat down they took it out and burned it a bit under the grill.

"Look!" Eve announced as she brought in the vegetable dishes. "These are from my vegetable patch – carrots and roast potatoes – all organic!"

Then, after Lawrence had served everyone, she paused and said slowly: "Prospero, there's something we want to know. The birds … the geese, or starlings, well no, not them, they don't seem to fly in a flock, but the others …" she looked up with a puzzled expression and raised her hands, "… I mean, how is it that when they're all flying in a flock they all change direction at the same time? I mean, how do they communicate? We've been watching and we can't see the leader, the one at the front of the 'V' – well I understand about the slipstream making it easier for the ones behind and the vacuum and all that – but we can't see him making any sign to the others about changing direction and anyway it must take time for the ones at the end to get the message but they all seem to move at the same moment, the ones at the back, too. I can't understand it."

Prospero looked at her and spread open his arms.

"Some unconscious web, snaring each and all, transmits reaction and over-rides all personal response. The world exists in an electric field, called zero point field. It covers – and is – the whole universe. And in it waves exchange all energy."

Prospero told them that these waves of energy were unconsciously felt by all animals. They exchanged them – took them in and gave them out. They were felt most by the simplest animals, including birds. He reminded them that dogs sometimes whined and howled hours before there was an earthquake.

"Oh, yes," said Lawrence suddenly. "Oh, yes. Remember how Ronald told me Harry knew there'd be snow when he saw the molehills coming up? And he forecast that we needn't worry about the flood, either."

"Don't be facetious, darling," reproved Eve. "That's not the same."
Prospero smiled gently.

"The waves all travel at the speed of light. One feels them and turns? So all turn at once."

"Well, the funny thing is," said Eve slowly, "we've noticed that the bigger the flock the more the birds fly together – you know, in one movement. You'd have thought the bigger the flock there'd be more likely to be birds straying."

"They're just like a crowd." Prospero pointed out. "The bigger the crowd, the greater effect. If their reactions are all just the same the whole's stronger than the sum of the parts."

"Like the instinct of love. It over-rides everything," said Eve. She sighed and disappeared into the kitchen for the last course, a chunk of Roquefort cheese. Lawrence threw a couple of logs on the fire and pushed them around with the poker to get a good blaze going. He brought out a decanter of port, filled three glasses and slid one across the table to Prospero.

Everyone agreed that even though it was now May there was still a chill in the air. That afternoon they had some showers of rain. They knew by now that North Norfolk's seasons always lagged behind seasons anywhere else in England – except for winter, of course. Winter was always on time, even early sometimes. In fact winter doesn't just come early. It doesn't know when to leave either for it always outstayed its welcome. So that night Lawrence had made a fire and drawn tight the velvet curtains in the dining room. Before the fireplace stood the armchairs they had brought from their house in Notting

Hill. The light from the flames flickered on the bookshelves that he had just built. Now they contained the books he had collected over many years from around the world.

"Zeus told us you wrote about ley lines and druids and stone circles and things like that," said Eve, inquisitive as usual. "He said you'd even written a book about the colour white."

Prospero smiled gently. "That's true. But that is not my secret work. I tell them that for fun. My secret work … ," he paused, looked at them for a moment, seemed to hesitate, then said:

"I am the interpreter of our dreams."

He told how people visited him every year for his explanation of their dreams. And how most of them were women.

"Why is that?" asked Eve.

"Women know the true mysteries of life," he told her.

She nodded.

"Of course," she seemed to be thinking. "At least one man knows this." She looked at her husband. "Well, perhaps two … sometimes."

Prospero continued.

"And their dreams unlock their hidden desires. I use their dreams to help my greater work."

"What's that, religion?" she asked. Then even Eve felt she had gone too far. She waited as Lawrence moved quietly around the table with the decanter. Then:

"Do you write about religion?"

"No!" smiled Prospero. "The need for that exceeds our human will."

Eve was puzzled, so he explained.

"No one wants to die – but live for ever. So wishful thinking, hopeful man's pitfall, is the placebo – our frailty's humour. Religion, it's called. And this is the way. Act – don't pray. Your good deeds make your faith good."

He asked if they'd been to any church concerts yet.

"Oh, yes!" cried Eve. "The Messiah at Blakeney Church. It was wonderful!"

He explained that the church's role as a place of worship and a yard-stick of behaviour were all strengthened with the help of the concerts.

"Yes," he said. "Music's magic key – that helps us to love."

She nodded – and sighed.

"Religion? God?" he shrugged. "Perhaps. But love's the aim."

"I think I need another drink," groaned Lawrence. "Eve, this heavy talk's making me thirsty." He reached for the decanter. "Anyone want some, too?"

After a refill and to lower the tension, they gossiped about the people in the village. Zeus and Leda – how close together they were becoming, almost an item, commented Eve.

"And then," asked Lawrence, "what about Justine?" Eve looked sideways at him. Justine seemed to be the free spirit of the village, somehow representative of it. Then there was the club of the Pottery family ... and Millicent, the cookery writer. Prospero was amused by their interest in gossip. But by now they had realised that it travelled almost at the speed of light, like that energy he'd just been talking about. Only the week before, Jill at the grocery shop had noticed that Eve had a cold. Ten minutes later, popping into the Deli on the way to the post office, Zeus had asked her if she was better. It was all a bit different from their wine shop in Notting Hill. Lawrence used to go in every other day for a bottle or two of wine – but they had always acted as if they'd never seen him before.

After Eve poured coffee the talk turned to the tranquillity of the village and how easily anyone could turn philosophical. They told him that Voltaire's idea of cultivating one's garden had helped them decide to leave London. This led to Freud, the Greeks and finally the oriental mystics. Prospero mentioned a mystic called Gurdjieff.

"I use his teaching in my own work here." Apparently Gurdjieff's aim had been to make people more aware of what lay behind ordinary life – the miraculous, the true reality, as he put it. "There is a Gurdjieff study group up here."

He told them it sometimes met under the leadership of one man – Gurdjieff's agent for North Norfolk, so to speak. They performed intricate and ancient dances. This mystic was, it seemed, a dab at dances. So who were his fans around here? By now the afternoon showers had turned into an evening torrent of wet and windy rain. They could hear it through the velvet curtains, lashing the windows as if trying to get at them. But everything was quiet and still inside – as if they were in the eye of the storm.

Lawrence poured Prospero more port and he gave them some names. A stencilliste from North Creake, a historian living on one of those straight roads inland from Wells, a serene acupuncturist in a nearby village, a reclusive sculptor near the market town of Fakenham and an artist with a studio in the straggling village of Hindringham. They all seemed to live secluded and anonymous lives, isolated in the inland spaces and villages of North Norfolk. And all were apparently looking for a reality behind ordinary life.

"But," asked Lawrence, "you said you used this mystic's teaching in your own work."

"He helps us to find the miraculous – the truth that Plato's shadows hide from us. My work builds a bridge between our dreaming and reality – the miraculous."

"But what d'you do with this miraculous, then?" asked Lawrence. "I mean, I can understand what it is … well, maybe. I sometimes get sort of carried away when I'm thinking about the marshes – or flints, for example."

"Yes, your consciousness … when it grows intense it will lead you to the miraculous." Prospero paused and look closely at them both.

"I'll prepare all those who conjure that force to plant deep the seed to fight the threat to England's way of life. If you'll both join me we'll all work to heal the wounds of England, and reinstate its former life – up here."

"That sounds wonderful," interrupted Eve, her eyes shining. "We were both worried about the way things were going before we left London. It was part of why we left, actually. But can it be done? Up here? In North Norfolk? Well, of course … maybe," she answered herself. "It's got such a lot already."

"I made myself the master of a plan. North Norfolk – it is England's fertile ground. Its womb gestates the seeds I'm planting here. My preparation's been as you can see. First came the commune – then the Pottery. It's here we'll build a new estate for all. And bricks? The folk who find they're destined here."

Prospero went on to explain how isolated the communities in North Norfolk could be. A man could live alone down an empty lane and hardly talk to anyone for months except at the check-out at Budgens – an exchange which could not invariably be expected to produce a stimulating dialogue. He might easily be influenced by any strange group. Many years ago a Rosicrucian sect had been formed in Norfolk – freemasons and a rosy cross, that sort of thing. He sighed and shook his head sadly. A man without a sensible friend at hand could easily believe in such things if he had a dominant leader. And that influence could turn malign. But this seclusion gave an opportunity, too. It meant that a community could turn its back on the world, at least for a time, to free all faults.

"And our coastline has such people in it! No such risks for us – we exchange our thoughts!"

When Prospero rose to leave, Eve and Lawrence felt bound to accompany him home. It was only a few steps. There was no danger of him being mugged in the lane, no traffic either. But as they walked in the black night they naturally continued their discussion and Lawrence felt it somehow symbolised how they belonged to the village. They lived not just inside Gibraltar House but everywhere in the village, too.

*  *  *

But there was a problem of reality at the bottom of their garden that even an oriental mystic couldn't solve. They needed to raise the height of their back wall to conceal the windows of an empty cottage beyond it. They felt overlooked even though it was empty.

They had seen a board up somewhere advertising a builder called Dick Crewe and went to check him out with Tom at his shop. They almost heard the argument before they opened the door.

"I don't give a bugger about your bloody forms." Tom was dressed in yellow oilskins and thigh boots and was busy pouring mussels from a sack into a big bowl. Scraps of seaweed were dropping onto the floor. Over the sack he was talking to a man in a trim dark suit holding a clip-board and looking as out of place as a nudist at a church service. "This is my shop and I'm selling it in pounds and ounces as well, so you can piss off."

The man hurriedly took a step back, opened his brief-case and dragged out a thick publication entitled "EU Retail Sales Regulations, Vol XXIX."

"Look, sir," he said, opening it. "It says here …"

"Take it away," Tom snapped. "Get back to your bloody office or wherever you crawled out of and you can go back to Brussels for all I care where all the other faceless little Hitlers like you come from. You lot would've loved it if he'd have invaded, wouldn't you," he snarled.

"And also, sir," continued the official nervously. "Are you aware of the new regulations concerning pregnancy leave for employees? It applies to businesses such as yours – "

"But Tom only has a few staff," interrupted Lawrence. "And they only apply to companies with over fifty workers."

The official turned to him and began to pull another thick volume out of his brief-case.

"I assure you, sir, that Her Majesty's Government produced this regulation in last month's Enabling Legislation. It is derived from the European Union and applies to all companies whatever their size – "

"Well, that's nonsense," said Lawrence. "Brussels said it was only for businesses with more than fifty people. Our government just made it cover any small businesses, like this one."

He looked back at Tom. "It's called gold-plating, reinforcing it so they don't get sued by Brussels ... I mean what can you do when your own government is against you?"

"Well, it doesn't matter, anyway," put in Tom's wife with a big grin. "I'm the only female he's got working for him and I'm not likely to get pregnant. He's out on his boat half the night as it is and by the time he comes home he's real knackered and no good for anything."

"But, sir," pleaded the official. "There are strict penalties against non-conformity to these ..."

But that was as far as he got. Tom marched round the counter and glared at him, his nose a few inches from the official's spectacles.

"In the SAS we ate buggers like you for breakfast," he barked. "And spat the bits out for the doberman."

He threw open the door and jerked his head sideways. As the official edged out he dropped his clip-board.

"Here, you can take your bloody forms with you. I don't want 'em!" He picked it up and slung it into the street, where it narrowly missed Jill's horse (chomping patiently at its food-bag) and was immediately ridden over by Millicent (passing by on a bicycle), which made her wobble dangerously (dropping a bag of olives bought from the Deli) and utter a strangled squeal as the fracas enveloped her. Tom thrust his visitor out and slammed the door.

"Why do they want to bother with things like weights and measures?" he asked the couple. "All we want is free trade with Europe. They'll be stopping us having our own navy next."

Lawrence let him calm down a little and then explained their problem.

"Crewe? You've asked that bloke to do the job, have you?" He laughed and weighed out a couple of dozen mussels for them. "Well, make sure you don't mix him up with his brother. He's a plumber."

"Why, am I likely to?"

"Their wives might," said Jill, grinning. She gave her husband a shove in the back. "Lucky I haven't got a sister."

"Well, I've got plenty of brothers," said Tom.

"I don't fancy any of them." She grinned again. And after a slice of gossip over the seafood, it turned out that one bitterly cold winter weekend some years ago the Crewe brothers had had a row and had swapped wives. Or the wives had swapped them. No one quite knew which but it hardly mattered. It had only been intended for the weekend anyway – or when the snow had melted. But when the snow melted the wives never moved back. They'd been sisters anyway.

"He's OK. But tell me when he's done it. The bricks'll all be new and I'll give you some of the slop I boil my crabs in. If you spray it over the wall it'll soon grow fungus and'll look fifty years old in no time!"

The builder turned out to be dapper and slick, with long and well-oiled hair. He wore a fancy waistcoat and check trousers so sharply ironed you could have cut your hands on the edge. He opened a slim briefcase and produced a small notebook computer and a measuring tape. He then spent two minutes recording measurements he made of the wall, replaced them in the briefcase and snapped it shut.

"I'll do it for you next week," he paused and looked Lawrence up and down for a moment.

"Two hundred pounds – OK?"

Lawrence said OK. He looked at Lawrence again.

"Materials extra, of course," he went on.

"Materials? Extra?"

"Nothing to worry about," he said soothingly. "Just a bit of sand and cement and a few bricks. I'll get you the trade price. Won't cost you much. It's always the labour that costs the most in a job like this."

He shook his head sorrowfully – then suddenly looked up.

"Got anything to trade?" he asked.

"Trade?" asked Lawrence.

"You know, instead of the readies ... "

They suddenly realised what he meant. But they didn't have anything he fancied.

"Never mind. We'll work that way when you've been here a bit longer," he said. "All right, half down now and the rest when I've finished, right?" he waited.

"OK," said Lawrence, slightly confused.

"But I'll need another £75 now to buy the materials with. OK?" he waited again.

"Well, that's – " began Lawrence. "Oh, well, OK" He gave up and began to write out a cheque.

"Oh, dear," said the builder.

"What now?"

"I'll have to add VAT and tax and God knows what if you give me one of those things." He shook his head sorrowfully. "I pay my book-keeper enough as it is. And he'll probably have a nervous breakdown if I give him any more work. It'd be wrong of me to do that, wouldn't it?"

"Oh, OK." Lawrence didn't want a book-keeper's nervous break-down on his head.

And between him and Eve, they managed to find £175 in cash and handed it over.

"I'll be round in a week or two to do the job."

"He doesn't look much like a builder to me," commented Eve later. "Those hands haven't seen much sand or cement. Nor has that hair."

She was right. Two weeks later a cheery Irishman knocked at the door. The day was warm and sunny but he wore an overcoat. Two bottles of whisky in the same pocket weighed down on one side (Lawrence couldn't help wondering why he didn't have a bottle in each pocket). Behind him a large trailer was parked halfway down the drive. It was loaded with a couple of thousand bricks, a huge mound of sand, a dozen bags of cement, five hundred flints, a pyramid of scaffolding bars and three ladders.

He saw Lawrence's face.

"Ach, the divil is always doing it," he said. "He told me I'd be needing all this. Never mind, I'll look after you even if he won't. Just sign here."

They did. It came to a good bit more than £275. But if they hadn't signed he'd never have been able to push all that load backwards out of the drive.

The job took him two hours.

"That's nearly £140 an hour," Lawrence protested to Eve later. "It's better than the barber."

"Don't be silly," she said scornfully. "Our Brylcreemed builder must have found him in the dole queue and promised him a couple of bottles of Scotch whisky. Or Irish," she added as an afterthought: "it's cheaper. Maybe the fellow had already been paid when he turned up. Remember those two bottles in his pocket? Anyway I hope Dick Crewe took one of his women out for a slap-up meal with what we paid him."

"Ah, well!" said Lawrence. He was learning to be philosophical. "But I bet he didn't invite his brother."

\*     \*     \*

Soon the weather improved and, presumably in sympathy with the frogs now emerging in the marshes, more and more low-flying aircraft began to appear. And, like the frogs, the planes stuck together in groups. At the same time every weekday morning they screamed in low formation over the windmill before banking out to sea beyond Blakeney Point. Lawrence didn't like it. Not many people did, except the windmill's caretaker. He was over for a drink once when a sudden scream of engines made the cat hide under the sofa again and Eve jump and drop her glass of gin. But to him it was heavenly music. Lawrence couldn't understand it. Then he turned out to have been a pilot.

For the previous few weeks Lawrence had been engaged in an increasingly unsatisfactory correspondence with some faceless civil servant in the Ministry of Defence. He had accused him of preparing for the previous war. He told him that low flying was obsolete. His accusations had been ignored. So Lawrence decided to point out why he was right. There was a new American ground-to-ground missile called the SLAM-ER that could hit a window (even a Whitehall Defence Ministry window, Lawrence reminded the civil servant) from 100 miles away. He gave the civil servant its full technical details. This information must have impressed them greatly because it was only on the drawing board at the time. Lawrence had read about it in a Sunday newspaper a fortnight before. He had waited that fortnight before writing about it in case the faceless civil servant might have noticed the same article. Even he might have recognised the source. But comment came there none.

In his next letter he described research on pilot-less miniature jet aircraft. They made conventional reconnaissance aircraft obsolete, said the same Sunday newspaper. It had published the details two weeks before. And a week later the same newspaper published details of the latest proposed "Uninhabited Combat Air Vehicle", made in the USA, of course, including its navigational system. He waited another fortnight and told the ministry all about that one too.

The faceless civil servant's next letter was a good deal more guarded. A few days later Ronald told him a couple of men in cloth caps and mackintoshes had been heard asking about him in the pub. It seemed as though they might be on the run. So Lawrence decided to attack. He produced a petition against low flying. He pinned it up in the post office for people to sign, went to the pub and waited.

\*    \*    \*

Aircraft noise was a wasp-bite compared to what was about to happen. A few days after he had begun his record of low flying, their estate agent rang with bad news. The Arab tenants had vanished. The agent had not known about it himself until an hour before. By chance he had passed the house. The front door had been swinging open. The house was empty and abandoned. Eve was horrified. Never mind the absent tenants. The last thing either of them wanted was a bunch of squatters. Luckily the agent had a spare set of keys and locked it up at once. But even a locked empty house could be a challenge. Professional squatters could easily get round the law if they had got in through an open window. It was simple to break one, climb in and repair it. Then they would claim that it had been open when they climbed in. Their bank manager had been quiet for a couple of months. Lawrence realised he should have known something terrible was waiting to happen. The Arabs owed three months rent and had apparently left the house in a filthy mess. There were some unsavoury stains on the drawing carpet. Two beds in the top floor bedrooms had been broken. The state of the bathrooms was too revolting to think about, let alone describe. One lavatory was actually smashed – how, let alone why, he never discovered. And there were some very dark deposits on the bathroom floors that needed a hammer and chisel to cut away. His only consolation was that they had long dried solid.

"Did you contact the embassy?" Lawrence asked.

"Of course," said the agent. "But they claimed diplomatic immunity and denied everything on his behalf. It's all too common nowadays."

It meant that Lawrence couldn't sue them for unpaid rent, let alone damage. Anyway, by now the tenant, his four wives and their caravan of children had no doubt returned to the Middle East. He asked their embassy to co-operate but they were as unhelpful as the Ministry of Defence (or the Foreign Office for that matter, whom he also approached) and a good deal less polite than either. Quite un-diplomatic, in fact. And, of course, it was no good trying to make the agent responsible for unpaid rent.

"Our job is only to find a tenant, check references and collect the rent," he told Lawrence, surprised that he didn't know. "Not to enforce payment."

He raised his eyebrows in surprise that Lawrence didn't know that – and told him he had another call waiting. As bad as lawyers, thought Lawrence in frustration. On second thoughts, he felt that nothing could be as bad as lawyers, not even estate agents – and then he remembered bankers. He sighed and decided to go down to London quickly, give the place a thorough clean out and replace the broken furniture himself. It had to be ready for new tenants as soon as possible. The agents were being quite realistic when they told him there was no point in showing it to anyone in its current condition. Even to other Arabs. As if he would.

"Don't be long, darling," said Eve. "And I want to tell you that we'll survive somehow. I do so want us to live up here. Somehow we'll manage it!"

"And I do too, darling. We'll manage."

She embraced him and they kissed deeply before he drove to Sheringham Station.

He spent a week in London. He found the place just as tiring and unattractive as when they had left. For one thing it was much too noisy. And there were too many people about and most of them seemed to be like the belligerent skinheads they had met in the tube the first time they had visited London. Tattoos competed with rawhide and bristles on their skin and some sort of stud filled almost every visible orifice. They seemed to like throwing empty cans of lager at each other and stamping around in huge boots. Hardly any of the rest spoke English. He didn't know which was worse. And the pavements were filthy. He missed terribly the skies and space of North Norfolk. Luckily he didn't have to use public transport. He remembered his last experience in the tube when they had come down to make out the inventory – and shuddered.

But things were even worse when he met his bank manager. The man was sympathetic enough about the Arabs. But he still wanted his money. He sketched out what would happen if he didn't get it; notice of foreclosure, court action, bailiffs and eviction – from Norfolk as well as from London. He was already three months behind in his mortgage payments. And they were too high to manage regularly anyway.

On his second floor study in London was an old solicitor's partners' desk he had inherited from his father. So far he had been unable to take it up to North Norfolk. He loved that desk. It was very handsome – made of English oak in the days of Queen Victoria. The top was inlaid with olive green leather and had been printed with a Greek key pattern round the border. There were eighteen drawers on that desk, three on each leg and three at the top, with the same number on the other side. Each knob was carved with a Celtic pattern. His father had once told him the pattern was connected with their family. He himself had inherited it from his own father, whom Lawrence did not remember – only from photographs. But Lawrence's father had sat at it ever since his first job in 1928. For forty years he had taken it from job to job all his working life. Here and there on the leather top were ink stains, giving memories of different moments over the generations. As a little boy Lawrence had so often been taken to "the office," and seen him sitting there smiling at him behind its wide surface. Before he died he had told Lawrence he wanted him to have it. And, of course, Lawrence had been looking forward to bringing it up to Norfolk.

He took it down to Christie's auction rooms in South Kensington. With the smack of a hammer it was gone. And what he got from the sale didn't even cover those three months' mortgage payments.

It was with a wounded and anxious heart that he had climbed into the Norwich train at Liverpool Street. For a few minutes he sat silently and near to despair. But he knew that the train would take him home to North Norfolk. And he was sure that, somehow, one day, all would be well for them, and that all manner of things would be well.

Back home Eve greeted him with a white face. God, he thought! What had happened while he was away? Some new catastrophe? Was she ill? Had the roof fallen in? Had they run out of gin?

"That horrible cat," she wailed. Cat? And then she explained. Half an hour ago, after the sun had gone down, she had gone into the garden to water the vegetable plot. And outside the back door was half a mouse.

"Nothing odd about that," he said. "She never eats all of a mouse, not at one sitting anyway. And sometimes she doesn't eat any of it. I've often seen one lying there dead without any marks on it."

"But it was breathing," she cried impatiently. "It was pregnant. Well, the bit that was left was. Its stomach was sort of going up and down."

She put her hands over her face and shuddered.

"And it was only stomach and back legs. There wasn't any body left. I mean, a bit, but only the stomach – and its womb." Her voice rose to a shriek – "that dreadful cat had eaten the rest. All of it above its stomach. The baby was in the bit that it had left and it was still alive inside."

Apparently a few minutes before he arrived home she had gone out to look at it again and it wasn't going up and down any more.

It was clear that Lawrence had returned home in the nick of time. He poured her a double gin and with a shaking hand she took a gulp.

"OK, where's the cat now?" he asked.

"It ran off over the back wall," she sniffed. "I shouted at it. I know it's natural … I know, I know. But I couldn't help it. It's hiding under the bushes next door."

She took another sip and soon her hand stopped shaking.

*     *     *

A few days later they bumped into blonde Marilyn and her Brian in the Deli. She was looking happy and his pigtail seemed permanently abandoned. Nowadays, Eve told her husband, they were definitely an item. Lawrence remembered Prospero had told them that Marilyn had studied with the Gurdjieff group but had left them. He asked:

"Did you leave them because you felt that your intellectual quest for the mystical nature of the esoteric enigma of life could not be wholly satisfied by your leader's emphasis on Gurdjieff's arcane dances and that you needed a deeper intellectual analysis of Hermetic gnosis?"

"No," she said. "It was because every time I opened my mouth he told me I was a stupid woman."

"A curious type, that fellow who runs her group," said Brian. "I must put him in one of my paintings sometime."

"Well, he's not that funny," Marilyn told him. "Definitely not."

This mysterious group resurfaced with a chance event a few months later. But until then the subject dropped from Lawrence's mind for he had become absorbed in watching the arrival of summer. Spring had long gone. Showers no longer drenched the garden, nor did winds chase the clouds across the sky. Now in late May, he noticed that the sky was definitely drier and the clouds ambled along as if out for a stroll and enjoying the view. Pockets of sunshine were appearing like troops advancing into foreign territory. As May had worn on, the heavy artillery of the sun had replaced the advance guard of the lone sunbeams. And, like a liberating army, it made everyone light and happy. General Winter had put up a desperate fight. He had even made some counter-attacks. But now he had definitely lost.

In the garden the dawn chorus took on a confident note. Tender buds had long since opened into flowers. The first tortoise-shell butter-flies had appeared. And swallows had begun to return from Africa. They swooped over the lawn in victory rolls as if back from a raid over enemy territory. At twilight so many gnats swarmed around the gable that for moments they darkened the sky. Several times now they heard frogs croaking when they walked besides the shallows to the sea.

Their overcoats and even their umbrellas hung neglected in the

185

cloakroom. Lawrence had long turned off the central heating. Rich green leaves hid the branches of the trees. Soon butterflies were everywhere. The grass on the lawn was thicker than ever. Now he had to cut it every week. And the borders of every lane were spilling over with wild flowers like trails of costume jewellery. Foxgloves doubled as sepia ear-rings, clusters of blood-red poppies formed brooches and fronds of cow parsley were now emerald bracelets. They were all strewn around the verges as if a vaudeville performer had just passed by without noticing that her bag had burst open.

And Eve looked out a sun hat.

*       *       *

*The end of May:* it was a week or two after I had bumped into Marilyn at the Deli that Prospero gave us a call. He knows we have a tow-bar on our car and asks if we would like to help him launch his dinghy into the water.

"All winter long it's stored beneath my trees," he says. "But summer's coming. Time to launch it now! You two have lived here nearly half a year. Time now for you to learn some river craft."

So early that evening we drive up to Prospero's house. He is waiting for us, no coat over his shoulders but wearing thigh boots. His assistant is doing something noisily in the kitchen. I see that his dinghy is named 'Circe.' "Yes," he says, "she is always here, temptress of my life." He smiles and we load Circe onto her trailer. I reverse our car and hook the trailer to its tow-bar. I slowly drive to the quayside by the windmill. I have to pass the concrete slipway. I note that it slopes down and vanishes beneath the water. I give it a wide berth and make a sharp right turn to put the trailer as much in line with it as possible. I know that backing a trailer means turning the wheel the way that looks wrong. If you want the trailer to go to the left you turn the steering wheel to the right as you go backwards – but not for too long. So I turn the wheel to the right instead of the left as I go backwards – and when it is nearly lined up with the slipway, gently to the left. I slowly back car and trainer onto the slipway and quickly ease off after only a couple of feet so that the trailer is properly lined up. But the slipway is narrow. It is hardly the width of the car. On each side deep mud waits for me if I steer the wrong way. And I wouldn't be able to get the car out of that in a hurry.

"Incomer baptises car while launching local's dinghy ..." would read the Eastern Daily Press headline. And it would be sure to print a picture. The pub would fall about laughing. Carefully I back the car an inch at a time. At last the trailer is on the slope. I stop the engine and pull the handbrake fully on.

*Prospero unties the ropes that have tied the dinghy to the trailer. It now lies loose and ready to float off when the trailer goes under water. He walks past it, takes the dinghy's bow painter in his hand, wades into the river and waits at one side. Eve unwinds a coil of rope that has been stored in the dinghy's forepeak, ties it with a bowline to the trailer and loops the other end in two turns around the tow-bar of the car. I take up this rope, now slack for a moment, lift the trailer's hook off the tow-bar and nudge the trailer sideways with my knee. This moves it off the tow-bar and I take its weight with the rope, holding it with the two turns Eve had wound around the tow-bar. As it begins to roll down the slipway I slowly pay out the rope by letting slip the turns so that the trailer rolls gently into the water. As it takes to the water the dinghy begins to float and Prospero holds it steady against the current with the painter. I tighten the turns of the rope on the tow-bar to stop the trailer following the dinghy into the water, take another turn round it and add two half hitches. Prospero pulls at the painter to guide the dinghy away from the trailer. I climb again into the car, start the engine and pull the trailer back out of the water and turn onto level ground. Then I reverse the car to the trailer, turn off the engine, climb out, push the trailer's hook down over the toe-bar, untie the rope from trailer and tow-bar, coil it up and, wading out to the dinghy, replace it in the forepeak.*

*Barefoot now and with trousers rolled, I wade into the stream to help pull the dinghy along with its painter to the landing stage several yards away. Prospero takes the painter and ties it with a reef knot to a post at the landing stage. I make fast a stern line with another reef to a ring on the transom and tie it with two half hitches to another landing stage post. The rope is very long and I make it shorter with a sheepshank. In this way Prospero can let the line out without casting off when he makes his first trip. So Circe keeps trimmed and steady as Eve and I stand in the shallows and bale out the water from the bilge. We pull the rowlocks from their sockets and tie them together to be taken back to Prospero's house. Finally, tearing dry grass from the riverbank, we wipe the mud from our feet. We leave the trailer at the side of the quay, ready to collect the dinghy at the end of the season.*

*Bearing the rowlocks, Eve goes on ahead. Shouldering the oars, Prospero and I both take up the rear. At Gibraltar House we sit together to drink sweet cider by the apple tree. The sky grows dark and slowly turns to night. We walk with Prospero to his own door and so retrace our steps to home and bed.*

# Summer

Summer has arrived! The earth has bowed to acknowledge the power of the sun. It's the time of year when everyone feels young and everyone smiles. It's the time when nature smiles too because the sun embraces everything. A month or two earlier spring's arrival in North Norfolk had been like a solo ballet dancer performing a pas seul across an empty stage – arching, pointing, darting quickly but hesitantly everywhere, beautiful, indeed delicate. But would it last? Then came summer and the thundering corps de ballet entered stage left and stage right, joined at centre stage and faced the audience to perform in powerful unison, backed by a few good blasts from the brass in the orchestra below.

In the garden the grass and leaves were still thick and juicy green. And in the countryside the whole of summer lay spread before everyone like a gorgeous picnic that would go on for three long months.

Lawrence stood at the top window of Gibraltar House. He looked south over their garden wall to the wall of the rectory's drive. It stood beyond one of the patches of waste ground that still existed here and here in the village. The wall was built mostly of flint and it curved elegantly round to the rectory's Georgian façade. The flints were all different yet all the same. They were laid in neat rows the way bricks are laid. Here and there small bricks were set in the wall too. Their burnet sienna colour made rectangular smudges amongst the regular pattern of the blue-grey flints. Tufts of grass sprouted from cracks in the mortar. Tangles of ivy grew over the top. They almost made it come alive. But the copingstones capped it all. They adorned the wall and showed an English craft that had been carried on for centuries, ever since brick and flint were used for building. Each coping stone was about six inches long and had the shape of a helmet – perhaps dating from the Wars of the Roses. Each was rounded but had a slight ridge over the top and a little ledge on each side as if to protect its wearer's ears. The ledge extended a couple of inches beyond the wall. This of course helped to keep the rain off the mortar between flint or brick. That was its function. But its size and shape looked good too. For they were regular and in proportion. And so, combining function and harmony, they were works of beauty, every one of them.

Lawrence called down to Eve, who was pulling up some carrots from her vegetable patch for their lunch.

"Come up here for a second, darling," he called. "Come and have a look."

A minute or two later she arrived in the top room, wiping her hands. He beckoned to her and they both leaned out of the window and gazed at the wall.

"Look!" he exclaimed. "That wall. That English wall. See it?"

"Yes, of course, darling." She looked at him and smiled. "And I know what you mean. And I agree. It's one of all those reasons why we came up here."

They stood and gazed at the wall together. They saw how it curved up to the rectory's front door in a graceful half-parabola. They saw the sunlight reflecting on the sparkling flint and warming the old bricks. And they saw how the coping layer took its place in English history.

The next morning, just after dawn, a series of violent crashes woke them. A cloud of dust was rising above a pile of scaffolding that a lorry had just unloaded. The developer who had bought The Cedars was already doing his worst on that bit of waste ground. Infilling was starting right there. Half an hour later the site swarmed with builders, a new house began to rise the following week and within a month the flint wall had vanished from their view.

\*     \*     \*

Since moving up to North Norfolk, there was one thing that Lawrence had wanted to do so much that he had left it to the last. It was like a choice morsel, a pièce de résistance that you keep to the last at dinner because it's the most tasty part of the meal.

And during the period that he had postponed it, Lawrence had been looking forward to it so much that the idea had begun to build up a real tension in his mind. He knew this would make him appreciate it all the more for the waiting.

It was probably thirty years since he had done it last, all those years when he had been wandering around the world. But he had thought of it – yes, he had thought of it all the time, really, because it was part of the Englishman's dream. In fact it told more of England than nearly every other part of the dream. It told more than a cottage, a farmhouse or even a palace. It told more than the food or the beer. It symbolised the English way of life and the core of English behaviour. And in one form it was something that you could find nowhere else in the world – only in England. No wonder Englishmen dreamed about it when they were far from home.

He'd never had much chance to do it in London, of course. He had been distracted there. Although, to be honest, it might just have been possible. In fact for the last few years before he left London he had felt annoyed with himself that he hadn't tried to do it and was upset that he wasn't doing it. It had been one of the things that had made him frustrated with London.

Naturally, when they did move up, it was the wrong time of the year. Winter and spring were hopeless, of course. But he supposed he could have prepared for it in the spring, asked around and so on. But in those days he and Eve were new – interlopers – and didn't want to feel pushy. But even early on he could see it was possible. For he'd had signs. He had seen that group photograph in the Three Swallows. And he'd seen the ropes on the green.

Ah, well! Now summer had come and one mid-June Saturday it was time for the annual Church Fête that would for a moment distract him from that dream. Just the day before, Eve had made several sprays of lilies, with a few foxgloves, for church next Sunday – it was a memorial service. Now they were all done and she wanted to show them to her husband. So after lunch they opened the door in their garden wall, turned their backs on the marshes and strolled up the dark alleyway towards the fête and the church. They passed the poppies and the foxgloves and walked along the quiet lane with its high banks of wild thyme. Maybe they would buy some of Millicent's marmalade at the fête. Perhaps they would have a go on the coconut shy. But they would definitely visit the Three Swallows for a drink. For some reason he suddenly felt thirsty.

But as they turned the corner below the church and passed the blossoming rosemary bush Lawrence saw what he had been waiting for all those years.

They were playing village cricket on the green.

The sight caught him unawares. He had been waiting for it for so long that he'd forgotten about it. But his spirit rose in less time than it took to make that one step round the corner. And by the time his foot had touched the ground again his remembrances of things past had flooded in at the speed of light – the Colts, captain of the school's first XI and an unbeaten season, college cricket, his college colours and his first century, the 'Varsity trial, that college tour of Ireland and cricket in the army overseas. He remembered that time he had hit three sixes in an over. His wrists and shoulders began to twitch. It was what he had been waiting for all those years. He felt suddenly happy – and laughed and Eve was laughing, too. She took his arm.

"Well! And what about that, darling!"

They walked arm in arm along the boundary line to the Three Swallows. Freddy Blake was sitting at on one of the benches outside the pub. Near him sprawled five or six players. They were all dressed in white. They lounged on chairs or sprawled on the grass. Pads and gloves were strewn around. Some of them already wore their pads ready to go in, like Spitfire pilots waiting to take off in the Battle of Britain. Next to them Freddy had a wide book open in front of him. Lawrence realised with some surprise that he must be the scorer.

He was delighted to see them both and enquired after Lawrence's health twice in two minutes and missed seeing the umpire's signal for a boundary. Lawrence made the mistake of telling him about it, so he thanked him politely and added two boundaries to the batsman's score. Lawrence saw he had a walking stick leaning on the table.

"Yes, my boy, it helps me get around, now that they stopped me using my scooter. Yes, the police. What? Well, I did go through a shop window in Holt – it was the fish shop. I got all greasy but no one was hurt. Dunno why they made so much fuss. But they said it might be worse next time and I might do myself an injury. I like walking, anyway, you know. It keeps me going."

It seemed that the village was playing a team from the King's Head near Letheringset watermill at the head of the valley. Lawrence learned that North Norfolk's cricket teams were drawn from the patrons of local pubs rather than from the villages. He made a diffident suggestion to Freddy.

"You'd like a game, Lawrence?" he said. "Of course you can. But you'd better check with Tom. He's skipper and we're fielding now so you'd better wait till tea."

Lawrence was keen but rather hesitant. He wanted a good look at the teams first. He wanted to be quite sure they weren't too good for him. After all, he was older now – just a bit, anyway. So he watched for a few overs and it looked possible. The bowling was sort of furious, with a good deal of arm waving. But the ball seemed to have slowed down by the time it reached the other end. And the batsmen seemed enthusiastic. As for the fielders he recognised them one by one. Tom was walking over from mid-wicket in short-paced quick strides, full of energy, to have a word with the bowler and gesturing to the fielders as he went – all full of energy. Bookseller Jekyll 'n' Hyde a fast bowler? Well, there he was and Lawrence watched as with a dark scowl and a purple face he pounded up to the crease and let fly with a nasty full-length in-swinger that kept low, nicked the inside edge of the bat, beat the wicket keeper's left hand (good Lord, isn't that Ronald from the pub?), sped past short leg (it must be Harry for Lawrence heard an incomprehensible oath and saw a lighted cigarette go flying as he shot a leg out and fell flat) and vanished fifty yards away into the long grass of the churchyard where it bounced off a startled sheep onto the table tomb of one of Admiral Sir Cloudsley Shovell's skippers and wasn't he one of those sailors who had singed the King of Spain's beard a few hundred years ago? Four runs! For once Jekyll 'n' Hyde's furious look was justified.

The ball seemed to be lost so there was an interval while a couple of waiting batsmen rose reluctantly from the pub tables and, glass in hand, strolled over to look for it. Their white-clad backs bobbed up and down like foraging sheep as they weaved in and out of the cemetery's long grass. The pause gave Lawrence time to recognise Derek at cover point and still wearing his navy sweater. Zeus was near the far boundary, sleeves half-rolled up, shirt open to the waist, a straw in his mouth and a floppy hat tilted over his head as, legs bent, he lay on his back at long-on. Eve noticed that, well really, he did have rather a well-built chest. Leda was sitting on the grass with him but presumably wasn't actually playing. As Lawrence watched them she leaned over and gave him a long kiss; caught-and-bowled-over.

At the far side of the pitch was a small round figure wearing a large sunhat and sitting on a stool.

"Look – it's Pippa and she's got an easel! She must be painting the cricket," whispered Eve. "Do let's go and see what it looks like."

They walked towards her along the square-leg boundary just as a horse and rider appeared and began trotting slowly around the far side. It was only when the rider pulled up at cover point near Tom and called out to him that Eve recognised Jill. Some message about the shop, Eve heard her calling. Tom ignored his wife, more of less. He was the skipper, he pointed out, and they were playing cricket. No time for women. And, immaculate in creased whites with a short hair cut and a straight back, he was now striding about between the wickets pointing quickly here and there and giving orders as if he were on the bridge of some ship about to come under fire. Victor was the square-leg umpire – wearing a wide straw hat. You needed a man of substance as a cricket umpire. While the players searched for the ball he waved to the pub and called for drinks. Someone came out with a tray.

When they found the ball – somewhat reluctantly, reckoned Lawrence, judging by their hesitation in throwing it back – play began again. Next over, and Tom beckoned to a relaxed and bearded figure and gave him the ball. Lawrence thought he looked like W. G. Grace. But he decided it couldn't be. That was going too far back, even for North Norfolk. He suddenly recognised him as the Guardian, who waved with both hands to everyone to move out to the boundary – except for silly point – and asked Leda to vacate the field if she wasn't going to play. As usual, he was carrying a newspaper, which he handed to the umpire like a baton in a relay race as he ambled past him to the wicket. Victor had his eyes down on the crease watching for a no-ball. Or perhaps he was half-asleep after that glass from the pub. The

Guardian sailed his arm slowly round in the way the village windmill must have done years ago. The batsman hit the first ball over the pub for six, rushed to the other end to shake hands with his team-mate, leaped out of the crease to try the same stroke with the next ball but missed, fell over backwards and lay there immobile, having – as it shortly appeared – knocked himself out. Everyone watched in silence as the ball trickled very slowly up to the crease, nestled comfortably between leg and centre stump and was hit by a bail that its gentle arrival had dislodged. Out! The fieldsmen's shout of delight woke up Victor who jumped, waved the Guardian's newspaper furiously – thereby knocking over the bowler's wicket – and bellowed: "Out! Out! Both of you!" This was followed by a derisive call from a lady sitting outside the pub – "Victor, you were asleep!" – who turned out to be his wife Pat. The Guardian told the batsman at the bowler's end he could stay, patted Victor on the back, took back his newspaper, found his place in it at once and continued reading while the batsman was carried off feet first by square leg and long leg.

Lawrence watched the cricket until the visitors were all out. By then he had completely forgotten about the Church Fête. But there it was, below the church and in the next field to the cricket pitch. A couple of dozen children were swarming around various stalls selling clothes and bric-a-brac. Two long tables were filled with dozens of jars of home-made marmalade and tins of cakes. Over it all, with her usual formidable authority, presided Millicent, cookery writer, chairman of the parish council, churchwarden, organiser of church flower arranging, chairman of the Church Restoration Fund Committee, caterer for its lunches, organiser of the Saturday morning bring-and-buy stalls on the church green, Flood Warning Officer and now, it seemed, Gendarme at the Church Fête Stalls. She caught two small boys with their fingers in a jar of honey and whatever it was she said made them back away and no mistake. Next door a heap of paperbacks overflowed another table. Beyond them half a dozen plastic ducks floated in a children's paddling pool.

"Fish one out and you get a prize," was Pat's genial call. "Lawrence, I hope you liked your wife's efforts!" She was brandishing a handful of bamboo rods with lengths of string and bent pins on their ends. The coconut shy was the next stall and her husband Victor was in charge, pretending to juggle three balls. "Just imagine that one of those coconuts is your bank manager," he suggested.

"But I thought you were umpiring," Lawrence complained.

"Ah, well, J 'n' H has taken over for a bit," he said. "We're batting now and he's going in at number eleven."

Nearer the church Ronald was organising a three-legged race. A dozen small children were having their left legs tied to their neighbour's right legs. There was a lot of high-pitched chatter going on. The boys enjoyed it all but the girls weren't too sure. Some of them were already pulling the hair of the nearest boys. Then Ronald blew a whistle but most of them fell over at the starting line. Ronald groaned, put his hands on his head and smiled at Victor. He had to line them up to start again. He shook his head at them, pulled a flask from his hip pocket, looked round, saw Millicent and put it back. Obviously it was hard work. Sacrifices were necessary.

But by some bales of straw Lawrence and Eve came across something new. Four drainpipes were lying on the ground. They were each a couple of feet apart but more or less parallel with each other. One end of each drainpipe was fitted into holes in a vertical plank of wood that formed one side of a small enclosure. Its other three sides were made from bales of straw. The drainpipes were numbered 1 to 4. Zeus and Leda were standing in the enclosure with four ferrets crawling around at their feet.

"Recognise their shape?" smiled Leda. "Long and hairy but with two legs at each end and whiskers and a mouth at the front." She laughed.

"We put a ferret into the far end of each drainpipe and let go – all at the same time," grinned Zeus. "Well ... if they don't bite you first. And you've got to take bets on which one will be the first out of the other end. It's quite a simple game, actually."

And they picked up all the ferrets and moved to the open ends of the drainpipes. The tournament was about to begin. It was certainly fascinating. It seemed to be a combination of a greyhound race and a cock fight. Harry was there with Derek the fisherman. Those two must both be low in the batting order, thought Lawrence. They put £2 bets on No. 4. He and Eve put the same on No. 3 and No. 1. Zeus and Leda held four ferrets and managed to shove one into each drainpipe at roughly the same time without being bitten.

Then everyone waited. Nothing happened. And nothing happened again. Harry said something almost incomprehensible, but it sounded like: "I'll be batting by the time those buggers come out."

"Well, I saw them go in," Derek told him.

Then after a few nerve-wracking seconds a little whiskery nose appeared at the opening of No. 2 – and twitched. There was a mild uproar from Harry (no one had bet on No. 2) in which the only word Lawrence recognised was "swizz."

"Wait a bit, Harry," said Leda. And sure enough the little whiskery nose stopped twitching and vanished back inside its drainpipe.

There was another pause. And then another little whiskery nose twitched at the opening of No. 4 and very soon its body decided to follow its nose into the straw enclosure.

"That's more like it," said Harry. Leda clapped and gave him and Derek £2 each.

"See you in the Swallows, then, Harry," said Derek.

Before they left for home, Lawrence had been offered a game of cricket by Tom for the following week and was then dragged into the church by his wife to show him her efforts at flower arranging, foxgloves and lilies entwined. He thought a little and said:

"Well, you didn't do that at our local church in London. Don't say you like it here?"

And she smiled happily and kissed him. But it was only after they reached home that they realised the Church Fête was organised exclusively by the middle-class members of the village. Its original inhabitants, like Harry and Derek, visited if they were around and put their pound or two on a ferret. But they didn't help organise the show. Lawrence and Eve noticed again that the village was divided. The Church Restoration Fund, the Church Fête, flower-arranging – these were the occupations of the middle class, their own little soap opera of Congregation Street. And none of the original locals took much notice of any of it. They didn't even mix in the Mitre.

"Never mind, darling," said Eve. "They're all a good lot and people like Millicent, Pat and Victor keep the village going. I'm pleased I'm part of it, too. In fact I was thinking I might start going to the Sunday services more regularly. Well, somehow it's not so much the religious side of it, funnily enough ... not really."

She paused, trying to work out the real reason. "I suppose it's because everyone is so happy and so nice here. They must be doing something right. And it has an effect on me."

"Yes," said her husband. "I understand. Isn't it called example?"

"And then there's Philip, of course. He's perfect." She laughed. "Different from London, darling."

As for Lawrence, he was looked forward to next weekend when he would be out on the cricket field. Eve was flower arranging again and he was playing cricket. They were doing well in the village community.

197

But on Monday morning after the weekend that feeling was almost completely crushed by a phone call from the London agents. It had only been a few days since the house had been redecorated after the Arabs had vanished and the agent had a list of people ready to show round it. But in those few days some squatters had got in.

"God knows how," said the agent. "There were eight of them and a couple of babies. But they were quick. They must have been waiting till they'd finished redecorating. What a cheek! Its about time the government did something about it."

He pointed out that he couldn't show anyone round, tenants or buyers, so long as they're there – nor kick them out.

"For one thing they'll hold the babies up in court and say we're all a bunch of baby-bashing fascists and start wailing all over the benches. And we may not be able to get in at all ourselves." He paused. "I'll check with our tame solicitor on the current legal situation but don't be too confident."

This was a disaster. They just sat there and felt more and more desperate. Even cricket was frivolous to think about. It was as serious as that. For a time they thought of giving up and going back to London, somehow forcing the squatters out. For a moment Lawrence wondered how much machine guns cost in Soho nowadays. They couldn't just sit in North Norfolk pretending everything was all right. Their dream was turning into a nightmare.

*   *   *

Meeting Hector – the great-coated pig rearer – was one of those chance events that might never have taken place if Jill had had some pork at the village store. But she didn't – so she told Eve where it usually came from.

"We get it from Hector, that weird blighter who wears a service greatcoat, remember?" she told her. "It'll be crisp, the crispest you've ever had – if he's got any left." Tom gave them more directions.

"Yeah, he wears a decrepit service greatcoat most of the time and he lives in Hector Hall," he grinned. "You know where that is? I mean, you can't see it until you're almost there. On the edge of the marshes between here and Blakeney, across the river from the village. Only half a mile away. You go down a long track. It's hidden in the trees. A bloody great mansion falling to bits but all you can see is the tops of tall chimneys, all twisted. And that's it. He breeds pigs."

Breeds pigs, wears a decrepit service greatcoat and lives on the edge of the marshes in a bloody great mansion falling to bits with tall twisted chimneys – no problem. Obviously not an accountant.

It was early afternoon on a hot Sunday in July, 80 degrees in the shade at least, when they drove to Hector Hall. Eve, just home from a church service, seemed to be floating on a cloud of contentment.

"I don't know," she told her husband as they turned into the drive. "It's just the whole atmosphere, you know, the feeling of putting myself in God's hands, it was so wonderful."

That was all very well, thought Lawrence. But when on safari in Africa he'd rather put himself in the hands of a good white hunter with an elephant gun and make sure that they both lived a little longer in this world, never mind the next – and certainly not just sit there praying. It was well known that lions were not religious.

They soon discovered that Hector Hall's drive wasn't much more than a straight track between rows of toothed briars, sharp furzes, prickling gorse and thorns leading down to a wood at the edge of the marshes with the sea about a mile beyond. Four or five chimneys showed through the trees. And, just as Tom told them, they were all twisted. It was the place they had seen when they had walked over the marshes in the winter. Every wall was built of flint or with the sort of bricks in their own house. And like their house it seemed to have grown out of the ground. Heaven knows how long it had been there. Its three old gables faced east. They would have been visible for miles along the coast if the trees hadn't hidden them. On an uncut front lawn a couple of rusty bikes lay in a pile that included a children's cricket bat and two tennis racquets, one with broken strings. A neglected Italian sunken garden lay between two wings at the back of the house and faced three or four barns. Beyond were stables, deep tracks, a little cottage with washing on a line, more deep tracks and a high-walled kitchen garden protecting strawberries, tomatoes, pota-toes, lettuce, radishes, cabbage and carrots from the north wind. But no pigs.

Eve and Lawrence walked over the lawn to the front door. It was a blackened oak slab criss-crossed with studs and hinges. Grass around the stone porch hid its lower hinges and a couple of fishing rods were threaded through the ring of the knocker in the middle. It didn't look as if it had been opened for ages. But Lawrence disentangled the rods from the knocker and gave it a bang. The result was merely a dull thud.

"He's not going to hear that." Eve took off a shoe and hammered at the door. No response either – not even an echo. She held onto the knocker, stood on one leg and put her shoe back on. They wandered around kicking at stones and looking for another door. The place seemed abandoned. They were about to give up when they heard squealing noises coming from behind a thick and untidy hedge. It certainly sounded like pigs. The noises grew louder and louder. Whatever it was, it was obviously heading towards them. Soon there was a sound of cracking as well and now and then a shout or two. Suddenly a swarm of piglets shot into view and darted in all directions – pink projectiles with tiny legs, curly tails and black eyes.

A few seconds later a very large and untidy old army greatcoat with a full colonel's crown-and-two-pips on the shoulders and wearing a trilby hat walked out from behind the hedge swishing with a cane at the pigs. It was a second or two before they realised there was someone inside – Hector, the pig breeder, at a wild guess. Since it was 80 in the shade let alone inside the greatcoat, he must have been allergic to the cold. By now the piglets had scattered. This man with the greatcoat, was he one of the Gurdjieff group? But Lawrence never got to ask. More important matters came first.

"Oh, I say, I'm most frightfully sorry," said the greatcoat. "Would you mind awfully if you helped me catch these little chaps. I've got to get them back into their sty. It would be most terribly kind of you."

He had a shock of black unruly hair and thick glasses, behind which his eyes blinked frequently. With him was a good-looking girl who, although very slim, was clearly in the last stages of pregnancy. She could have doubled as a rugby club's mascot.

The four of them spent the next ten minutes chasing around together in the undergrowth. Hector gave the instructions. His hat fell off twice but his wife turned out to be remarkably good in the scrum, although Lawrence was a bit worried that at any time she might deliver amongst all the piglets – or was it convert? Eventually they got them all back into the sty. A sow had been lying there, taking no notice of her offspring but grunting gently from time to time. Hector slammed the gate shut and said:

"Did you remember how many there were? I thought I had nine," he gave a broad grin, pulled a handkerchief out of his greatcoat pocket, wiped his face and blew his nose loudly. By now his spectacles were falling off. He pushed them back onto his nose with a finger and scratched his hair. "By the way, who are you?"

Eve explained – and he led the way indoors.

"You went to the front door? Ha!" he turned his head, smiled at her and blinked quickly through his spectacles. "It's been kept locked ever since great-great-grandpapa left through it for the Boer War and didn't come back." He shook his head sadly. "Oh dear it was such a frightful pity. He'd just taken a First in Latin at King's, you know. He was a real classics scholar, was Desmond. Did a bit of scribbling, too, actually. And he'd done very well in South Africa. He had his regiment by the time it happened."

Desmond turned to them.

"Mafeking, you know." And he added, almost apologetically. "The family put up a plaque for him in the church, actually."

They felt embarrassed but he held up the sleeve of his greatcoat. "Don't worry! I'm carrying his mantle, so to speak. You see, he was wearing this when it happened."

He led them to an arched side door that they hadn't noticed before, although it was open. On the gravel outside were a heap of oyster shells and a pile of old jerseys, trousers and other debris.

"I'm in the middle of a clear-out," he said and kicked a pile of empty shot-gun cartridges out of the way.

"I suppose if you're newcomers you won't yet have any exchange?" he asked over his shoulder, as he led the way inside. Exchange? Of course! But no, they regretfully told him. They were rather embarrassed.

"Never mind," he smiled at them. "It takes time."

Stacked around in the hall were five umbrellas, three tennis racquets, two pairs of waders, one of them encrusted with dried mud, a cricket bat bearing the signature of Leslie Ames and dated 1935, one ski, two cartridge boxes (one empty), assorted shrimping nets (two of them torn), a couple of long fowling guns and a rusted Boer War service rifle. Hanging from a hat stand in one corner were two cricket caps, a black stove pipe hat and a pith helmet marked "Mesopotamia" that had turned green with mould. A WWI Norfolk Regiment officer's cap with a bullet hole in it lay on the floor.

"That one was great-great-grandpapa's," said Hector as he picked it up and stuck it back on the hat stand. He saw Eve's expression as she looked at the bullet hole.

"Oh!" he said reassuringly. "No ... don't worry. We had rather a rowdy New Year's Eve Party some time ago. Someone got out of hand. We had to dump him in a pig trough in the end." He smiled at them and continued:

"Actually poor old great-great-grandpapa was killed trying to raise the siege of Mafeking. He was leading his men smuggling an ammunition wagon into the town after dark. He felt that as their colonel he had to show an example. One of the horses went berserk and he took hold of its reins to calm it down and ran with it while the Boers were shooting at the wagon to try to blow it up. He wouldn't let his men anywhere near it in case they succeeded. Well, they did." Hector wiped a tear away. "Sorry. Must have got some grit in my eye."

Suddenly he stood to attention, clicked his heels, pushed his spectacles back on his nose, saluted the hat stand and barked: "Well done, great-great-grandpapa. We will remember you."

'The price of empire,' thought Lawrence as they followed him through a drawing room that Miss Havisham must surely have abandoned the day before. The wallpaper seemed to have been the model for every curry house in London. Amid the cobwebs were a couple of chesterfield sofas. One of them sprouted horsehair from a torn seam. Over it had been stitched part of a McCarthy tartan rug. In the fireplace a large copper kettle hung from a hook above a mound of glowing ashes. Steam hissed gently from its spout. Half a dozen grimy but clearly priceless Persian carpets were strewn over the floorboards. The edges of most of them were curled and parts were threadbare. Between the sofas and the tall, half-shuttered windows were three glass cases of stuffed birds and an elegant Sheraton table piled with newspapers. Stacked against the walls were rows of books (early bound volumes of the Illustrated London News) and oil paintings in gilt frames ("Stag at Bay, Ardnamurchan, August 1935."). Walking through the room, thought Lawrence, was like working on an archaeological dig in Ancient Troy. In fact, following Hector around made him remember something ... hadn't there been someone there of the same name? But North Norfolk couldn't be that old, surely?

They walked past a three-legged Chippendale side table. The legless corner was propped up by a complete set of the Encyclopaedia Britannica.

"I must do something about that one day," he said and dropped great-great-grandpapa's greatcoat onto a sofa, where it fell off onto the floor. Following behind him his wife picked it up. In a dimly lit corridor Lawrence and Eve passed a line of bookshelves overflowing with neglected volumes of The Spectator going back 200 years. They followed him into a kitchen that had clearly been modernised before great-great-grandpapa went off to the wars.

"There are early fourteenth century foundations under here, you know," Hector told them as they walked along. "Quite old, I suppose. We've had the place quite a time, really."

But the kitchen did have a large deep-freeze with lots of bits of dead pig in it. And Jill was right. That night they ate the freshest pork with the crispest crackling they had ever tasted. Lawrence roasted it with some cloves and sauce from some of their apples and remembered to spread marmalade on the skin. It tasted as like ordinary roast pork as chalk did to cheese. What had they been eating in London all these years?

And as they crunched Hector's pig's crackling, they wondered whether they could have found Hector and his house anywhere else in the world but in England.

"And not just England but in North Norfolk, nowhere else but in North Norfolk," Eve claimed. She was right. And the house showed again how independence thrives on this coast. For Hector didn't give a damn.

"What if the place had been in Surrey, somewhere like Dorking?" asked Eve. What if a banker had got hold of it? They shuddered with horror, poured each other another glass of wine and drank to Hector.

"Yes! And to North Norfolk!" said Lawrence, smiling at his wife over the rim of his glass.

Discovering Hector, like discovering Troy, pushed more urgent activities from their minds. So when they awoke at dawn next morning to remember the squatters in their house, their anxiety hit them all the harder. But later that morning their agent rang with good news. The squatters had been kicked out an hour earlier. He had checked up as promised and there was a new law, effective from the week before. It allowed landlords to evict squatters without waiting six months before they could get to court. They could do it at once. In fact the agents had obtained an ex-parte injunction the day before to get squatters out that morning. There wasn't much damage, either. Not, at least, on the scale of the Arabs' devastation the month before. A couple of chairs had vanished, one mirror was broken and a casserole dish was full of dried up condoms – used, according to the agents, although Eve said that was something she didn't want to know about. They confirmed that they had changed the keys and locked the ground floor windows. He asked them to find some more tenants. And reliable this time, he added with an exasperated note to his voice. No third-world diplomats, again, thank you – however rich the diplomats were and however desperate they were. Before ringing off he thanked them for their quick action. It was the sort of sudden change in fortune that happens often to those living on the edge but hardly ever to those following a regular life.

*       *       *

Silence, darkness and a candle. Around the candle sat two men and two women. It was a deep July night on the sands of a North Norfolk beach. Lawrence and Eve were with Zeus and Leda at his beach hut west of Wells. Behind them bulked woods of cloven pine, almost shapeless in the twilight. Ahead, the sands vanished into the darkness that hid the sea. Now not even a flash of surf told that it was there.

That morning Zeus and Leda had shown them the compact little village of Burnham Market. It lay across farmland beyond Wells to the west.

"Very pretty," Leda had said. "Very civilised. It's got all you want, a lovely green and a smart pub, a fish restaurant, an antiquarian bookshop and a new bookshop too and a Deli – though not so good as someone's ... " she had smiled warmly at Zeus.

"Well, it is very pretty," he said. "Lovely houses, too, almost like a picture post-card, everything all around the village green and just the sort of village foreigners think of when they think of England."

But they all knew there was something special about their own village. It was more raw, less civilised. It was rougher, nearer the sea and closer to the edge. It wasn't pretty – no, but it was searingly beautiful. Lawrence and Eve had been shown the other villages thereabouts. They were all called Burnham something – Norton (wind-wracked far into the marshes), Overy Staithe (pretty creek, small boats, educated children, residence of a property developer) and straggling Thorpe (birthplace of Norfolk's Hero Nelson, houses hidden behind long grass by an undulating stream, an ancient pub drowsing by a green).

"Everything asleep. No wonder the fellow wanted to leave." Lawrence had remarked.

"It gets even emptier further west," Zeus had told them. "With sand dunes and marram grass miles long at Brancaster and there's Scolt Head beyond it, that's an island, more or less, with all those shifting sands, it changes its shape over the decades, well, that's the same for all our coast line, either bits of it are falling into the sea or the sands are changing shape, and it's all crawling westward an inch or so a year ... and then there's Holme beach beyond all that ... you'd think the country was half uninhabited there."

It had been early afternoon when they had reached his beach hut. But now night had fallen and everyone was silent. The landscape and the empty space had worn them down and in the end it had overcome them completely.

Far to the west, beyond three or four miles of empty sand, the sun hung low over the horizon, watching the world like a primitive god. Slowly it grew bigger, the earth rolled slightly away from it and it sank under its own weight. For a few moments a line of molten gold bubbled along the horizon. Soon only a wide purple wash was left to stain the western sky. The twilight subdued them and they noticed how it changed everything. The mass of silence filled the night and even the birds were quiet. The last of the holiday makers had left, the world had shrunk to the glow of their candle and they were alone.

During the afternoon random swarms of families had roamed the sands with children and dogs all running everywhere. They had not been intrusive, although at one time there had been some sort of commotion near the water. If the beach had been in the south of France travel agents would have ruined the place with package holidays. Somehow this coast had been overlooked.

Soon it was high tide. They took a quick dip into the sea – just to get their appetite up, they said. There was a slight swell running. Somehow the groups of children had vanished. Then back at the beach hut Zeus had suddenly stood up and pointed to the east, to the channel leading out of Wells harbour to the open sea.

"Look!" he cried, "the Albatross!"

And there she was, gliding out of the Wells channel on the tide between red and green navigation buoys and less than a couple of hundred yards from them. Its up-thrust bow-sprit carried three billowing jibs and a flying jib at the top of the foremast and then those two raking masts were fully rigged fore-and-aft with its main-mast and mizzen booms wing to wing, port and starboard, to catch the wind. Everything she had in her sail locker was on those masts.

"Well, she has to, she has to have everything rigged." Zeus turned to explain, his eyes glistening, "full sail – there's not much wind. She's just left the quay at Wells and she's got to get off-shore as quick as she can."

And then –

"Hey, isn't that Justine on board?" He turned to them, grinning. "Look!"

Everyone leaned forward to stare at the figures on deck.

"Well, it could be," admitted Leda. And then – "Yes! She's seen us. She's waving."

And everyone saw that slim and aquiline figure with the flowing hair and the straight back standing by Jan at the wheel and waving to them.

And everyone waved back. Eve began to say –

"But I thought she was with, you know, the Village Marxist." She turned to Leda, a woman-to-woman appeal, "we saw them together at the Easter concert at Blakeney Church. It was the Messiah. We sat with them."

"Well, looks like you were wrong, darling," interrupted Lawrence. "But you know what these shipboard romances are like. She'll no doubt be back with him as soon as she gets onto dry land."

Eve made a face at him and stamped on his toe. Leda laughed.

"You never know with Justine. And perhaps the VM will wait for her," she remarked. And she grinned at Zeus and dug him in the ribs. "What do you think, Z? " Then she paused and looked at him. "Actually, I know what you think."

They stood and watched silently as the Albatross cleared the bar and sailed due north out to sea and the figures on deck became smaller and smaller. Soon the schooner met the swell head-on and her bows began to rise and dip into the waves. After a few minutes they saw her gybe, and her main and mizzen booms and jibs swung over to port. The crew quickly trimmed the sails as she wore to starboard, her wake following her round as she took up her new course.

"Yes ... outward bound for Rotterdam out of Wells," murmured Zeus and nodded to himself. He licked his fore-finger, looked round and held it up.

"Force Three or Four from the south, I reckon. And now she's heading nor' east. That'll keep her out of trouble. But it might change – this is North Norfolk, even out at sea. So even though we're not a lee shore Jan will probably hold this course for an hour or so to give her ten, even maybe fifteen miles of water to get her round the coast just to be on the safe side, because she can't be doing more than eight knots if that, and there's a lot of shallow water off Cromer. She's changed course to put the wind on her starboard quarter. He's done that to save her being pooped in case the wind gets up but she's still heading offshore. You see, that swell looks as if it could get heavier and she's down to her gun'ls as it is."

He slowly scratched his chest through the hairs as he stared out to sea. But they could hardly see her sails now for already she was far off.

"Well, Jan has to get right out to sea," he explained, "even at high tide. They must be nearly half a mile offshore already."

"Z, darling," smiled Leda, and put her arm round him, "don't you just wish you were on board?" She reached up and kissed him. "Even if Justine wasn't there?"

Eve and Lawrence looked at each other.

"You, too?" smiled Eve. And kissed her husband as well.

With their quick dip and the excitement of seeing the Albatross, they suddenly realised they were starving. Zeus wrapped a shirt around the barrel of his chest, opened a few bottles of red and white wine at random and laid out the food he had brought from his Deli. First out of the hamper were some olives, a few stuffed vine leaves and a couple of dozen quail's eggs – just to get in the mood, as he put it. After that came the serious eating. This involved a creamed and chilled casserole of pheasant. With it were new potatoes with parsley, mushrooms from the marshes and some of his own yoghurt culture. Nothing special, he claimed with a grin. But all fresh and all local. He opened three bottles of Brown Brothers white wine.

For some reason they were soon just a little sleepy. When at last they roused themselves the light, like the holidaymakers, had vanished. But the primitive mystery of the coast of North Norfolk was still around them. They sat together in the darkness with a candle, shuddered with pleasure and smiled to each other. Over a final glass they toasted their own wisdom in finding such a paradise. At last 'they all took hands to drift along those yellow sands' and made their own way home.

It was only the next morning, when they opened the Eastern Daily Press, that Lawrence and Eve learned that during that sybaritic lunch of theirs, two little children had gone missing, believed drowned – at that very beach, the one they had described as a paradise.

*       *       *

Now it was late July and they still didn't have a buyer for their house in London. But the squatters had been thrown out and justice had been done. And somehow this convinced them that one day all would be well for them too. So Lawrence's contentment was crowned when Freddy Blake got him a place in the village's cricket team that weekend.

Lawrence had bumped into him outside the Pottery. He was looking much frailer than when they had first met. His face was flushed and he was coughing a lot. And now he was walking with the aid of a couple of sticks, not just one.

"My legs aren't doing that well," he said. "Doctor said I wasn't to use them much and I'm not feeling too well all over. But," he stood still, leaned on one stick for a moment and waved the other in the air, "I'm going to get to the pub for my glass of stout if it kills me." He grinned. "I shouldn't be saying that, now, should I? But I'll be scoring the match at the weekend. I'll tell Tom you'll be playing." But he began to cough and had to break off. Lawrence put his hand under his elbow and led him to the pub for a medicinal Guinness.

They were to play against a team from a pub at the catholic enclave of Little Walsingham about ten miles away. Amazingly enough the pub was called the Bull. Tom told Lawrence this was their first season of cricket and apparently they had wanted each side to play with twelve men, on the grounds that there had been twelve apostles.

"I told them I'd been twenty-two years in the navy but that didn't mean I could have twenty-two players," he said. "If they wanted twelve men, A. N. Other could be Judas but as for us the village only had eleven people who knew how to play and that was all they could have, too."

He jerked his chin upwards.

"They'll be wanting Jesus as umpire next."

The opposing team arrived wearing brown habits and sandals and their captain brought out a silver flask and sprinkled some water on the coin that they were going to toss with.

But it didn't work. The devil fought back and Tom won. He decided to bat and put Lawrence in at number eight. That upset him. It was too far down the batting order.

"I've been in the services, too," he told Tom. "And I didn't go in at number eight when I played for the army in Cyprus."

"Well, that was long ago, so long ago that it was part of the colonies," he grinned. "Now you've got to start all over again."

But as Lawrence waited to bat he was anxious, to put it mildly. He could remember all the strokes but could he play them? Ronald told him just to put his bat in the way of the ball and keep at least one of his feet inside the crease. Easy enough to say, he pointed out.

"Well, if you miss," he said, "at least the keeper can't stump you. And if you hit a six on your first ball I'll pull you a pint."

Lawrence reckoned Ronald would be quite safe. He was.

Prospero was one of the umpires and wore his white coat over his shoulders. "It's an arcane game, so it suits me well," he told Lawrence, who was padding up outside the pub. The Bull's umpire at the bowler's end was a monk in a black gown with a silver cross hanging from a chain around his neck. Prospero gave him an official warning when he began to use it to reflect the sun into the batsmen's eyes. He begged Prospero's forgiveness but Prospero explained that his mansion was in a different house. It was bad enough when their bowlers faced the batsman, for at the very moment of delivery they often crossed themselves before they bowled, a sort of atonement in advance. It was rather effective because the delay meant that the batsman had usually completed his stroke by the time the bowler actually bowled the ball. Sometimes the bowler didn't cross himself but just bowled. When that happened the batsman wouldn't have had time to make a stroke before the ball reached him. And there was nothing in the rules against it. Tom was disgusted. Even worse was when every time they took a wicket the whole team knelt down and gave thanks to God – facing roughly towards mid-off (or deep third man), that being the approximate direction of Jerusalem. But at least, everyone agreed, there was none of this modern kissing.

"Well, those fellows at the Bull wouldn't have liked it anyway," pointed out Lawrence. "Judas kissed Jesus that last innings and look what happened to him later. To both of them, in fact."

Once at the crease he discovered that their bowling, making crosses or not, was much faster than he thought. Yes, he played the right strokes – more or less. But he usually made them half a second too late. Still, he scored three runs not out and was secretly pleased. But he decided not to display his college colours cap just yet.

When the Bull went in to bat, things were delayed every time a wicket fell. After taking guard the incoming batsmen knelt on the pitch and prayed for the soul of the bowler. Jekyll 'n' Hyde, the fast in-swinger, got really annoyed about that and began to bowl bouncers at them. They invariably turned their backs and let the ball hit them on the back or shoulders if it didn't miss altogether. "Scourged!" one of them murmured with a beatific smile as he was carried off after the ball had hit him on the head. Ronald, not being a Christian, stood at a safe distance from the stumps. The results were one monk bowled, twelve byes, thirty-one leg-byes and six monks retired hurt. But this was statistically inconclusive of the efficacy of prayer.

As for Lawrence, he spent the rest of the game in the mid-wicket outfield under that English heaven. He was unaffected by all the prayers and swooped with eagle eye on any ball that came his way (in village cricket everyone is all dead keen). He drifted around in a state of bliss to have discovered an almost perfect occupation. At last he was taking part again after so many years away. He realised what he had been dreaming of and had been missing for so long in his life. It was indeed what all good Englishmen dream about in the bush. When he was fielding and trying to concentrate on every ball he became aware of the game's rhythms. He saw how, at the end of each over, the players strolled with unhurried confidence to their new positions as if stepping to a minuet without music. He noticed how the fielders contracted towards the batsmen as the bowler came in and then subsided again, like a sea anemone in the tide's ebb and flow over some hot rock pool. And he experienced again the little rituals like the courtesy of clapping-in a new batsman. "What other country does that?" he thought. He saw how, at the finish, the batsmen walked back to the pavilion first and how they were followed by the fielders and then by the umpires, each side clapping the other – with pleasure, too. Somehow this marked the English genius. And all these things he saw as if for the first time, for he would not have recognised their authentic nature so many years ago. And now, for the first time too, he tried to analyse the strokes and movements of the game. The batsman's drive, hook and cut, the grip, run-up and follow-through of the bowler. And like much human activity taken to extremes, it made no sense. He decided that all players must drink deep, or taste not, at the bar of cricket – in their case, the functionally named Three Swallows.

At tea the home side held back until the visitors were served. Tea was an English feast prepared by a rota of English wives. There were egg sandwiches with thick brown bread. There were slim cucumber sandwiches with thin white bread. There was current cake. And there was hot sweet tea. And, not for the first time, he noticed how providing food brings out certain feelings in women. They were smiling and joking and being very attentive to the players. Impassive in the background stood Millicent, not just cookery writer, chairman of the parish council, churchwarden, organiser of church flower arranging, chairman of the Church Restoration Fund Committee, caterer for its lunches, organiser of the Saturday morning bring-and-buy stall on the church green, Flood Warning Officer and Gendarme at the Church Fête Stalls, but also Feeder of the Cricketers at Tea. She didn't actually do anything but as usual just supervised the village wives, Eve now enrolled of course, who passed around the tea. The current cake was hers and Lawrence knew how rich it was. Eve gave him three slices.

The village won by ten runs. The team from the Bull knelt on the grass outside the pub and forgave the village for beating them. That was the part that annoyed Tom most.

"They wouldn't have lasted ten minutes in Vietnam," he growled – and threw a pint of beer down his throat. The team had waved them good-bye and returned inside the pub for the ritual post-mortem on the match. Half an hour later everyone agreed that everyone had played extremely well. Their team was the usual English egalitarian mix that demonstrates the English genius – a fisherman (Derek), a banker (Victor), a potter (the Guardian), a sailor (Tom), a shop-keeper (Zeus), a book-seller (Jekyll 'n' Hyde), a fisherman (Derek), and an OAP (Freddy Blake, scorer).

So had Lawrence ever dreamed, in his decadent miss-spent early years, as shadow lengthened across close-cut grass and late sun glowed upon flint-walled ancient church with homely pub below, that he would be heaving a roller and helping to fence in a cricket middle in company with a publican, a banker and a fisherman? No! And he loved it.

*　　　*　　　*

*July: Another call from Prospero. Would we like a trip down the river in Circe? Eve was due at an evening service at the church but she gives me her blessing and into a picnic basket I pack a couple of bottles of red wine and a small flask of cognac. Vital supplies, I tell myself. For even in the summer we're still in North Norfolk. It can be cold on the river.*

*At the last minute I pull on a sweater and a pair of gum boots. By now we have realised that we are likely to need gum boots at any time of day or night. Luckily by now we have four or five pairs on a long wooden boot rack I made and fitted into the conservatory.*

*The sun is beginning to melt itself on the rim of the horizon by the time Prospero arrives to collect me. His golden retriever dances around him. According to the local newsletter, high tide is at 9pm today. But even then, he tells me there is a bar further down the river, where it enters that big inland sea called The Pit. It will only have two feet of water even at high tide. And if we are more than an hour either side of 9pm there won't be enough water for Prospero's boat. If we are too early, or too late, we'll have to climb out into the water and drag it over the bar.*

*When we come to the riverbank by the windmill his assistant, that hunch-*

back who speaks little, is pushing out the boat. Soon he begins to start the outboard motor. After a moment or two it catches, breaking the silence. And so home he trudges, leaving the golden retriever with us, who at once climbs on board and sits at the bows, staring intently ahead. Prospero helps me aboard, puts the helm round and turns *Circe* down the river. Twilight is approaching and the earth turns towards Venus. Soon it appears from below the eastern horizon. Unblinking in the clear sky, it watches as we run between the river banks that slowly widen and stretch ahead below the night's bowl.

In a few minutes the river will cross the bar and lose itself in The Pit. Far to the west, past the coastguard's house, lies its exit where beyond it waits the sea.

As we cross the bar the tide is near the ebb and there is little current. The dinghy's bows sigh through the water. No one speaks. The sound of the outboard motor is lost over the marshes.

Prospero suddenly stretches his arm seawards.

"See those masts at sea?" he says quietly, "beyond the sand dunes?"

"Oh, yes. They're moving too. Going west, aren't they? But what is it?"

"It's the *Albatross* inward bound from the continent for Wells."

"Oh, yes!" I tell him that we had been in Zeus's beach hut when we saw her set out from Wells.

"We saw Justine on board. She was sailing to Rotterdam with Jan."

Prospero turns to me and nods gravely as if to confirm that everything is going according to plan.

The earth rolls away from the sun, which abandons us to twilight. Lights begin to come on inland near the harbour at Blakeney. On the skyline of the dark hill behind stands its outlined church and beside it in a tower the spark of a lantern. After a few more minutes Prospero runs the bows into the bank and we climb ashore. The golden retriever leaps out at once and vanishes among the tufts of long grass. For a moment I'm not exactly sure where we are.

But Prospero points out that it is very simple. All we have to do is to lie on our backs amongst the reeds and the sea lavender. "Hear the birds above? We lie and listen!"

And we do. In line astern the shellducks approach us from the east and cackle to each other. At fifty feet their white breasts still catch the last rays of the sun, now below the western horizon and out of our sight. The birds cross the sandbank to the sea. To the west and forty yards above us a kestrel hangs, wings outspread and black against the sky.

"You see?" says Prospero, "we could be anywhere at all."

He's right, we could be anywhere – North Norfolk, Nova Scotia, Newfoundland.

Suddenly his dog reappears and nuzzles him at his ear as if he's telling him

*something. And Prospero lies still, as if listening. At last he moves his head slightly, looks the dog in the eyes and nods slightly. The dog buries his nose in Prospero's neck for a moment, gives a great leap and vanishes again.*

*Together we drink some dark red wine. I take a sip. Prospero asks me if I had ever noticed how the taste of what one ate and drank was affected by where one was.*

*"The palate of place?" I ask him.*

*"Red wine on the marsh? The seasons unfold. First it's hard as earth in winter – so hard. It has quality but it is sleeping. And then it expands – it bursts with colour. Like the earth in spring it is young and fresh. But soon you know it will be full and ripe. But then, don't swallow! Keep it in your mouth and roll its rich aroma all around. Quite soon it will expand, like summer's feast. It has fruit, like the berries in the hedge." He pauses and we both fill our glasses.*

*"And then it gets dull. It's lost its young spark. The marshland's damp taste seeps into your mouth. Quick! No time to lose! You throw it all down – and so it fills you." He turns to me and smiles.*

*"But you have what's left, wherever you are! The wine's memory, summer's memory. You sit by the fire, a crusty old loon. Autumn comes and goes – and turns to winter. You think of the marsh, the wine we drank there."*

*"You're right!" I agree and refill his glass. "Funny, though," I add thoughtfully. "I didn't quite get that feeling with the wine they gave Eve and me at that Church Restoration Fund Lunch."*

*And we lie under the sky, arms and legs outstretched on the soft turf. Our beds are the reeds, the clusters of pliant grass our soft pillows. We see the stars but not each other, so we talk easily as if we are in a confessional. We speak of Copernicus and comets, of constellations and celestial spheres. Our limbs seem to stretch to infinity. And we feel free. We are alone on the empty marshes. The nearest people are a mile or two away. But still we whisper. The centre of the universe? We are there. And for a time no one exists in it but us.*

*The spell stays with us as we turn for home. We pass over the bar with only an inch or two to spare. Once we scrape along the bottom for a moment but a quick twist on the outboard's throttle pushes us through. As Circe moves forward into the river the night's chill meets us. I am glad of my extra sweater and to be doubly sure I pour us both a glass of cognac from my flask. The outboard's exhaust drums against the river's banks. When we reach the windmill Prospero switches off the motor. The sudden silence, the silence we had forgotten, increases the spell and in fact locks us both into it. For a moment it is almost as if we find it difficult to breath. Now we clearly hear the rippling water. Somehow, with engine off, we perform the ritual of nosing in to the landing stage. Silent now, we hear the reeds rustling and soon they are well above our heads. The dark mill leans over everything except Venus, now a shining dot high overhead. A swish through half-submerged plants precedes the dull clunk of the bows against the landing stage. We tie up, ship the rowlocks, lift out the oars and lock the outboard motor as if still in the dream. We speak quietly and slowly. We do not want to break the spell.*

*I bring Prospero back home for a drink. But we are behind schedule and Eve wasn't at home. Never mind – I pour us both a glass of wine. And soon she returns. Apparently the delay had worried her. After all, she hadn't wanted to come all this way from London to have her husband drown on the marshes. So she had done the sensible thing. She had called round to the pub. She had asked Ronald if Prospero and I had been washed up there. No, we hadn't – and the amusement this produced at the bar didn't make me any more popular now that she has found us both at home with drinks in our hands. Like Derek, I suppose I'd have had more sympathy if I'd actually drowned.*

*"Anyway," she says, "the boys rang. I didn't tell them you were probably drowned."*

*"Oh, are they OK? Where are they now?" I pour us all another glass of red wine.*

*"In the Greek islands. Mykonos, actually," she says. "They've both got jobs at a strip club there."*

*"Good God!" I reply. "Are they actually stripping? Well, I suppose it's better than asking us for money – that is, if they can find anyone who wants to pay*

*to see them naked. I mean, they're young and slim ... but all that's quite common nowadays."*

"No, silly!" she laughs. "They're waiters. And they said to tell you that if you're interested the club's at the second café on the left when you get off the boat."

"Not tonight, Josephine." I grin and raise my glass to my wife. "But I'm open to persuasion."

*       *       *

Soon it was the end of July and Lawrence and Eve were due at an open-air performance of a Restoration comedy at the rectory, a hundred yards from their house. The actors were strolling players from an Anglian company. The backcloth for their play was the rectory's late eighteenth century facade. After all, its pillars and sash windows were genuine and there were stables behind if the script called for a Restoration romp in the hay. The auditorium was the front lawn. Everyone had to bring their own chairs or rugs. Behind were the elms and then the open meadows. Across the lawn and near the shrubbery little groups of people were busy opening bottles and even hampers with tablecloths on the grass. Philip had emerged from the front door and was moving around exchanging greetings with his flock. Now and then the pop of corks punctuated the conversation. No chairs for Lawrence and Eve – they had carried a cane sofa up from their summerhouse. Very comfortable, they explained to Victor and Pat nearby, who were surrounded by a cornucopia of cold dishes. Victor was preoccupied with the ordeal of opening a bottle of Krug 1975 while sitting in a well-upholstered film director's chair with gold tassels and marked "Mr Toad." Pat sat opposite him supported by a half a dozen large cushions. She presided over a dazzling white tablecloth bearing a feast of caviar, foie gras, lobster and wholemeal bread.

"Come and have a drink, you two," she called out. "Victor has chilled the glasses and he might be able to get the bottle open before it starts."

"Don't distract me," he grunted breathlessly, straining at the cork.

A few yards behind them Brian and Marilyn sat and winked at Eve. They were propping each other up back to back on the grass with a bottle of white wine and a cheese salad. Lawrence noticed Brian was wearing curious orange sun glasses that were hinged like a visor.

"Just back from a show I held in the States, my lad," he told him.

"These things are all the rage over there. They're called shades nowadays."

Sitting nearby in chairs from the Pottery, the Rhine Maiden and the Guardian waved to them. He was writing in his notebook.

"He's hard at it – it's a chapter on local architecture," she smiled. Eve waved back.

"Almost Congregation Street," said Lawrence. "But where's Freddy or Tom? Not many old villagers here. But I see Justine over there, back from the sea. And she's got the VM with her. Look – behind us. You know I'd seen the Albatross when I was out with Prospero?"

"You didn't tell me!" she protested.

"Well, you were too busy being annoyed that I hadn't drowned," he replied, grinning.

"That's not fair. I was worried."

But she turned her head – carefully, so as not to be noticed, pretending to look at the trees. And, true enough, behind them Justine and the Village Marxist were sitting on an old rug and seemed to be engaged in an intense discussion. She was looking down at the rug and at one stage he spread his arm out and waved his hand in what looked like frustration. Justine shrugged and almost imperceptibly shrank away.

"Ah!" said Eve.

"What d'you mean, 'ah'?" demanded Lawrence.

"What I mean," she replied, not taking her eyes off them. He groaned.

Soon shadows began to stretch across the lawn. Lawrence noticed the tall figure of Prospero, coat over his shoulders and motionless and hardly visible between some trees at the edge of the lawn. He got up and walked over to him but Prospero put his finger to his lips and smiled.

"I need to watch these people's subtleties," he said. Soon the players appeared, the audience settled into silence and the play began. The plot quickly developed in the gathering dusk. Spot lights appeared, directed here and there on the front of the house. Soon all else was pitch black. This transition to a universal dream made make-believe child's play. Soon everyone was ready to imagine anything – cloud-capped towers, gorgeous palaces, solemn temples, even the great globe itself. But by Act II they were transported to a Mayfair drawing room. There were crinolines and wigs, frivolity, witticisms and political intrigue. At last the play's climax came with a stylish flourish.

Eventually the applause and the laughter died down, the spot lights went off one by one and the silence of the night sank over everyone. Slowly, and in little groups, they rose and gathered up their chairs, their hampers and their bottles. And in ones and twos they wandered off and vanished into the shadows. Lawrence and Eve took up their sofa and walked the few steps home.

"Remember our last trip to the theatre in London?" he asked Eve with a smile. "To make sure we'd be on time and find a parking space we had left Notting Hill at 5pm – nearly two hours before the play started. What was it? Ah yes! Les Miserables."

"Yes, you'd dropped me at the theatre, the Palace, it was on there, in the West End," remembered Eve. "I had an hour and a half to wait and went and had a drink somewhere."

"Well, I drove for twenty minutes, further and further from the theatre, looking for a safe place to park the car," he said. "I ended up the other side of Euston Road, I think. Anyway I had to walk all the way back to the theatre, maybe half a mile or more. None of the taxis would stop. And of course when the play ended the car had vanished. I put you in a taxi, remember, and rang a police car pound to find out where they'd put it. I took another taxi to somewhere underneath Hyde Park, walked half a mile again and spent a fortune before they let me have it back."

By the time he had reached home, he remembered, it had been nearly 3am.

*        *        *

But a few days later the couple found a local activity that was possible at any time of the year. It was the noble sport of wine tasting, an art form of North Norfolk. Well, not quite a sport, although it did exercise the palate. And he guessed it had its origins in local habits.

Years ago, supposed Lawrence, people living in North Norfolk often spent the evenings slowly getting drunk in quiet corners of isolated pubs. More and more indifferent to the torrential rain falling heavily onto the increasingly dark and muddy fields, they would have become heavier and heavier and sunk lower and lower into their chairs as the night wore on. Muttered oaths, garbled last orders (around one in the morning, after the landlord had drawn the curtains and locked the door) and a faulty juke box playing "Some enchanted evening" would have been the only accompaniment to the sound outside of rain lashing the fields of sugar beet that surrounded the pub. But to the newer and more travelled population a wine tasting was a natural habitat. They had no doubt drunk themselves around the world before settling on the coast. And a big difference between a wine tasting in London and one in North Norfolk was that on the coast whoever arranges it is likely to be a friend. And that meant there was no nonsense about spitting out the wine. And with a friend organising a wine tasting you can have a second taste and not have to pretend that you've lost your notes. Your friend knows very well that in North Norfolk no one really makes notes. No one talks about noses or butter either, let alone wood shavings. And the local master of a wine tasting par excellence was, of course, Zeus.

So when late in June he announced a wine tasting at a Blakeney hotel, Lawrence and Eve knew they must be there. And what a feast! By the entrance a table was piled with his cheeses. Some were cut into handy chunks. Some were cartwheels and there was Bleu d'Auvergne, an enormous round of ripe Brie, something crunchy called Lincoln-shire Poacher, a richly veined apricot Stilton and a pile of olive-spiced bread baked in the village. Lawrence suddenly felt hungry. The cheddar got him going. And then he felt thirsty. Zeus welcomed them with a big grin, his shirt unbuttoned already and his sleeves rolled up to the elbows. He gave Eve a hug.

"Actually," he told her confidentially, "I've got a special reason for this wine tasting. It's a celebration. I've moved in with Leda. She's got a cottage near Matlaske, its about fifteen miles inland. She used to live there with her husband before he died. But, well, life goes on. Anyway, you must come and see it soon. She's a lovely girl. I think I've got some-thing permanent coming over me."

Then he grinned. "I'm not used to it!"

He winked at Lawrence and turned to greet a few more wine tasters. Lawrence recognised Victor, Jekyll 'n' Hyde and Ronald.

"I've arranged the wine in a new way," Zeus told them. "I've made it like a game of cricket."

He led them over to a long table on which he had set out a row of twenty-four bottles.

"Look, I've got eleven whites here on the left. They're doing the bowling," he grinned. "Then on the right we've got the reds as batsmen." He slapped Ronald's back. "You've got to laugh! I call it a new marketing technique. And I've got red and white port as umpires at the end. You should try it in the pub."

Ronald stretched out a hand.

"Just give me a glass of beer, Z. I get enough of all that from the wholesalers," he said.

"But," asked Jekyll 'n' Hyde, "since I usually open the bowling am I supposed to be this sparkling French Limoux?" He held up the first bottle in the row. "And what are those wines next to it?" His eyes narrowed as he peered suspiciously at the labels – "Reisling and Moselle? They're close together and if I'm bowling in-swingers they must be the leg slips."

He poured a glass of Limoux for himself and one for Lawrence. Its bubbles came straight for Lawrence and hit the back of his throat and he jerked his head back as if he'd been bowled a bouncer. And you don't argue with a bouncer on your first ball. You just get out of the way. Lawrence put the glass down slowly. Then he had an idea.

"You gave me only half a glass, J'n'H," he said, "so that makes it a no ball." And he appealed for another.

Victor tapped him on the shoulder.

"I didn't call it a no ball and I'm the umpire," he protested. "More like a short run."

He took a mouthful and looked at his glass.

"J'n'H, I think mine was a short run, too," he added and held it out for a refill.

That was the end of the over. Lawrence sprinted to the pavilion for some cheese to purify his palate, a morsel of ripe Brie on bread baked with olives.

Ronald was wandering around looking for something.

"I can't find the wicket-keeper," he grumbled. Zeus gave him a can of lager and he looked at it suspiciously. The Guardian was further down the table, trying some Australian Chardonnay.

"Elegant, round and deceptive," he murmured to the Rhine Maiden next to him.

"Like me? Or your bowling?" she smiled warmly at him and topped up his glass.

Then to the slip field. First slip's label gave the French negociant's address in Dijon – Burgundy country.

"A good start," commented Lawrence, before he tasted.

"Yes," said Zeus. "But it's from the lower Rhone, not white Burgundy." Huh! Not that subtle.

To tell the truth, they were economical with that negociant. It was the only glass Lawrence didn't finish (there was a spittoon somewhere

219

but he didn't notice it).

As Zeus said: "It's not that bad, an everyday white, but I must say I've never seen you not finish a glass before."

"Nor have I," added Victor. "Eve, are you sure your husband's all right?"

They both visited the pavilion again for more cheese. A nice bit of Lincolnshire Poacher, wonderful! Efficient, too. Lawrence had a second helping just to make sure. By then they were ready for the medium-pace bowling.

"I get sick of affected wine descriptions," Eve was saying to Leda, who was serving behind the long table. She poured Eve a glass of mid-off – Touraine Sauvignon. "It's cheaper to buy the gooseberries, or the black currants, let alone the wood shavings."

"Ah," she laughed. "Eve, I quite agree. Mind you, I'd draw the line at wood shavings but sometimes, I mean he's got a good palate, but sometimes I think Z would drink anything." She paused for a moment, looked at Eve, and smiled as she shook her head. "Or anyone."

Then the reds. These were the batsmen, Zeus explained.

"Look, you two," he said. "I'm opening the batting with a couple of stylish young light-weights from the Loire – a Bourgueil and a Chinon."

They were stylish young players all right but slow scorers, intended to tire out the bowlers rather than score runs – like tiring out the bulls at the start of a bullfight. But they had no weight. A straight bat was not too interesting. So Eve and Lawrence were off to the pavilion again for more cheese, this time a hunk of Stilton to give a bit of weight to the batsmen.

First wicket down was the Chinon – caught by (or drunk with) some Bleu d'Auvergne at first slip – and in came a Chateau Lafite, an aristo-cratic Bordeaux Premier Cru at number three, a gentleman who had his initials before his name, who had seen it all before, even at prep school, and knew how to deal with an upstart colonial who thought syrah was spelled shiraz.

"What style! That one must be C. B. Fry!" cried Lawrence. "The forward drive of the first dry taste and then the body's follow-through. Classic wine-making!" But it was taken off after one glass.

"You're too expensive, Lawrence," Zeus protested.

Then came a middle order of heavy-hitting Rhones and Australian reds. Number four was a Gigondas, a quality Rhone with a terrific body. It was like a full-bodied half volley with a magnificent follow-through. Over the sight screen for six. Zeus told Lawrence he had once bought five litres from a Gigondas winery. He described the uneven earth floor, the huge old oak barrels eight feet high and twelve long and the old winepress in the corner reeking of wine. You could smell it even inside the church next door, he remembered. And when he had asked to taste some wine the winemaker washed his hands carefully, produced a tiny tasting glass and held it carefully in a purple-veined fist as he climbed a ladder to the top of a barrel to siphon off a few cc's with a long pipette. When at last he returned home Zeus had buried the wine in the garden. This ages it quickly, he explained. But when he drank it a year later it was like tasting the blood of a dead man.

"Oh, well, you must know, Z," said Lawrence. "But there's no gooseberry or blackcurrant nonsense here," he said.

"Yes. It tastes like wine. Have some more."

Fourth wicket down was a rich tannin Shiraz cross-bat from the Barossa Valley. Was this the great Don Bradman? Lawrence remembered that Bradman had been from South Australia and quickly drank four sixes over mid-wicket and Eve managed a couple of slices of Roquefort over the heads of the slip fielders before Zeus appealed against the light and took or, rather, led them both off.

Finally – the batting tail. Hardly worth worrying about. A couple of thin rosé wines from Provence and Anjou. They came and went before Eve and Lawrence could make up their minds whether they were red or white – batsmen or bowlers.

The post-mortem was a glass of white port and then of red port with the umpires – Prospero and Victor. Prospero, jacket over shoulders as usual, had arrived late with a lady friend from Milan. She examined the bottles up and down the long table and couldn't understand why Zeus had no wine from her country. She told them she would bring them all some Italian wine to taste.

Lawrence noticed Prospero giving Zeus a book he had written on druids and receiving a couple of bottles of the Gigondas in exchange.

"I said it's worth three, perhaps four bottles!" Prospero smiled at Lawrence. "But he said he would not really read it. It's for the Deli's new window display. It pulls in punters, maybe boost his sales."

After a last slice of rich current cake as a finale, they made for home. But yes! They did remember to buy a few bottles of wine.

\*       \*       \*

They had only just recovered from Zeus's wine tasting when something wonderful happened in a little church near their village. There hadn't been any announcements. There was nothing on Anglia TV. There were no lines in the Eastern Daily Press. And no one had put up any notices in shop windows.

But one August day the simple village church of St Andrew and St Mary in nearby Langham was filled with more people than had ever met inside its walls since it had been built so many centuries ago. Lawrence and Eve were there because Tom had strode round from his grocery shop an hour before and had told them to come and why they had to. And when they knew why they dropped everything.

Were there two hundred? Three hundred? Who knows? But every pew was packed, even the choir stalls were full and there was standing room only by the door at the back, where the late-comers were crammed in shoulder to shoulder.

Everyone was there for the funeral of Tom's mother Iris, the first person they had met in North Norfolk. The cancer that she had battled with for so long had at last been too much for her. They had known, as everyone had known, that she was very poorly. Two or three days earlier Eve and Lawrence had gone round with a bunch of flowers. It was all they could do and she had looked so well. But she had died the next day.

She had been born in the parish and lived all her life around this little part of North Norfolk. It hadn't been a long journey. Born in Langham, moving to Salthouse only a few miles away, then to the village and now back to Langham to be near her mother who had been buried there twenty years before.

But it was a journey long enough for her to bring up eight children; Tom, the eldest, whom Lawrence and Eve knew best, of course, and then four more brothers, one of whom had rebuilt part of their flint wall after the storm during that flood, and then the three girls, too – and all happily married.

She had brought them all up with the help of Harry, local parish councillor, fisherman of vast experience and friend, a gentle man if ever there was one. Their children had given them continuity – a couple of dozen grandchildren and great-grand children. Even when Lawrence and Eve came to settle in the village they were all still living in that little part of North Norfolk, give or take hardly any, establishing the continuity of life so naturally they had never given it a thought. And if anyone didn't know this family they must, as they might say round here, come from east of Cromer. And Lawrence and Eve knew them.

Her tiny figure with abundant snow-white hair had been well known in the village, of course. She had always been around, either helping in the shop or cooking at the Three Swallows by the church. She had had an unshakeable manner and an unhurried quiet smile. Her round easy vowels had rolled like the Norfolk landscape – gentle, unassuming, slow to rouse – yes, English. At times Lawrence and Eve had felt her almost saintly. Not always, though. Once, they remembered, she had called them interlopers. But they even got to like the smell of the boiling crab at Tom's shop.

There is a brass plaque on the north wall of that little church at Langham. It is in the tradition of the wall plaques in churches anywhere in England. And it says this:

> "From the fields between this church and the sea during the wartime summer of 1940 a small band of young men, who had volunteered to journey half across the world to our aid at a time of desperate need, flew to the defence of these islands.

> "Many of them were destined never to return home again, but to be lost somewhere across a waste of sea with their final resting place unknown to this day."

Lawrence shivered when he read it and the hair stood up on the back of his neck. She would have been seventeen in that perilous year of England's history. Everyone in her little village would have watched those fighter planes take off across the North Sea, wondering who would get home. And who wouldn't.

Even in those days Iris had stood out, according to the people who know. Rita Hayworth wasn't in it, apparently.

So now all the family was there and filling the front rows of the church. Perhaps puzzled, because of the cancer that had taken her life, but accepting surely now and with their hearts bursting with memories as they stood silently before her little coffin.

And they were not alone. They stood together with all their friends and neighbours from Langham and the North Norfolk villages nearby, Morston, Stiffkey, Wells, Blakeney, Salthouse, Kelling, Letheringset, Binham … people they'd known all their lives like Horace Nelson, Freddy Blake, Derek the fisherman and his son Mark, dozens and dozens of them from everywhere around. Lawrence and Eve recognised Karina the Log Lady, who gave them a sad smile, and Anton, the historian plumber. And then the later people, the ones she had sometimes called interlopers, Zeus and Leda of the Deli, Prospero the man of mystery, Ronald from the George and Dragon, Justine the free spirit (this time with Jan), silent Moses, Pippa the artist and poet, Victor with his wife, the good-natured Pat, and everyone from the Pottery. The church was crammed.

To add distress to the sadness, one of her grandsons had been stricken with meningitis less than a day after his grandmother had died. He was only three years old. His parents had been numbed by it all. Only Tom's quick thinking had brought the medics in. At the very moment when Philip was beginning the service the tiny lad was on a heart-support machine at Addenbrooke's Hospital at Cambridge. Well, he pulled through, thanks to the nursing staff. But nobody was sure of that while they were all standing there in the church.

And then the wonderful thing happened – the singing ... the singing of all her family and friends. First, the 23rd Psalm. The great declaration of faith: "The Lord's My Shepherd, I'll Not Want."

It was just a normal elderly church organ and a bit wheezy by now. But the simple formality and the gentle singing gave beauty to this plain and unadorned church. It rolled into all its corners and filled it and everybody there with kindness, trust and peace.

Then came "All Things Bright and Beautiful, All Creatures Great and Small," a favourite round here, Tom told Eve later. Simple and easy, the singing made the dust dance in the rafters. How often must she have sung her children to sleep with this happy tune, while the sea mist crept in over the marshes.

And finally: "Abide With Me, Fast Falls the Eventide. The Darkness Deepens, Lord With Me Abide." Deep, resonant and trusting at the hour of our death, it is the most powerful of all the Church of England's hymns, ancient or modern. Nothing to be said about it. Nothing to fear after it. No sting to death nor victory to the grave. No farewell. Just a confident au revoir, for we know we shall all meet again at the communion of the saints.

And as those simple strong chords marched slowly onward, as simple and as strong as the trust of a child, it was the turn now for those with grave bass voices to be heard. And the church was filled again, this time with the certainty that had brought everybody together. By now, some people were a bit misty.

Lawrence and Eve were sad to have to be there, but strangely happy that they had been expected to join with everyone in sending Iris home. They felt they had come to know her well and to know her family too. And now they stood with them all in that little church. They had seen how everyone had dropped everything to be there together, confirming to each other their community spirit as well as their faith. This church service could have been held anywhere in England. The pattern is the same in Cornwall as in Yorkshire. And because they were in the countryside, where everyone knew each other and worked together, the feeling that everyone was responsible for how things went was stronger than if they had lived in a city.

It had been part of their dream to live not just in the English countryside but also in a community where everyone knew everyone else, and knew what was expected of them. Lawrence and Eve glowed with pleasure and privilege that this was happening to them and that they fitted in. And they felt too that, in some strange way, Iris was now even closer to them all than when she had been alive.

After her funeral the spirit that had filled the church filled the village too. Everyone was a little quieter now. The atmosphere had been restless and uneasy during her struggle with cancer. Everyone had been unhappy, having to wait for her to die. But somehow, now, things were settled. The village seemed reconciled to Iris's death and recognised that it was just part of the cycle of life. It wasn't so terrible. It was continuity, like summer leading to autumn and autumn to winter. You accepted it. It was unnatural not to. The continuity was the proof that an old and well-loved friend was with you to reassure you that things were as they should be and that you were not to worry. For no matter how painful the trial and how hard the road, all would be well in the end. You were full of confidence that you were not alone, for you knew your old friend loved you and had whispered, "Yes, I will abide with you."

\*     \*     \*

After the following weekend Lawrence and Eve heard from the agents that they had found some more tenants. They were a university professor and his family from America. That sounded respectable and they felt really relieved. And at the same time they picked up an idea that was going around. Why not make the house the prize in a lottery? They would calculate how much they wanted for it and sell enough tickets at, say, £100 to reach that price. If they sold four thousand tickets, they would have £400,000 – and so on. And the person who had the winning ticket would have a £400,000 house for £100. It sounded irresistible! Who wouldn't take up that chance?

But who should they sell the tickets to? To reach the punters they would have to advertise. So they wrote to a few magazines to ask them if they'd like to take part and sat back to wait for their replies.

While they waited Lawrence checked out the number of people who had signed his low-flying petition. It had reached eighty-two, not bad for a village of less than a hundred houses, he thought, especially one with not a few Blimps. A couple of elderly regulars at the pub had disagreed. They said that everyone should do their duty and present a stiff upper lip. The Hun might strike at any minute.

But Lawrence and Eve felt that the Blimps' obsolete views needed to be balanced. So of course it was only fair that any of their family and other visitors up for weekends should sign the petition too. They had to be locals, of course. So the petition was signed with illegible names who claimed to live at 'Pansy Cottage' and 'Gay House,' not to mention 'The Hanger', 'Grounded' and 'Pranged.'

That weekend Lawrence decided to send the petition to the Ministry of Defence. The faceless civil servant failed to mention it in his reply. And this gave him the chance to attack them for ignoring public opinion – "an arrogant and incompetent display, showing your true colours of total indifference to the opinion of those who pay your salaries, not to mention of gross offence to the public," was how he put it. He was beginning to enjoy it all. Then his Sunday paper printed details of proposals of the "Future Offensive Air System" (FOAS to them), virtual-reality pilots, flying saucers steered by exhaust-gas and mother craft with aggressive detacheable tiddlers. Exciting stuff – and all real. He waited a week or two. Then he told the Ministry all about them, in case it might help them in their work.

\*     \*     \*

*Mid-July: Prospero telephones. "Come, my friends!" he says. "It's time you sailed to The Pit." He suggests a trip to that inland sea off Blakeney. This time I am able to persuade Eve to join us. He has a plan to for a picnic among the reeds. So we decide to bring sandwiches and wine.*

*We arrived late and Prospero reminds us that we must be in time to pass the bar at high tide. As usual, his golden retriever sits at the bows, keeping watch ahead.*

*Eve and I had learned some time ago that a colony of seals lived at the edge of Blakeney Point, where The Pit meets the North Sea. So Prospero takes the*

*dinghy through The Pit, all empty now though he says it will be full of sailing dinghies when the Regatta races are on next month. Soon we are in open water and the sea becomes choppy. Now we are past the end of that long spit of sand dunes that has been slowly extending itself westwards for a few hundred years. At its very tip lie dozens of seals. Most are asleep, though some raise their whiskered faces and gaze at us through tiny jet-black round eyes. They move by humping themselves clumsily along the sands. But when they take to the water they become elegant twisting black sleeves, dancing half in and half out of the waves. It is early evening now. The earth has already rolled away from the sun, which although out of sight still streaks the eastern clouds with rose. Overhead hundreds of seagulls scream as they dive and dart above the seals. In the distance a boat approaches us and soon we can see that it holds Zeus and his two young sons. He has taken them to see the seals and they return with us. By some uncanny co-incidence he has a bottle of wine with him. Instead of a picnic he proposes something we never knew – another of North Norfolk's art forms. Take two dinghies, hitch them both to the same buoy in the middle of The Pit and hundreds of yards from land, open several bottles of wine and drink; food optional. So we follow the instructions. Glasses of wine and lamb-and-chutney sandwiches pass each other back and forth over the gunwales. The boats sway slightly. The light fails gently. Ours are the only two boats in The Pit and its water is flat and quiet. Above us spreads the vast dark dome of night.*

*And naturally this sort of isolation stops the clock and we forget the tide until Zeus suddenly remembers we have to cross the bar at the mouth of the river. Sure enough, we are too late. As the banks close in both dinghies gently slide to a stop. No amount of revving of outboard motors can help. In fact they make things worse. So Zeus rips off his clothes ("Don't look, Eve," he says, with a provocative grin) and leaps out. He has muscular shoulders and blacksmith's arms. He soon pulls both boats over with a couple of tugs. His two sons jump in, too, but leave their clothes on. Eve and I, each with a glass of wine, sit watching him and cheer him on. But the golden retriever watches Prospero.*

*   *   *

It was mid August and outside the village whole fields were laid with carpets of buttercups and daisies. Tourists were everywhere. In fact there were more of them walking about the marshes all day than the flocks of birds wheeling over the house in the evenings. In any case, if Lawrence wasn't playing cricket, he didn't want to leave the garden. After a barbecue lunch, probably even a pheasant revolving on a spit, they would doze in the shade beneath the apple tree. They would watch the bees struggling noisily from flower to flower. And they would become mildly irritated at their buzzing. A whisper would set the blades of grass stirring. The thud of a falling apple would bring on a nervous twitch. Perhaps they would begin a game of croquet. But the heat usually ensured that the game would peter out. Yes, they began with the aggressive intent against each other that croquet demands. But they often undermined it by lying on the grass and gazing up at the sky while waiting their turn. Now and then they would sip at a jug of iced cider. Whoever's turn it was to play somehow found it difficult to stand up and look for their mallet. This was often enough a reason for the game to be abandoned. And they would try to concentrate on a book instead. But then they'd find themselves reading the same line fifteen times. Sometimes they would rest their heads on a cushion – just for a moment, of course. As they dozed off they would conclude that they couldn't think of a better place to be. And if they doubted it, all they had to do was to walk down their gravel drive and look at the immobile iron snake of cars full of tired and grumpy families and probably a char-a-banc or two of trippers from Leicester. Inside any of them were usually a red-faced father tapping his knuckles impatiently at the wheel, a mother staring grimly ahead or, if she was lucky, asleep and two children fighting in the back seats. Lawrence could never understand why no one had thought of detouring inland, maybe only a mile or two, where the roads were empty and the countryside just as beautiful.

So walking down the road was an obstacle course that added nothing to the magic of North Norfolk. And it was as near as those in the cars ever got to it. In fact, as Victor would have said, they were the jam jar that you put on the ground near your picnic. But there were still times when Lawrence and Eve might have had to brave the obstacle of the road – when, for example, they ran out of wine and had to visit Zeus at the Deli.

But they knew how to avoid the road. And that was by using the system of those narrow alleyways running from one part of the village to another. They could reach them through the door in their garden wall. Like smugglers they could vanish down them and emerge somewhere else. In full summer you had to fight your way past hundreds of hollyhocks leaning across the path – a forest of yielding swords. It was on one such an afternoon, when Lawrence had made an emergency detour to the Deli for another bottle of Pimms, that he had bumped into Prospero. As usual, his assistant was following behind him with a bag of groceries. It was the weekend and tourists were everywhere. The Guardian in the Pottery waved as he wrapped another large order. The Rhine Maiden smiled happily to them from the window, behind which she was turning a new pot on a wheel. It was hardly surprising that they were almost run down by a police car arriving from Blakeney and turning right at the Deli towards the church. This was the first time Lawrence had seen one in the village.

Behind them in the Bookshop Jekyll 'n' Hyde tapped on his window. He smiled and beckoned them both to come in. Prospero's assistant waited outside and glowered at them through the glass.

"Nice of you to drop in. All these tourists must be a nuisance for you. Blighters don't buy much here, anyway. Incidentally, did you see that police car just now?" he asked. "Well, I had an idea. I was thinking I might ask one of them to come into the shop every day. It might make these buggers buy something! What d'you think?"

Without waiting for their reply his face went purple and he bellowed at a man engrossed in a book entitled: "Flagellation through the Ages (65th edition)."

"Do you desire flagellation, sir?" he demanded. "Yes? Yes? Is that it, sir? Flagellation, sir, indeed? Hard back, bound, uncovered and cut, sir? I can supply it, sir. Do you desire it, sir? I'd be most happy to oblige you, sir. Step this way, sir, if you would please to be so good, sir!"

Jekyll 'n' Hyde unrolled his left arm in an elegant gesture towards his office and inclined his head in the manner of an Elizabethan courtier.

The man flushed, looked terrified and put the book back on the shelves.

"No, no, well, oh no, not today, I mean ... not ... " He sidled out.

"That bugger's been standing there reading that book for twenty minutes, you know. What a wally, eh? And the country isn't much better either. Look what's been happening! I just read it this morning."

He thrust a newspaper cutting at them but before they could read it he scrumpled it up and threw it into a waste-paper basket.

"Oh, well, I'll tell you." He pounded the desk with his fist. "Those faceless bureaucrats in Brussels ... they've actually produced a map of Europe that doesn't mention England. We're all split into regions. East Anglia is inside the Eastern Region. But it's got Scotland and Wales on it all right – but not a word of England, just these regions. And what are we doing about it? Bugger all! But why? That's what I can't under-stand." He paused and smiled charmingly, pulling out two chairs. "Do sit down, my friends. Would you both care for a cup of Assam tea? It's rather delicate, you know. My dear wife loves it."

He boiled a kettle, filled a teapot and poured three cups. "I do hope you also will find it to your satisfaction."

Prospero sat silently but Lawrence ventured that the English had a tendency throughout history to be slow off the mark. Look at Drake and the Armada – playing bowls and all. Look at the 1930s, for that matter. Nearly missed the bus that time, as someone said.

"And we haven't been trampled over for nearly a thousand years," he pointed out. "And being an island, maybe we forget about foreigners."

"Dead right!" said Jekyll 'n' Hyde. "Here, have one of these." He snatched a leaflet up from a pile on the bookshelf and gave him one.

"It's about some Eastern mystics. Another lot of nutcases," he snarled. By now Lawrence was becoming a little confused, so he stuffed it into his pocket and they both escaped.

As they walked down the street Prospero laid his hand on Lawrence's shoulder.

"Look upon that document – but beware," he said. "Now my friend, something else you should do here."

He told Lawrence that in the summer people sometimes went on a midnight barbecue on the beach. It took everyone back – not to 1935 but to many thousands of years ago. He suggested, if he and Eve were free, that they all went out that night.

He need hardly have asked. After arranging a time to meet, Lawrence retraced his way home down the dark alley. He opened the green door. Again he enjoyed the miracle of exchanging the alley's gloom for the garden's sunlit peace. The traffic's hum had stopped. Eve was dozing in the hammock. Her glass of Pimms lay empty and forgotten in the grass. The Sphinx was sleeping on the paperback on her lap. And he realised that they would never have met Prospero, Zeus, Jekyll 'n' Hyde or the others if they hadn't opened that door.

After dusk that night they drove to the beach and walked towards The Point with Prospero, a few steaks, a portable barbecue, some sausages, three bottles of wine and his dog. As usual the golden retriever danced around, vanished for minutes at a time but always returned to nuzzle Prospero briefly, as if reporting on events. The clouds were low and soon faded into night. Now they could only hear rather than make out the sea, snoring regularly somewhere like a mythical beast. Inland pricked the lights of Blakeney – quite near, only a mile away. Further west straggled pin-points marking houses along the coast until they merged into a rich galaxy less than ten miles away – and that was Wells. Between those lights lay the dark coastline. As their eyes became familiar with the sky, the night space filled with more and more stars. Now the only sounds were the irregular crunching of three pairs of shoes on the pebbles and the snoring of a mythical beast.

At length Prospero called a halt. They drove a couple of posts into the sand and wrapped a screen between them. It was more a barrier to the emptiness of the beach and sky than protection from any wind. They soon had a fire glowing and the sausages hissing. Almost out of sight beyond the fire the golden retriever sat motionless and quiet. He watched Prospero as if awaiting orders. But Prospero merely opened the bottles of wine.

"Stone Age!" said Lawrence. "Apart from the wine."

Prospero nodded.

"That's it – it isn't just a time-warp here. When as tonight the sky is wide and clear sometimes I search it with my telescope. The silence that's here, different from my house ... it's millions of years since light left those stars. Imagination cannot grasp their size, yet they're simpler than the pulse of an ant. Perhaps that ant's pulse or a lover's dream lies between us and the one big bang that brought out time and space. And all in the book was written since then. And here I feel how magic fills my life. Eve and Lawrence, you both will feel it too."

Lawrence and Eve were silent. He looked at her.

"If we'd listened to everyone and not bought Gibraltar House before we sold London, we wouldn't be lying here now. And we're only a mile from home – we're not on a holiday."

"You're right, darling," she said, putting her hand in his. "And I'm glad we did it. We'll manage somehow – whatever that bank will try to do."

They were sure Prospero was right, too. But soon they all dozed off and half an hour later woke to the gentle lapping of the waves before they trudged quietly home.

At lunch the next day Lawrence fished out the leaflet Jekyll 'n' Hyde had given him in the Bookshop. He poured himself another glass of Chardonnay and unfolded it.

"Those who are interested in the teaching of Gurdjieff, the Anatolian mystic, please write in."

He remembered Prospero had told him about the Gurdjieff group in North Norfolk. He was curious. So he replied. And a few days later he was driving through the empty lanes inland to the house of the mystic's representative near Fakenham.

It was a sombre drive. That morning in the shop Tom had told Eve that the two little children had been found, the ones who had vanished near Wells beach. That was three weeks ago. During all that time their bodies, lifeless and swollen, had drifted eastwards with the current. Only a month before they had played together at their school. Now, for twenty miles, brother and sister had rolled and turned together in the swell. They had drifted half-afloat, half-submerged and more and more bloated. In the end they had become almost unrecognisable. They must have passed Wells, Stiffkey, Morston, Blakeney, Weybourne ... all those charming and picturesque holiday villages along the coast ... until at last the sea had grown tired of playing with the little bodies it had so grotesquely disfigured and had spewed them out onto a hard and empty beach.

Had it been at night when the current had taken them past their village? Perhaps when they had been dining by candlelight in their conservatory? Or when they were lying on their lawn and sipping cider one hazy and idyllic afternoon? Or even – unbearable to consider, thought Eve – had it been the night of their barbecue on the beach with Prospero? They could have drifted past only a few yards away. Either way, beauty's canker had riven the North Norfolk coast. But it had made it all the more vital, too.

So Lawrence was rather quiet by the time he arrived. How afraid must they have been. How soon must their struggle have ended. And how their parents' agony would never end.

An elderly man opened the door. His expression suggested a badly digested lunch. Lawrence introduced himself. The Gurdjieff disciple grunted and marched down a corridor. Was he rejected already, Lawrence wondered?

The interrogation began with a lecture intended to deflate him. The atmosphere was malign. He was not encouraged to interrupt. It was clear that he had been invited as domination fodder. And he was treated to a curious physiology lesson.

"Gurdjieff, yes ... he teaches that we all have three brains," he announced in a voice that brooked no contradiction. "One is in the head. Another is in the heart. And the other is in the stomach."

"But surely," Lawrence began, "we only have one brain. There may be other nervous centres like the solar plexus, but besides being autonomic..."

His voice died away as his host glared at him.

"This is not a discussion meeting," he said. But worse was to come.

"Gurdjieff had analysed pre-Christianity. It is very esoteric ..." he murmured. According to Gurdjieff Christianity originated, it seemed, with sacred dances expressing secret knowledge on the Upper Nile in Ancient Egypt. The Resurrection? Smoke and mirrors. Forgiveness of sins? Wishful thinking. Love thine enemies? Quaint but rash. St Paul? Inconstant, changeable. Lawrence opened his mouth – and shut it again. Who was going to tell the Pope?

Then came a pause. Lawrence had just mentioned Gurdjieff and the miraculous, and he expected a comment in reply. But nothing came. After a silence for after about twenty seconds – a long time in an ordinary conversation – Lawrence realised that his interrogator was trying to force him to speak first. The discussion had become a battle of wills. What a cheek, thought Lawrence. So he was determined that he would not be the one to speak first. He knew that if he looked at this male Medusa something would force him to speak. So he stared instead at a book he had caught sight of on the shelves. Its title was "The New Small Garden," by C. E. Lucas-Phillips. Its cover had a photograph of a garden with lawns and lots of yellow and pink roses in the foreground. He remembered it for months afterwards – not surprisingly, because he fixed his gaze on it for sixteen minutes. And that's a long time when you're alone in a room with someone who's trying to crush you. In the end his host spoke first. He asked Lawrence if he thought his visit had been useful. Lawrence said that it had. And it was true. For he knew he needn't waste any more time there. And he escaped as soon as he could – never to return.

His car rolled gently homeward along the simple and sun-dappled North Norfolk lanes. It sailed through the innocent villages of Little Snoring, Thornham, Hindringham, Binham and Langham. He felt liberated, as if he had escaped from some mental enslavement. So North Norfolk wasn't always what it seemed. It was not always the pretty countryside filled with poppies, little cottages and simple round-towered flint churches. When Lawrence and Eve had come to live there they hadn't expected to find serpents with malignant minds. But now he remembered the words of Sherlock Holmes when one of his investigations took him and Dr Watson by train from Waterloo to the depths of Hampshire.

*"These happy country landscapes, Watson … see the simple farmer toiling in the fields, see the smoke spiralling sleepily upwards from the chimneys of homely cottages nestling below the church. See the big house, where the squire looks after his trusting villagers, those innocent families who work together in tranquil communities of faith and good-will." Holmes taps his pipe out and glances at Watson. "But, my dear Watson, the truth is so different. The walls of those grand houses hide ambitions of greed and manipulation, lust for the possession of men's souls and malign indifference to their fortune."*

Perhaps that was the danger of living deep in the country, where people often have to be self-sufficient. In North Norfolk Lawrence had already learned that without contact with people different from your-self, you could lose your sense of proportion.

He had never considered the dangers of isolation before he came to live in North Norfolk. London … ah, that was different. In most London pubs you could find people with half a dozen different world-views, all battling it out between them. Isolation in the depths of Norfolk had encouraged a tradition of religious non-conformity. That was the extreme. There had been no one to react to such ideas. So there was no balance. Alone they sat. They lost their proportion and they never knew it. Lawrence and Eve had already learned about the extremes of weather. Was it a co-incidence that Norfolk had also harboured some extreme characters? Sometimes it produced great thinkers. It would be difficult to beat Thomas Paine, champion of the rights of man – maybe the first East Anglian Marxist? And he had been foreshadowed by Reggie Kett who led a rebellion against land enclosures in the sixteenth century. It was put down by a Norfolk bishop, a professional Christian who believed in coveting his neighbour's land. So he helped slaughter three thousand other Christians who didn't. So much for authority. Then there were the powerful and distinguished East Anglian women. Julian of Norwich shut herself into a cell at the age of 38 after hearing voices – and wrote about God. Edith Cavell declared she must bear no hatred for any man – after which the Germans shot her. Who has Norfolk got to compare with them today? Formidable as Millicent was, perhaps even she couldn't match up to Boadicea.

By then Lawrence was becoming defiant. Maybe he was becoming a Norfolk man at last? Life is not Gurdjieff's "miraculous," he told himself. It's not Sufi, Subud, scientology or even religion, it's not "works" or prayer or knowledge. Life, he said to himself – life? It's other people.

And Lawrence thought of those two little other people, whose moments of excitement had lost them their existence and torn apart their parents' hearts for ever. What could Gurdjieff possibly say to them about "the miraculous"?

Eve was much relieved when he reached home. She had feared that he might have signed away their house to those Gurdjieff-ites. So to celebrate his safe return they opened a bottle of Zeus's champagne. And they thought with compassion of those little children and their parents and with contempt for Gurdjieff.

"He'd have done better to have spent his disciples' money on lifebelt installations," said Eve bitterly.

Besides being other people, life was ironic. No sooner had they decided to sell their house with a lottery than the agents found them a buyer. And at a price they could live with.

"Drop that auction idea," they said. "It would never have worked." Probably right, thought Lawrence. Or was it that the agents wouldn't have got any commission? So they cancelled their proposal to the magazines. They told their solicitor to draw up the sales contract. And they went round to the pub for a drink. What a relief. But was it true? Was it going to happen?

\*    \*    \*

235

It was Sunday and warm even just after dawn, even for August. And the day got warmer as time wore on. Even by midday, the marshes were full of tiny figures tramping in single file on the long tracks to the sea. And the traffic was the usual immobile iron snake.

Lawrence and Eve decided to join the crowds for a change. They felt they were due for an English seaside afternoon. And they arranged to take Zeus's two little boys to the seaside. Eve made up a picnic from the Deli – just some wild boar paté, a loaf of wholemeal bread, slices of cold fried aubergine, a handful of olives, a lobster and a bottle of Chardonnay.

"Why not two bottles?" asked Lawrence. "Are we going broke or something?"

She looked at him.

"Is that meant to be a joke?" she asked. "Well, we probably are. Well, probably tomorrow, anyway."

"Ah!" he said. "Tomorrow? Give no thought for the morrow. For tomorrow is another day. Didn't someone say that?"

"Yes, two of them."

And with the second bottle he threw in ginger beer, peanut butter sandwiches and gob-stoppers for the boys.

They headed east to Cromer, where they had begun their search for a house in North Norfolk. Like Wells, it's a seaside town – and that's their only similarity. The two together show North Norfolk's variety and extremes. Wells is an authentic fishing port. A lot of its income comes from working on the sea, as well as from the sea-side. Its shops sell sailing gear such as anchors and shackles and it only modestly acknowledges the nearby caravan parks. But Cromer is the compact if decayed watering place – with Victorian hotels and level sands. Its great church towers over its centre. Cromer has no harbour and caters less for sailors than for those needing sun tan lotion and fresh crabs and who like to play golf and tennis. The sea is there to look at and maybe even paddle in but not to be quite trusted – hence its lifeboat service; although it has a famous crab industry. It still wears its streaked coat of decay and seems almost proud of its appearance today – thanks to a confidence inherited from its hey-days. And that confidence is as English as cricket and warm beer, even warm ginger beer.

Deck chairs? Only 50p this year. The candyfloss machine was almost out of control. The tide was out and two teams of fathers and sons were playing cricket on the sand near the pier. The ball didn't always bounce but everyone took the game seriously. In England we know that cricket isn't just a game, especially on the beach. There was no boundary and whenever the ball vanished into the waves the batsmen just ran and ran until some small boy swam after it and threw it back, usually into the waves again. Once, by the time the ball returned to the wicketkeeper, the batsmen had run so much – two fathers, Lawrence noticed – that they were lying exhausted between the wickets. Whereupon they were both run out, Oedipus style, by their own sons. While Eve found a spot near the lifeboats to unpack the picnic, Lawrence found a father who agreed to let Zeus's sons play too. It involved lots of splashing of other boys, sometimes running after the ball and sometimes even batting. They were both excited by it all until one of them fell flat in his face in the water, burst into tears and had to be cuddled by the ever-ready Eve, who saw her chance to make up for her own boys being away from home. Lawrence rolled up his trousers and stood in a small pool near deep extra cover hoping someone would ask him to play. But no one did.

His attention had wandered anyway. Behind the wicket keeper the world's largest woman was struggling into the world's smallest bathing costume. If she'd been doing that in the main street a hundred yards away she'd have attracted a huge crowd and been arrested. But here no one was interested.

Then a rival group of fathers began building the world's largest sand castle with a moat, a portcullis and even a flag. The only problem was that they'd built it on the cricket pitch – at mid-off, to be precise. Belligerent words were exchanged with the players but the incoming tide threatened them both. At this point the Salvation Army Band arrived – as if to calm the savage breasts by adding the judgement of Solomon to the defiance of Canute. The Band marched to the promenade above the beach. There they halted and formed fours – all in navy uniforms, brass buttons and flat caps with a red band. Their instruments – the bassoons, the horns, the piccolos, the tubas and even the drums – all flashed in the afternoon sun. The conductor tapped his music stand and they struck up the rousing tune of 'Men of Harlech'. The music certainly seemed to sooth any antagonism. One or two fathers even began to sing along with the band. Lawrence and Eve lay back in their deck chairs: the English miracle had happened again. They looked around for the boys and saw them safe. So they tilted their handkerchiefs over their eyes and dozed off.

It was when the deck chair attendant woke them up to demand his 50p that they saw it – the Albatross! Or rather only the tops'ls on its two masts. The old schooner was almost hull down on the horizon and heading east.

"She's bound for Rotterdam," said Lawrence, gazing keenly out to sea, the palm of his hand shading his eyes from the sun in true nautical fashion.

"Remember Zeus's beach hut in Wells? She was outward bound then, too. And I saw her on the way back when I went out in Prospero's boat – remember? Now she's out again for another cargo."

When it was time for home they were all a little sunburned. The boys were sleepy, one of them had lost a shoe and there was sand everywhere in the car. Lawrence didn't expect much traffic so he was surprised to find a traffic jam even before they had reached Sheringham. There didn't seem to be an accident anywhere and he couldn't see any obstacles. It was only after a few minutes of stop-go that they saw the problem. A hedgehog had decided to cross the road. But it was crossing very slowly. Now and then it stopped for a rest. By the time Lawrence and Eve came up it had reached the verge, having totally ignored the chaos it had caused on the road. But no one seemed annoyed; in fact everyone was laughing. In Notting Hill that hedgehog would have been a smear on the tarmac in three seconds – flat.

And once home the boys had potted shrimps on toast before bed.

*     *     *

Prospero's Italian friend whom they had met at Zeus's wine tasting had returned to Italy and was now back for the summer. She had decided she wanted to buy a cottage in North Norfolk, for she had recognised the magic it held. This was the way England assimilated Europeans, thought Lawrence. But then he had a feeling there was something else about it as well, that he'd been trying to work out since they'd come to live up here. Meanwhile he and Eve took her house hunting. They had become long-term residents by now and so qualified as guides.

Moreover she had kept her promise and had returned with some Italian wines – deep reds and a few dry whites. She told Eve that she thought Zeus might like to taste some and perhaps make a bulk order. She was serious, they could see that. Business was business, even for Italians. But they both felt it possible – certain, in fact – that she had brought these cases over in her battered Alfa Romeo as her contribution to their life in North Norfolk and not really to do business. That was just the excuse.

But the game had to be played. So Eve called at the Deli to make a date with Zeus for a wine tasting, that famous North Norfolk art form.

"What about our garden for it, Z, one evening soon?" she suggested. And so it was agreed.

It was full summer by then and day had followed day after day of summer warmth. On the morning of the wine tasting Lawrence and Eve had cycled east along the coast to Salthouse. They had planned a picnic on the hill behind, a rising heath covered here and there with brown furze.

They opened parasols and placed their chairs to face north at the edge of the bosky ridge. A field of ripening corn sloped below them to the village.

"Nearly time for harvest," said Lawrence, looking over the cornfield as they settled down, uncorked a bottle of Sauvignon and opened cartons of Russian salad and cold tongue. "And I'd never have said that in London."

"Well, obviously, darling," said Eve, smiling and shaking her head at him. "There aren't any cornfields in London, are there?"

Beyond the cornfield a dozen flint cottages huddled around the church and overlooked the marshes and the hazy North Sea beyond. Spitzbergen lay somewhere over the horizon.

Later, the tongue and Russian salad long gone, Lawrence regretted as usual not having brought another bottle. Talk petered out and they both dozed. At last the sun swelled up, became again a pot of molten gold, flowed along the horizon's edge, lowered itself into the sea and vanished as the earth gently rolled away from it. Time to pack up and freewheel down to the coast road. Sticky and warm in the evening glow, they cycled contentedly home. It was one of Norfolk's summer days that seem to last for ever and only fades away when gentle twilight yields itself with the ritual token of modest resistance to the night.

Home at last, they wheeled their bikes down the dark alleyway, opened the door and stepped into their protected garden. Its flint walls, its lawn, its apple tree, its summerhouse and its hammock were still glowing from the heat of the day.

Later, stars scattered the deep sky by the time Zeus and his home-sharing lover, the beautiful and calm Leda, arrived with their Italian friend. Zeus had a bag of a dozen bottles over his burly shoulders.

"We need candles," he announced, putting down his bag, undoing a shirt button and rolling back his sleeves. "And somewhere to put the wine."

Lawrence and Eve carried the garden table to its place beneath the apple tree. During the day it stood near a patch of hollyhocks and usually supported some plant pots, a watering can and a sleeping cat. Its top was a rough surface of old pine. But candlelight and a patterned tablecloth soon transformed it into a mythical surface where every shadow hid a mystery. Lawrence produced the candles and lit them. Eve put down a few bowls of olives, nuts, cheese and bread. Leda laid out a stack of note pads. Their Italian friend lined up the bottles. Above the candles the apple tree's branches swept down over everyone's heads. Now they became the gleaming framework of a tent – apples and emerald leaves its ceiling and darkness for its walls. Twice that evening an apple plopped onto the ground behind them. Once or twice blossoms of pink and white floated down to the table.

"Now listen," instructed Zeus, handing out little note pads and pencils. "These are for you to make notes with, OK? We have to take this seriously – really! Now, the labels. The more information, the more you can tell and the more likely it will be of good quality. After all, the label of a cheap bottle isn't going to tell you much about its wine, is it? For example, 'Red wine from EU countries,' – you see? God knows what it's got in it and what it will be like. In fact the bottle and cork are probably the most expensive part. But don't let any of that distract you from the taste."

His Italian friend leaned over.

"If you like, I can give you the prices, Zeus," she said. "It's not a guarantee, but it will help." She wrote them down for him. And so they began.

Zeus had his hands full opening the bottles, numbering the labels, looking at the colour through a candle flame, having a preliminary sip, rolling it about in his mouth, spitting it out on the grass, making notes and maintaining order, let alone looking at what was written on the labels. So everyone sat there, each with their little pads, and entered their comments as they sipped and swirled and spat. Or that's how it started.

The problems began when they realised there were so many bottles on the table that they could hardly see each other over them. Or perhaps they had all begun to sink into their chairs. Either way Lawrence began to suspect that some people were not spitting but drinking - not him, of course.

In any case the candlelight was glinting on the glass of the bottles. And that made it difficult to read the labels. Zeus told them it didn't matter – they all had numbers anyway. Then, although they made their notes and spat out the wine (at first, anyway) there were regrettably times when they liked the wine so much that they had another taste. And this time they forgot to spit it out.

The problem was made worse when they decided to have yet another taste. And perhaps this time it would be a bigger one because it was so good. Oenological recidivism, Lawrence remembered calling it, although he wasn't sure he was able to pronounce it properly by then. In any case he had to explain the word to their Italian friend who, not being English, didn't know it. Until –

"Si! Capisco!" she said. "Niente self-control?" She had it in one. A short sharp shock. Eve took another sip of a Barola. At least, she thought it was a Barola. She knew it was red, though. The next step down the road was when they forgot which bottle they had taken a sip from. By now the candle flames were beginning to waver, there was a lot of wax on the tablecloth and most of the bottles were empty. Someone knocked a full one over, Leda began to laugh so much at a joke of Zeus' that she spilt her wine, Eve complained she'd lost her notes and Lawrence had gone to sleep.

"All right, we'll stop. You're all red-hot with drinking – reeling ripe, in fact, if you've heard that before," said Zeus, winking at them. He put away his notes.

"Anyway I think I have what I want," he went on. "You've got a good dry white here which would fill a gap in my stock. I'll order some from you and see how it goes."

Finally they woke Lawrence. He stretched, knocked another bottle over, shook his head twice and helped them gather up the empties, snuff out the remaining candles and put the pots and the watering can back on the table. The cat would arrive later – with the sun.

Another evening's hard work was over. All were pleased with themselves and with each other. And all showed it with hugs and kisses in the dark garden before they separated for the night and soon to bed.

\*　　\*　　\*

Besides wine tasting, Lawrence and Eve soon discovered another art form in North Norfolk – the private view. They were invited to them because many of their new friends were artists. Most of them held private views and their private views had one thing in common with private views in London. You were bound to meet your friends. But in North Norfolk that's true in spades. For everyone knows everyone else. The artists weren't only painters. There were potters, stencillistes, sculptors, poets, dancers and writers. And it's not just that there were so many. Their influence in the community was so strong. It played a bigger part in everyone's lives than if they were in London. There, after all, everybody goes backwards and forwards every day to work in some cramped office. They rub shoulders with civil servants, solicitors, money dealers, architects, bank clerks, shopkeepers and even accountants. In London it's almost as if art is something you do at weekends – not something which affects people all the time as it does in North Norfolk. All for the better too. No formaldehyde sharks in Norfolk. But possibly quite a few unmade beds.

As for what's on offer at the private views – yes, the drinks are free. But whereas in London you're quite likely to get champagne (or at least Spanish sparkling), with elaborate canapes (or at least small sausages), up here it's usually white or red – and none the less welcome, for that matter.

It was Pippa who had invited them to her private view late that August. By now they knew her well and had become fond of her warm heart and her courage in living alone up here. She was in constant battle against the weather and her finances. She did nothing else except paint and write poetry. No work in computers or advertising, no state subsidies or inheritance, not even a job at the checkout. Just selling her work wherever she could. After having been acquainted with only passing examples of integrity over the years, Lawrence and Eve were beginning to learn up here what it really meant. And what it cost, too.

She was "showing," as they say in London, at the village hall in the caravan park of Morston, two or three miles west along the coast. They decided to cycle and after pushing their bikes up the hill to Blakeney they freewheeled laughing and with the wind in their hair the mile downhill to Morston. A yellow-haired harvest covered the fields. Near the woods inland a combine harvester was cutting the corn. It gave out a spray of chaff that was quickly lost in the heat haze. From time to time the clatter of the engine carried to them over the fields, always a second or two later than the puff of smoke. A few sunburnt sicklemen gathered up and bound the sheaves. And as the couple freewheeled along, the grey tower of Morston Church loomed up over those honeyed fields. Tacked to its lych-gate was a large sign. "PIPPA's EXHIBITION", it said and an arrow pointed past the pub, where another sign said "TRIPS TO SEE THE SEALS", and down a track towards the marshes. The village hall was a large wooden building with bare floorboards. It was surrounded by caravans. Behind them were the municipal conveniences. And beyond them the marshland spread to the sea.

"White or red, you two?" cried Pippa, as they arrived. "Make holiday, put on your rye hats!" she giggled. "Heard that before?"

Breaking off for a moment from a noisy chat with some friends, she spread out her arms affectionately, sleek hair flying and eyes gleaming. She was clearly holding court, and loved it all. So did Lawrence and Eve. With paper cups of earthy wine (it had a bouquet of marsh), they strolled around the hall – gallery wouldn't quite be the word.

Her show was called "Myths, Marshes and Moses." For sharing the private view with her was Moses, the shy and biblical owner of the Smoke House. His papier-mâché figures were robust and recognisable. The Flasher was there (priced at £10,000 – "yes it's a lot but, well, he needs it at the Smoke House and hasn't got time to make another," explained Pippa). But this was eclipsed by a pièce de résistance new to Lawrence and Eve. It was a large motorboat, also papier-mache, steered by a half-naked papier-mâché man ("a local solicitor from Holt," Pippa giggled), complete with spectacles on the end of his nose. The crew was a fierce group of three papier-mâché beauties, also half-naked. Each one had scarlet lips, a blonde coiffure and a mere gesture of a black bikini, literally painted on. They were balanced at impossible angles, arms and legs in impossible positions and all had impossibly laughing faces. Beneath the motorboat was a papier-mâché sea of crinkled green waves surging and spilling in all directions. The whole thing was about five foot square and three foot high.

"I'm not quite sure exactly what market he has in mind for this," said Lawrence. "Its size puts it in the category of bank foyer sculpture, like a Henry Moore, but it doesn't seem quite the thing for Coutts or even Barclays."

"And it's much too good for our bank – that deserves a formaldehyde shark – it would suit its character." said Eve. "He made it for his own satisfaction, the way some men have a private store of pornography."

He looked at her.

"Is that a fact?" he asked, and paused for an answer. "And how do you know?"

"Look, there's Moses!" she cried, changing the subject and pointing across the room.

He was presiding over the gathering from a corner of the hall, head and shoulders over everyone else and massive beard swaying slightly beneath eyes glinting with ironic amusement. And again they never heard him utter a word.

Two or three couples were doing the rounds – all friends of the artist, as one would have expected. Jokes, yes – but serious appraisal too. They were looking at big canvases of Norfolk landscapes. Vast and joyous blue skies rode above yellow pastures. And together the colours spelled fertile green. In one canvas a tiny church was clinging to the land just inside the frame as if the landscape was so wide that it pushed everything else out of sight.

"Isn't that the field near our house?" asked someone. She wore an ankle-length flowered dress that revealed a tantalising glimpse of green welly. No fancy art language or brittle chatter here. No smart gear either – not even jeans. Dark clothes, a shabby overcoat or two, long scarves and a straw hat clearly coming apart round the brim.

But there were other pictures, too. And they were different. There was a trapeze artist poised at the top of the swing and just about to swoop down into the picture. Then there was a little boat rising to a wave and about to dip down.

"She's painting the moment before the action," said Eve. "Do you see? Look at that dog, too!" She dragged Lawrence by the sleeve to a close-up of a dog's head on a beach, gazing into the distance. "His nose is twitching. He's waiting for something!"

Lawrence suddenly had a flash of recognition.

"Well, it can't be twitching," he told her. "It's not a film. But d'you know who she's like? She's like Gauguin! You remember his picture 'The White Horse' – three horses, one drinking, two with riders ...? They're all waiting, something is going to happen. She does that, too. Remember the famous one – 'Bonjour, Monsieur Gauguin?' the man and the girl at the gate with the moon behind? He painted them as if they were holding their breath."

Lawrence pointed to a picture of a girl holding a violin.

"This girl, too, she's motionless, she's not playing, she's staring ahead – waiting for something, maybe the conductor? It's like lots of Gauguin's portraits, too."

"Yes, dears." Pippa had come up behind them. "It's a good theory and Gauguin or not you're right. That's how I see North Norfolk. Sort of poised between the past and the present."

"Not 1935!" Lawrence and Eve laughed together.

"I love this one," Lawrence was pointing at an enigmatic portrait of a seductive Ancient Egyptian woman, black hair framing mesmeric eyes.

"D'you think they will sell?" Eve asked her.

"Ah!" She made a face and wobbled slightly. Her paper cup spilled some wine. "Probably not, Eve darling. I wouldn't mind if one or two did, though. But how's your water colour painting getting on?"

"Ah, not too good. I keep on making mistakes."

"Well, why don't you try oils?" Eve felt that was too ambitious, but Pippa pointed out with a toss of her black hair that with oils you could paint over the mistakes – or even scrape them off. "That's what we use a palette knife for, mostly! So nobody knows you've made one!" she giggled.

Eve felt that such good advice deserved an effort on her part so they scraped up enough money between them to buy a small canvas of a field with a tree and two jays. They wanted to show they appreciated her achievement. As for Lawrence, he wanted to buy the enigmatic Egyptian face but couldn't afford it.

"Perhaps one day. I love it," he told her. "And something will turn up, I'm sure!"

They didn't like to ask for another paper cup of wine. Only two bottles were left. And Pippa's private view was due to last for another two hours. Besides, underneath the table was a bag containing her lunch – a couple of sandwiches and a lettuce. And they didn't want to deprive her of a paper cup of wine with that. Anyway, she was coming to supper with them the next day. So with laughter, giggles, kisses and good wishes all round they were off home on their bikes. Pippa found a big envelope for Eve's painting and put it in their bicycle basket.

"There, darlings, thanks so much! And find a nice place to hang it. See you tomorrow!" She kissed them both.

On an impulse they decided to cycle home by the marshes, starting at Morston Creek and following the path to Blakeney. It would at least be flat – at sea level, in fact.

And so they took the winding coast track home. They cycled together in silence. It was hot and high summer. The sedge had dried out and by the path only the cry of curlews high above them or the faint trumpeting of geese broke the silence.

In a creek near the path five sailing dinghies were anchored in line astern. Their sails were stowed. "MORSTON SAILING SCHOOL", said a faded notice on a post. A light wind had come up and the dinghies' wires rattled against their masts. Waves appeared and gave a few flat slaps to the mud. The two cyclists shivered a little as they passed. Later, the regular swish of their wheels on the path was interrupted by a sudden splashing and a fluttering of wings. Four mallards had settled into a shallow lagoon ahead of them. To the north, beyond the marsh's reeds and the winding mud creeks, lay the sand dunes that kept the sea away.

Suddenly Lawrence called out.

"Look!" he cried, staring north. His bike wobbled and he nearly went off the track but he just managed to push his leg out to keep on the path. He pointed to the sand dunes. "Look – can you see?"

"What, darling?" She too had stopped, both feet on the ground, and was looking out to sea.

"Those two masts! Above the sand dunes out there. D'you see them? I bet it's the Albatross again!"

"Oh, yes!" She was thrilled. "It must be returning from Rotterdam. It was only a week or so when we saw it going out, remember? When we were at Cromer with Zeus's boys?"

"Of course!" Lawrence was gazing out to sea and hardly heard her. "I can only see the sails. But it's the tops'ls, two of them. And there's no other ship on this coast like her." He was calculating, almost speaking to himself. "Yes, she must be the Albatross!"

He turned and looked at her.

"How wonderful!"

They climbed back onto their bikes and rode in silence. He was thinking how that ship shuttled backwards and forwards along the coast and sewed everybody into it.

Soon The Pit came into view. Fifteen minutes of silence and easy pedalling brought them to Blakeney Harbour. They walked their bikes up the hill to the main road and freewheeled down it again.

It wasn't their fault that Zeus and his Deli were on their route. So they had to call in and see if he was all right. Anyway they felt thirsty. By another lucky North Norfolk co-incidence he was at the bellows in the wine department and opening a bottle of some new white wine for a customer. He insisted they try it, too – pretending he didn't know them.

He grinned, stroked his black beard and shrugged to his customer. "I've never seen them before. So if they like it, you'll know it's good."

So they tried it. They pronounced it "topping." So the customer bought six bottles before he left. Zeus grinned to them.

"That's the way to do it!"

When Pippa arrived for dinner the following night, she brought with her the picture of the enigmatic Egyptian figure that Lawrence had admired the day before. And she gave it to him.

And that's how a private view goes in North Norfolk.

\*　　\*　　\*

Her painting was looking a little less enigmatic next morning when the post arrived. Their solicitor had sent the buyer a contract but he refused to sign it until he'd had a survey done. Lawrence rang and told their solicitor that the buyer needn't expect to get the price down if the survey report was bad. He had a feeling that the market was picking up. But he knew he could have been wrong. He usually was.

The survey report wasn't really very good news and true enough the buyer wanted a big whack off the price. Lawrence refused, gambling on the market going up. The buyer backed out and a few days later they heard from the agents that he'd bought another house in the same street. They felt isolated. They'd done the wrong thing again. Obviously they would have been able to drop their price. But they didn't and now they'd lost the buyer. The news was even worse next day. A letter from their bank warned them that if they didn't repay the mortgage within four weeks recovery action would begin without further notice.

"You've got it wrong." Eve put her head in her hands. "Oh, why didn't you accept that offer?" Lawrence had lacked the soft grace of patience needed to await a buyer. He had forced the pace. So he contacted the magazines about a lottery again, but they seemed less interested now. Apparently there was a legal problem. They didn't want to get involved any more. It was all becoming frantic. Their dream was again more like a nightmare. Their albatross was back.

*    *    *

*End of August: Prospero knocks on our door early one evening, notices our dejection and suggests a trip down the river. "In time of trouble," he tells them, "always go to sea!" He points out the absence of land-rooted ties: "Of course they exist, but cannot reach you while you're out at sea!" Anyway, he tells us, today is Blakeney Regatta and dozens of sailing dinghies will be racing – a magnificent sight. High tide is in fifteen minutes so we must hurry to catch it.*

*And he's right. Once aboard Circe, even while we are stowing our picnic basket and preparing to cast off bow and stern while Prospero pulls the starting cord on the outboard motor our worries seem to fall away from us as if we had thrown off heavy overcoats. I almost imagine being able to laugh if the bank manager's car had suddenly drawn up just as we cast off and he leaped out waving a possession order at us. I'm even more relaxed once we move off the berth, glide downriver and are concealed by the tall reeds lining each side of the narrow channel. Eve and I smile to each other and she squeezes my hand.*

*"Don't worry, darling," she murmurs. "We'll be all right. I know you'll find a way to keep them off." And arms around each other we sit back and watch the sky rotate above us as Prospero takes the helm.*

*Soon we are out in The Pit and open water now stretches each side of the dinghy. The wind is blowing from a point or two east of north. Far off to the west dozens of tiny dark triangles stud the horizon. Prospero tells us that the course of the race takes the yachts north to a buoy beyond The Point and back to the finishing line in the south. Many of them are still close together but already there's a big gap between the leading boat and the stragglers.*

*Despite the distance it's not long before we are among them. Their burnt-umber sails are high overhead now and blocking out the sky. They are close too, and constantly they cross our path tacking port and starboard into the wind. Prospero turns the dinghy to line up with their course, cuts the outboard motor, climbs across a thwart to the bows and hurls out a drogue anchor.*

*"That will keep us head to wind. Now listen!" he says. "We'll hear the music*

*of these little boats, the same tunes played by those big battleships before Trafalgar and our Hero's death."*

*He turns to us and smiles.*

*"Our Hero! Never far from us up here."*

*And in the sudden silence, the sounds come as if made by instruments in an orchestra. First comes the alto violas' underlying rippling wave piano continuo theme of elided semi-quavers as if they're all murmuring and gossiping together. Then, when the dinghies tack into the wind, comes the violins' allegretto "pluck-at-will," the pizzicato throaty allegro crack-crack-crack of the sails as they fill after the dinghies cross the wind. Then, in largo tempo and a minor key, a double base or two pluck semi-breves as the masts creak and bend to the wind's new direction and a bassoon groans out a rising swoop of quavers as the helmsman shifts upwind across his thwart. A shackle clunks — a commanding major key of random staccato semi-quavers from the first fiddle's desk. Perhaps a crewman lets out a muffled cough — a soloist preparing to come in. An oboe's interjection snaps a forte crack when the wind fills the leading dinghy's sails as it quickly tacks again. White water rushes up its stem in a tumbling flurry like a drum's mute ruffle and is repeated da capo by the others. Then the drummer makes a series of final muted slaps as the bows chop a little and cross the waves head on. All these sounds overlap each other in counterpoint as the dinghies constantly change course. Beneath them all is the padding of Circe's strokes against the waves like the soft and regular slap of a dark and muscular palm on a jungle drum. And, like night tales, the dark sails sweep above us and hide the sky as, ignored, we rock amongst them.*

*And by the time we reach home we've forgotten that nasty bank manager's nasty letter.*

\*     \*     \*

The earth still bowed towards the sun. Summer now was rich and strong. At dawn the air was always still. All day the village held its breath.

So when Lawrence threw up their bedroom window in the morning its squeak was quite distracting. Even the cat, already sunbathing half-asleep on the lawn, looked up in reproof. No need to mow the grass, now worn and fading into straw. Every day more apples fell beneath the tree. And every evening they watered the flowerbeds.

The unchanging summer days passed so effortlessly that Lawrence had completely forgotten that he hadn't seen the Log Lady for months.

In the winter they had dressed carefully. Often the rain had already been lashing down. They had always been sure to wear their thickest sweaters and corduroys. But in summer – well, in summer they just slipped into a pair of shorts, pulled on a T-shirt, eased into their sandals and tried to remember where they had left their sun hats the day before.

In fact their sandals had become hard and brittle through spending much of the time in seawater. Their feet too had become tough and encrusted with salt. Their hair was thick and bleached near white. The sun and the wind had seared their skin russet-red. By now they were both almost the colour of the bricks on their gable. And their financial crisis made them agonisingly aware that this first summer in North Norfolk might be their last one too. So they were determined not to let the crisis ruin it – which made their pleasure all the more intense.

In this limbo of waiting for something to happen they often walked eastwards along the bank of the shingle beach. After half a mile they had left the beach café far behind. Any wandering bird-watchers had been outstripped. They would be alone save for the absent-minded tumble of the waves on the beach. Perhaps a curlew wandered high overhead. One afternoon they saw the Albatross sailing half a mile off the coast, heading back to the continent. They waved but of course Jan wouldn't have seen them. They just waved as a sign of comradeship – of belonging. For they increasingly felt that they did belong on this wild coast, among these wild people. Sailing before the wind on that course (what was it, thought mariner Lawrence – north-east by east?) the Albatross was usually fully rigged with three or four jibs and wide-stretched mainsails. By sailing away it seemed it was able to escape from financial worries and it cheered their spirits, especially after they had turned down that offer the week before. Surely they would wake from their nightmare? Wouldn't they?

Often during those afternoons they would dip down into the reeds inland to seek a secluded space. It would be out of sight of the sea yet high enough for them to gaze inland at the line of fields beyond the edge of the marshes and watch as the heat set dancing the windmill and the houses of their village. There they sunbathed, talked, perhaps read a bit, or just lay and dozed under the high and silent sky. They were hidden – and that suited them. It was the next best thing to a hole in the ground. And it helped them forget the pressure from their albatross and their bank – and, for a time, pretend that everything was all right. One of those afternoons Eve began a painting of the distant inland landscape with the windmill – now in oils, the change that

Pippa had recommended.

"Slap it on! Make a big stroke!" she had told Eve. "It's the only way to start."

And she did – and it was. And her worries had drained away.

In the late afternoon they would rise to leave for home. By then the wind would have sprung up. And the sea would be filled with dozens of foaming mountain tops heading steadily towards the beach. They were ships in a convoy, a squadron of Spanish galleons. And they were stately wide and high. They had ledges and frills and tiers and curls and traceries. And every one of them seemed to have the density of icing on a wedding cake. They all kept their distance from each other. And when they crashed on the beach the stately rows of balconies and towers and terraces and turrets crashed too. Very quickly all that remained of the galleons was a tumble of froth that was already turning yellow.

By the time Eve and Lawrence reached home they were tired and stiff. Usually they were slightly sunburned. And they felt sand in uncomfortable places. But they were satisfied. For at the end of every trip, once their sandals had crunched down their gravel drive and they had closed the front door behind them, they were full of the great contentment of knowing that this house was their home. They weren't tenants who would have to leave on Sunday evening. They weren't guests who had to be polite to their hosts and offer to 'do something.' They were in their own home, a home that they were fighting to keep. The key in the front door was theirs. The photographs on the mantel-piece were of their family. On the shelves were the books that they'd colleted over many years. The sofa that the cat had scratched was theirs and so were the muddy shoes beneath the hall table. They were all theirs. And their anxiety made them theirs all the more. They would put the kettle on for a cup of tea. They would wander slowly around the house or sink onto a sofa. They would run a bath. And all the time their minds would still be on the marshes and the silence they had found there. It was a silence broken only by the caress of the wind like the sound of a hand through hair, the gentle murmur of the surf like a lover breathing in their sleep and now and again the wild cries of birds like the whimpering of a dozing pet. They were living on the edge of the marshes and the sea. The seaweed hanging on the staircase wall, the bowl of knapped flints on the landing, the bag of samphire, the bouquet of parsley and the dish of dressed crabs in the fridge; these all showed where they were. Yet they were sheltered within the village and were safe. The barometer, the sun hats and the sandals in the hall, the umbrellas, the wellington boots and the waders in the conservatory and the sou'westers and scarves hanging in the cloak-room, the massive fireplace in the dining room, the Aga in the kitchen and the central heating everywhere all showed that they were ready for the seasons and were well protected. The rain on their faces or the sun on their faces. They welcomed them both. And they were ready for both.

*     *     *

Lawrence and Eve had seen a notice somewhere about another church concert. It was to be next Saturday and only a few miles away inland at Great Snoring church. Mozart's Requiem was to be performed by the Fakenham Choir. And what more did anyone want?

It was early evening by the time they reached this ancient church in the fields beyond the village. It was built of flint and stone and almost looked as if it was part of a quarry. This was how most country churches looked in North Norfolk. Some were tiny. Sometimes they had thatched roofs. Others were like the huge church in their own village, evidence of a pious and prosperous past. And most of them had round towers. This church at Great Snoring sat next to an Elizabethan rectory. Both buildings had clearly been planted in the earth. The rectory brickwork was like an old tree – or like their own home, for that matter. Tall chimneys spiralled above the gable and Tudor windows tucked themselves away under the eaves.

Although they were now deep into August the weather had been damp and sometimes windy. But the rain had stopped now and the sky was rinsed clear of colour. Only a trace of china blue remained low in the east. Here and there a few wisps of high cloud reflected the sun like fresh blood leaching through a bandage.

Lawrence parked the car by a hedge. He and Eve walked through an apple orchard to the church and its thatched porch. Apples lay in the long grass but the trees were still heavy with fruit. The grass was wet from the rain and it smelled of England. A couple of pheasants ran from beneath their feet. Their feathers were the same burnt umber of the chimneys' bricks. Soon they came to three yews that shaded the pathway between rows of crumbling tombstones. It was twilight now but they could make out four wreaths on a newly dug grave. Bright they lay against the black earth. Beyond the yews the church door still stood open and in its shadow Eve could see an usher beckoning. The first chords of Mozart's Requiem were swelling out to them. The concert had just begun. The music filled the air like a massive yet delicate thundercloud. Despite the usher's entreaty Lawrence had to stop and listen for a moment. He had just discovered that he couldn't walk and listen to Mozart at the same time.

The church was small like the church in Langham, scene of Iris' funeral service. They crept in and found a seat behind the font (fourteenth century). Plaster and whitewash covered the flint walls (fifteenth and sixteenth century). And a Restoration plaque (seventeenth century) hung below the belfry (repaired in the eighteenth century) near the porch (nineteenth century). Stuck away in North Norfolk, was this church. And you'd have thought something more than a few notices on a tree would have been needed to fill the place. But the news had got around – as they had discovered it always did in North Norfolk. And of course the church was packed. Everyone was clearly local except for the adventurous ones who must have travelled a good ten miles.

The Fakenham Choir gave full voice and the Requiem Eternal swelled out over everyone, a clear expression of faith in eternal life and you knew the choir believed it too. It was a marvel to discover that the church had perfect acoustics. For the sound came pure, clean and without an echo even to the group behind the font. It put the Albert Hall to shame. And it wasn't just the acoustics. The audience's hair may not have been cut by Trumpers in Curzon Street. After all North Norfolk is rather windy. Everyone had dressed up that evening but the men's suits of variable loose tweed were sometimes in conflict with their owners' figures. But they looked more settled than a London audience and all different, too – which was more than you could say for the passengers on the 8.30am from Dorking. Yes, Eve and Lawrence felt glad they had moved up to North Norfolk. Everyone was here from a love of God and Mozart. And in that order? Well, as Lady Bracknell said, the order was immaterial. There were no bankers' corporate seats here. No half-naked society women dripping with diamonds and looking bored. No plump City bankers in Savile Row suits, flushed from a glass or two of champagne at Covent Garden's Long Bar and trying not to burp or fall asleep. Here it was more likely to have been the weather than champagne that had put colour into their faces. But it was true that during the interval the vicar had offered the couple a glass of warm and sweet Riesling. He had beamed at them and exclaimed, in the captivating and innocent way of English vicars,

"What heavenly music!"

After the opening choral theme had worked itself through, and Mozart had hedged his bets and added a pious coda to his usual brief and elegant preamble, there was a pause and the four soloists emerged from the choir. They stood before everyone, their backs to the rood screen (fifteenth century). Its painted figures of early saints were faded and their faces blank. Cromwell's men had done their worst (seventeenth century). Those figures were nothing special in England. Hundreds of country churches still showed such remnants of that attack on the early faith. The vestiges still showed their simple, child-like style. It was a style that gave notice of the artists' faith more steadily and openly than any work of Rembrandt. Or so thought Lawrence, when the soloists began their supplication. The alto led, followed by the base. After those two had sung together the theme was enforced by soprano and tenor. And then all four voices soared up to the hammer beams above. By now darkness was clouding the high corners beyond the nave. They were vanishing as daylight faded at the open porch. Inside, the only light came from a single candle at the piano. It became brighter as night fell outside. And in the pauses of the music Lawrence could have sworn he heard a fluttering of wings high above the altar – although he wasn't sure if they were pigeons or angels.

It was during the interval that they met someone from their village. They had seen him often enough. He was always striding up and down the road in shorts whatever the weather – even in winter, even during the flood and the storm. They had learned that he was an international authority on birds and took bird lovers around the marshes. He was short and sturdy and he had a big bristly beard and a keen gaze beneath a pair of huge eyebrows that worked away like a pair of brooms. Although they had seen him often neither of them had spoken together. But now they greeted each other with delight. It wasn't the first time this had happened. It was how they had met Victor, Pat and Millicent. After the interval they found seats together. And when the final chorale had died down, the church had emptied and they had sought their cars, they drove home in convoy. On the way, and for the first time this summer, their windscreen was spattered by summer rain. But they didn't mind. Another neighbour had become a friend.

\*      \*      \*

Soon it was time to visit another outdoor theatre – this time at Felbrigg Hall, a formal Jacobean pile near Cromer. They were putting on a play by Shakespeare. The actors were the same group of strolling Anglian players who had performed the Restoration comedy play at their rectory. The couple wanted to be there. And it was now or never, too. They had a feeling the weather wouldn't hold for much longer.

So late one Saturday afternoon Lawrence and Eve turned off the main road and rolled through parkland along a private drive. Through the railings a herd of pedigree cattle watched them drive past. The woods rose up against the sun, which made its exit, stage right. Lanterns soon lit up the courtyard. Jill and Tom had joined them for the evening and everyone felt warm and expansive. It wasn't just the usual expectation before curtain-up. After all, nothing was hidden since there wasn't a curtain. No, it was the sky – dark and wide and overhead, too! Naturally, that also meant danger. By now Lawrence and Eve had learned what an English country summer was like and the wise ones amongst the audience had brought umbrellas. Just as well, too, for it bucketed down in the second act and everyone sat huddled together under the deluge. The well brought-up offered to share umbrellas with any next-door neighbours who had forgotten them.

No matter about the rain. For again they were warm witness to how everyone could enjoy themselves in the country. The actors were lively and the audience actually laughed at the jokes of the tipsy shipwrecked sailors. Everyone had forgotten that Shakespeare was "culture" – meant to be taken solemnly.

So everyone was in good humour when they stood up, stretched themselves and folded their umbrellas at the end. And it was only then that Eve and Lawrence found so many village friends in the audience. Two rows in front sat Victor and Pat. And from behind them came a call – the Rhine Maiden and the Guardian. And beyond them wasn't that John Hurlingham, their favourite butcher in England? They were all there. And now they all laughed and joked together. And wasn't that Prospero, too, in the distance by the stage, that tall lean figure standing in the shadows, his coat over his shoulders and shaking hands with the producer? Why was he shaking hands with him anyway? What did he have to do with it? But when they looked again he had gone.

Slowly and reluctantly, as if unwilling to break the spell, the couple and their friends found their cars and creaked open the doors. There wasn't a traffic warden within a hundred and fifty miles. They climbed in, started their engines and rolled through the parkland to the main road. The full moon rode high above them. It seemed to light up all North Norfolk. And beneath that moon Eve and Lawrence sailed along in convoy with their friends.

Neither spoke. Nothing disturbed their memories of the play or the thoughts that reached out beyond it. At last, as they neared their village, their friends one by one gave farewell toots as they peeled off, each one for their own homes. At last they too gave their final goodnight and turned into their own drive. Their wheels crunched on the gravel and they awoke at last from Ariel's spell.

It beat the car pound beneath Hyde Park every time.

# Autumn

It was one morning in early September when Lawrence and Eve awoke and realised that summer would soon be leaving them.

It wasn't so much the noise of the rain gusting around outside their windows. The summer had been a particularly English one anyway. And at their picnics and barbecues they'd never been certain that rain, like Banquo's ghost, would not arrive as an uninvited guest. They had long discovered that a North Norfolk summer was unlike summer anywhere else. It could be tingling hot with no wind, breathtaking and still – perfect! And next day it could throw rain at you. What's more, all the fields were now stripped bare of corn. After all, it hadn't been long since the day they had noticed the hay-makers in the fields when they had cycled to Pippa's private view. Perhaps it was Eve's roses that had given them a stronger hint of change. They were still going well. But more and more petals were flying around in the gusts of a wind that seemed to be just a little bit cooler every day.

And then there were the small boys on the cricket pitch. Last week they had played against the Three Horseshoes from Wareham. It was still sunny and everyone had played as if it was a tie-breaking test against Australia. But a few small boys had been kicking a ball around at the scoreboard by the pub. They seemed to know that football was on the way. And they took no notice of Freddy Blake who, although still the scorer, was by now in crutches and couldn't stop them. He had resigned himself to wagging his pencil at the ringleader – who happened to be the son of his sister, who lived next door – and marking the home side up by another four runs.

The end of summer was not really sad since there was still something reassuring about it. Autumn was about to follow summer and that was as it should be – even if, like today, the village lost by nine runs despite Freddy's contributions.

Only last Sunday, ignoring forecasts of a high summer day, rain had spattered over their walled garden before lunch and a dozen apples had thudded down from the tree. Lawrence had dashed out to cover the lunch table. Even after their guests had arrived – Victor and Pat with Zeus and Leda – a sudden shower had chased them all into the summerhouse. There they watched the pheasant turning on its spit on the barbecue (now covered by an umbrella), drank lemon rum together and waited for it to pass.

But this time there was something chilly about that rain. And the clouds overhead were grey and threatening. Yes, that morning the sun had indeed broken through once – to flood the garden with glorious brightness. But it had arrived like an ageing film star. He was keen to demonstrate his former brilliance. But he could only manage a brief appearance. A daily matinee, let alone an evening performance, was too much to expect. They'd have had to have a doctor in the house – every day.

Now, more often than not, the wind tore apart the clouds that raced across the sky. The same wind was tussling the trees in the garden. More and more apples lay waiting to be gathered. Sunset, they noticed, came earlier and earlier. Sometimes a pearly haze appeared in the late afternoon sky – a sure sign of autumn. And the evenings were just a little cooler. The central heating had been off for over four months. Now Lawrence turned it on again. And, as if to prove that summer was over, Prospero's Italian friend had, like a swallow, left on her journey home to the south. A month or two before she had found a cottage in the village that she loved. She had bought it on the spot and spent the summer renovating it. Lawrence and Eve were secretly delighted. They were no longer the latest incomers. They had taken her to several North Norfolk country auctions. She had bought chairs, corner cupboards and a table for her new cottage. Afterwards, they had often lunched together at one of the country pubs nearby. She built a new fireplace and had bought a valuable old beam from Tom. He had a store of them hidden somewhere on the marshes – but wouldn't tell anybody where it was. She used it as a mantelpiece. Only last week she had given a house-warming supper party before her new fireplace.

But yesterday she had packed her suitcases. She had crammed her car full of all the objets trouvés that she had collected during her visit. She couldn't bear to be parted from them until she returned next year. With a last bottle of champagne together they celebrated the memory of their first summer in North Norfolk. They remembered their exploration of their shared paradise. They talked of what they had done together – the auctions, the country pub lunches, her wine-tasting party beneath their apple tree and long discussions under the stars. Their reflective mood suited the onset of autumn. Lawrence and Eve were sad now that summer was over. But they were pleased to have shared it with her and to be able to share its memories, even though she would be leaving. Now, they all agreed, they could draw breath after summer's pace. They could look forward to the autumn. They were about to come upon that sad and sweetly contemplative season that arrives after maturity has been achieved, when the harvest is in and the year's waning begins.

Out on the road they waved farewell to the swallow and watched as she turned the corner to begin her journey south, her tail lights vanishing into the evening dusk. She would be crossing the Channel next morning and would reach the warm Mediterranean sun by nightfall.

Meanwhile clouds had appeared over the village. Back inside, Lawrence closed the window shutters and poured his wife a large gin and tonic with a double whisky for himself. As always during the summer they spent their evenings in the sitting room. Eve called it the summer room, for its French windows opened to the garden. But it seemed unusually empty and the air was almost chilly. Lawrence pulled on a jersey.

"Shall I light a fire in the winter room?" he suggested. It held their library, that dark and secret room. Eve smiled and they crossed the hall. Soon the fire was roaring. The chill vanished and they were mildly reassured.

But Eve was sad. Like a sleeping beauty the garden, her creation, was shortly to begin its decline into a winter sleep from which only Easter's sun could awaken it. Her efforts had already begun to show results. The vegetable garden, the roses and the lavender were both flourishing. The jasmine was now well established. Lawrence had laid a little area with York stone and built a flint wall round two sides. There he had set an old cast-iron pub table with a couple of chairs. It was an alcove, a place for them to drink a glass or two in the last warmth of the sun. Eve had trained sweet pea up a trellis near the new flint wall. Lawrence had put down more turf. Together they had planted five weeping laburnums around the outdoor lunch table. And everything was doing very well. All they had to remember was to plant some bulbs before winter. It was time for them to watch the leaves of the Virginia creeper turn into the rust of ages. Time to sit at the outdoor table and watch the leaves flutter gently to the ground. They were a symbol of the year's decline. Summer's over, they said to themselves. No more days of wonderful Norfolk heat waves, where the air sizzled and nothing moved on the fields. No more beach parties with bucket and spade. No more cricket on the Cromer sands. No more Salvation Army brass band. No more barbecue lunches with rosé wine. No more croquet or afternoons lying on the lawn drinking Norfolk cider. No more straw hats, no more shorts and no more bare feet. No more velvet skies or still night air.

But now! Now Eve can bottle their fruit, for they have dozens of apples and plums. She will put the plums into rabbit casseroles and bottle the rest with brandy. She will make chutney with most of the apples and freeze the rest for later. And now they can pick blackberries and elderberries along the lanes.

They can look forward to the first mussels of the season and an autumn and winter of pheasant and partridge. Now it is time to expect driving rain. Time to look out gumboots and darn a few sweaters. Time to be on the marshes in early morning to pick mushrooms. Time to make bonfires of the fallen leaves and to watch their smoke rise into the still and melancholic air.

Soon the village will be free of holidaymakers and the noisy snake of traffic. Soon they will be able to stroll down the middle of the street. And soon the marshes will revert to a wilderness, abandoned beneath the cold North Norfolk skies. Soon fog will roll at nightfall across the marshes to carry inland the sound of the sea and the honking of geese as they cross the coastline. Soon Lawrence will light fires in the late afternoon. And soon he will feel again the rain on his face.

Their friends will return from summer adventures overseas and will visit the couple in the winter room. They will tell of climbing the Matterhorn or of horse riding across the Hungarian plains. They will all be cheerful and refreshed for the bleak season to come. When their friends leave Lawrence and Eve will watch the flames flicker on the bookshelves and will draw the thick burgundy velvet curtains. They will pull up their armchairs and cup their glasses in their hands. They will gaze into the crackling flames, listen to the rain rattling the windows outside and they will smile to each other. They will become more thoughtful. And once again the house will fill with the smell of wood-smoke.

A few days after their swallow had left for the Mediterranean the Ministry of Defence wrote to say that they had received Lawrence's petition. Since he was making such a fuss a team would spend a week in the village to monitor any low flying. And he mustn't mention it to anyone. They would demonstrate their monitoring equipment to the assembled villagers who, of course, would tighten the string around the knees of their trousers, pull the straw from their hair and gaze dumbstruck. Millicent had not signed Lawrence's petition. He had only just arrived but here he was organising petitions already! Maybe she had considered that organising a petition was the work for the cookery writer or chairman of the parish council or churchwarden or organiser of church flower arranging or chairman of the Church Restoration Fund Committee or caterer for its lunches or organiser of the Saturday morning bring-and-buy stall on the church green or Flood Warning Officer or Gendarme at the Church Fête Stalls or Feeder of the Cricketers at Tea, rather than for an interloper. But she heard that the ministry was taking his actions seriously. So she decided to join the bandwagon. She announced that would do the catering for the men from the ministry.

"That nice Flight Sergeant," she said later. "He was so helpful."

"Well, I hope he liked your sandwiches."

"Sandwiches!" she spluttered. "I beg your pardon! I gave him vol-o-vents, vine leaves stuffed with anchovies and sliced strawberries."

A week later they wrote to Lawrence, not about the sliced strawberries but to report that no low flying had been monitored during their visit. Amazing, he said to himself. He replied that this no doubt was because they'd told their lads to fly over some other unfortunate village for that week instead of his. An indignant silence was their pained reply.

*     *     *

*Mid September: Prospero telephones – time for the last trip down the river before he takes Circe out of the water for the winter. At the moment Eve is occupied bottling plums. She will mix some white wine and a little cognac with them before she seals the jars until next summer. It is a delicate operation. But she wants to come. She knows it will be her last chance before next summer. So we three glide down the river, Prospero's golden retriever on duty at the bows as usual. The sound of the outboard motor is muted in the autumn's quiet. It is the sort of quietness where nature holds its breath when the summer's heat is over. Even the water seems calm and level. Only now and then do ripples disturb its surface. Perhaps the calm is the calm before the wild storms of winter.*

*We travel contented. We speak little and merely look around us. Our wake disturbs five baby moorhens with their mother. Where the river widens a dozen seagulls screech together high overhead. The sky's pearly shade of cloud covers us like the shell of an oyster. We reach The Pit and it reflects the sea back to us. If I half-close my eyes I can hardly tell whether I am looking at sea or sky. Only a wheeling galaxy of starlings proves that I am watching the sky.*

*"Prospero," says Eve, "the dreams you interpret. I suppose they aren't your dreams ... but I'd love to know of someone's dreams that they asked you to explain."*

*Prospero turns and looks at her and smiles slightly. Then he steers towards a buoy, ties the dinghy's painter to it and begins to speak. He mentions that he does not discuss such things to those not involved but the one he is about to describe involves our community. He tells us that recently Justine came to him with a dream. He assumes we know that she was unable to choose between the love of Jan and that of the Village Marxist. Apparently in the dream she is on a big sailing boat on the sea. There is a strong wind and high waves – which she loves – and she was tempted to jump in for a swim. A bit hesitant but, well, the sun is shining and the water inviting. So she pulls off her clothes and jumps in. "The high waves were so exciting," she said. But the sailing boat is drawing away. No worry, the beach isn't far off, but she is drawn to return to the boat – although to try that was more dangerous than the safer option of heading for the beach. The waves get higher and she becomes frightened. Then she sees the Village Marxist waving frantically to her from the beach. He seems so far away now. Can she reach him? She doesn't know what to do, which way to go. The waves are getting higher and higher and she is terrified that she will drown. Prospero looks at Eve.*

*"Is that all?" she asks. He nods.*

*"But what did it mean? Did you work it out?" He nods.*

*"Did you tell her?"*

*"Not yet – she must wait. Her dream's importance gives expression here to what draws us to this wild cut-out coast. Waiting gives time to understand herself."*

*And he smiles briefly again and lets slip the painter from the buoy. As we turn and begin the journey back up the river to the windmill we see seven swans in line astern gliding downstream towards us. They are near the far bank and silhouetted white against the black reeds. Their feathered white breasts swell out of the water like foam. Their long necks rear back in a proud curve. Each swan's orange beak and jet-black eyes point ahead with elegant menace.*

*"Seven white swans are found where man and woman, joined, create the world. Their cleansing white gives beauty, purity. Each swan's the symbol of a family," murmurs Prospero almost to himself, but he glances at me for a moment. His dog turns its head and looks at him questioningly. But Prospero gives a barely noticeable shake of his head and the dog turns away from the swans.*

*And as we glide effortlessly into The Pit it occurs to me that those swans symbolise the difference between our village and Blakeney, so close but so different. Blakeney – the Mecca for holiday sailors. A village of picture-postcard prettiness, indeed of beauty. A flint-cottage-lined main street winding gently down to wharf and creek where children play with bucket and spade, where dinghies lean in decorative positions on the mud. But perhaps – in a twist of Pirandello – a village where many of its cottages, empty out of season and crammed in season, sometimes seem in search of residents.*

*But our village is basic, rough, weather-blasted, secret – not pretty but gut-scrapingly beautiful – and inhabited by a company of strange and divers people spun together in a web of intrigue and desire. The swans represent not just the wild beauty of the village but also its community spirit, the idealism of the pottery folk and the individuality of the entrepreneurs living here – Zeus, Jekyll 'n' Hyde and Prospero himself.*

*We travel the final stretch to our mooring in silence. The season's change has marked all three of us.*

\*     \*     \*

It was a rather optimistic idea for September, but there was to be a garden party in the village on Saturday evening. Lawrence and Eve had been invited. Apparently it was to celebrate the birthday of Millicent, the village stalwart. The hosts were kindly and retired schoolteachers. They lived a couple of hundred yards away along the coast road. They would never really have met before moving up. But now they found they enjoyed their company and hoped they felt the same. They knew that most of the guests would resemble their hosts. They would be the village's quota of the comfortably-off retired middle class.

Eve and Lawrence strolled down the middle of the road to the party. They were a little late. They had felt they should make an effort and both were well scrubbed and well dressed. Lawrence was even wearing a tie for the first time in nine months. But soon they reached their hosts' garden wall and heard the hum of conversation. They came up with Tom climbing out of his truck outside his own house next door. His sou-wester and boots were covered in dried mud and the truck was full of lobster-pots and marker buoys.

"You look exhausted," said Eve. "What's happened?"

"Oh, don't ask me!" he groaned. "I got caught last night by the tide. I was out fishing all day and there was a head wind coming off the coast and I was late getting to the bar at Wells channel. The tide was too low by the time I got there and I hit it. I was lucky to get off backwards, actually."

"But where's your boat?"

"I had to run it up on the beach offshore and lay out an anchor in a sand dune a hundred yards from the channel. That was difficult enough 'cos the tide's strong there. But then I had to walk back to Wells. That's a mile or so over the dunes and at the end of it I had to swim across the harbour – I mean ... I had to ... my truck was parked on the quay. I got back in the middle of the night and I've been working in the shop all day."

He threw his arm over the tailgate and leaned against the crab-pots in his truck. "I'm knackered."

"Is the boat still there?"

"No – I had to go back to bring it in as soon as we shut up the shop this afternoon. Otherwise it would have been out all night again. It might have floated off."

He shrugged. "Anyway, where are you going, all dressed up like that?"

"A garden party at your neighbour's. You know, just the other side of this garden wall here?"

"My neighbours, huh! Well, I might just turn the garden hose on. It's been a bit dry recently. So don't go near the wall on the other side." He winked at them.

Not for the first time did Lawrence and Eve realise that the village was divided. It was like those theories of different universes existing side by side but never meeting – except of course via Tom's garden hose. Here, though, it was the English disease again. Perhaps it was the same everywhere. But at least they had a foot in both camps.

*    *    *

Soon the damp and chilly weather began to set in. It had been only the week before that their friend had left for the south. Since then the season's change from summer to autumn had been like the arrival of spring – but in reverse. Once more the man had come to dinner but, with a stormy downpour after the port and no car, had been invited to stay the night. Come the morning and a hint of a warm Indian summer? Barely able to hide his reluctance, he announces his imminent departure. But gusts of rain appear after breakfast – the usual soak-tease of the coquettish English summer. So he asks his hosts if, well, could he perhaps wait until after lunch? The rain might have slackened by then. He sits with a book in the conservatory and tells them he is so embarrassed about staying so long. Soon after the shower the sun comes out again and he squints secretly at his watch. He rises from his chair, perhaps a little too reluctantly – and pretends to look for his hat. Just then the fog arrives in earnest. With disguised relief he smiles helplessly at his hosts, forces his expression into a grimace and throws up his hands. He takes off his hat and settles on the sofa. He persuades one of his hosts' daughters to tuck him up in a blanket and give him an extra cushion. And he watches television. The leaves fall. Evening comes – dinner too. Later it's clear that he'll have to stay the night again and his hosts find themselves entering into the game of pretence by enquiring a little too solicitously about his comfort if he sleeps on the sofa. But next morning no guile or fake protests can compete with the bright sunshine. So, after a last-ditch pretended anxious gaze at the sky ("will this sun last?") he begins his long walk home. And, of course, halfway back he gets soaked.

One morning the mist lay low on the ground and half hid their valley. Suspended in the air, water vapour had turned it into a Chinese landscape. Three or four broad yet accurate strokes – and the side of a hill appeared, delicate to the gaze. Thick but light smudges, more or less horizontal – and there's a water meadow. A cluster of dots? Geese in formation. More ordered strokes, the merest hint of a not-so-straight line as roughcast as a flint wall, and half Wiveton Church emerged from behind a cloud. Eve found it irresistible. She turned to Lawrence.

"It makes walking a sort of adventure – you don't know what's going to appear next," she told him and proposed a walk somewhere – perhaps Stiffkey Marshes and the pub later?

As they took the coast road west at the Deli Millicent cycled past them on her way to church. She wobbled a little but smiled and gave them a wave.

"Just off to organise communion," she called out. "Churchwarden's duties. Philip calls! Oh, Eve, see you tomorrow about Sunday's flowers?"

"Of course!" Eve nodded and waved back as Millicent pedalled steadily up the valley lane towards the church and slowly disappeared into the mist. Lawrence turned to Eve. She looked at him.

"You don't have to say it," she smiled. And with a feeling of deep contentment, she laid her head on his shoulder. "It's England."

They had set off late this October afternoon. By the time they reached the Stiffkey marshes the mist had become a winding sheet wrapped over the body of the marshes. A roll of clouds was gathering over the sea like a cavalry regiment before a charge. And soon the charge began. The wind began to drive the clouds inland. It looked like rain. And soon it was rain.

Lawrence had seen it all coming a few days before. He had rung the Log Lady for more wood and she had arrived with a truckload of hard dry oak. Nowadays Lawrence and Eve called her Karina. Apparently last year her husband had been asked to cut down an old oak that had been split open by lightening. It was on the Holkham Estate beyond Wells – and two hundred years old. By now it was well seasoned. Karina

266

had left off her combat gear but wore a red track-suit, four-inch heels and a dazzling smile. The wood burned all the better for that, too.

Early that morning Eve had spent an hour mushrooming in the marshes east of Salthouse where the road swings inland and up the hill to Kelling. Although someone had been out earlier, her basket was soon full. A herd of cows had been grazing there for the last few days and cowpats were everywhere – good for flavour. She had grilled some mushrooms for a late breakfast, laying them on thick wholemeal bread. It had been baked only a couple of hours before.

They welcomed the seasonal changes. Such natural forces were all part of their move to the country. They had been mesmerised by the still air of the Norfolk summer that had just left them. And now they were gripped by the thoughtful beauty of autumn. They reached the edge of Stiffkey marshes and headed north towards the sea. The marshes were so wide and empty that the couple felt all the more close to each other. After all, they could see there was nobody else for miles around. So intimacy was there by consent – more than if they had been forced together in a prison cell. That alone was worth making a new life in North Norfolk. And so they walked together arm in arm.

But there was another change too. Since they had come to live here they had both felt a release of creative energy. Eve was expressing this with her flower arrangements in the church, of course, which also enriched her feeling of belonging. But her painting was improving now that she was using oils. As for Lawrence, he had begun to write some poetry. They both felt that a spring was uncoiling inside them and bursting them with energy. It was as if some exotic creature had escaped from the box called London and was now leaping and bound-ing around a marshy box open to the skies called North Norfolk and flexing itself like some fabulous untamed beast – a unicorn perhaps, or even a qoxarchl. It had all come about through the change in surroundings – the fresh air, the wind and the rain, but most of all the space! Space most of all had released their self-expression and helped them deal with their mortgage anxiety. So that anxiety had shrunk to an irritant of a grain of sand that helped them become creative almost without trying. It also gave them the state of mind that helped them understand themselves. And, of course, that was the one big reason why Lawrence and Eve had wanted to come to live in North Norfolk.

Yet they knew there was something else that it represented. Something that included everything of all they knew but something more. Though what it was they still weren't quite sure.

By now clouds had closed over the sky like a giant's candle snuffer and they were almost in the dark. Again the only bit of open sky left was a strip a few degrees wide all round the horizon like a stage curtain that had got jammed. And after another ten minutes of walking in this half-light they again came across Jimmy Blake sieving mussels in a creek.

"They're the first of the season," he said. "Big and juicy. You know how they've got like that?" he winked at Lawrence. "Well, they've been living in The Pit off Blakeney, haven't they, where all those holiday trippers have their boats. They've got fat from all that ..."

"Ah!" Lawrence interrupted. "It's called recycling, isn't it?"

"Eh? Yeah." He picked up a shell, flicked it open, scraped out the mussel with his thumbnail and swallowed it. He tossed them a handful and they did the same. They were luscious and plump, a real round mouthful with a full meaty bouquet, like an Australian Chardonnay with a dash of salt and iodine or a lowland malt without the alcohol.

"You want a bagful?" he asked. Just then a shower of rain hissed down near them. The next gust drenched them. Jimmy took no notice. Feet planted in the mud, he swallowed the mussels and tossed the shells into the creek.

Suddenly Eve felt chilled. "I think we'd better get back."

"Look," asked Lawrence. "Can you fill a bag for us, and we'll see you in the pub in half an hour? Settle up there?"

Jimmy agreed and as Lawrence turned to go he looked out to sea and caught sight of the now familiar black hull with its pair of fully rigged masts.

"See that?" he said to Jimmy. "There's the Albatross. Look! She's coming back to Wells with her cargo. We saw her going to Rotterdam, it must have been, to pick it up, the cargo – about a couple of weeks ago, remember, darling?" he turned to Eve.

"Oh, ah," Jimmy hardly looked round. "That big boat? Some foreigner's got it, hasn't he? Must have cost him a packet, bugger must be crazy. See you in the pub, then."

He still hadn't seemed to notice the rain at all. In fact he made fun of them for retreating. They obviously had a long way to go in coping with Norfolk weather. And the rain chased them all the way to the Red Lion. By the time they reached it they were both soaked. But it didn't take them long to dry out. The pub was only just open. The bar was empty. The sawdust was clean. The fire had just been lit. And again it cackled like a sack of chickens. They threw their coats on a chair, stood before the flames and dried out. Over the mantelpiece Admiral Nelson was still locked in a compromising grapple with Lady Hamilton. And the church jumble sale was still on for 2nd September 1935.

There was no one around, not even behind the bar. Lawrence was just wondering whether he dared leap over and pull himself a pint when someone appeared. It was their young friend Mark, their one-time gardener. He grinned and his eyes twinkled under his short black crew-cut.

"I'm working here now, Lawrence, only for a week or two, though. Been on the marshes, then?" He polished a pint jug, one with a handle, and held it up.

"The usual? Nelson's Revenge? Handle?"

"Handle!" He knew Lawrence pretended he couldn't hold steady the first glass of the day unless it had a handle.

"And a glass of white for you, Eve?"

"Gin-and-tonic, please, Mark, love," said Eve. "No ice either. The weather's cold enough today without that."

"How's that Irish yew then?" he asked, grinning. What a cheek. He'd almost burned it down in the spring.

"It's still alive," replied Lawrence. "Even if it hasn't recovered yet from when you got at it."

"Sorry about that," he grinned again. Why did they always forgive him? "Never mind. You can get plants and stuff at the auction at Aylsham," he said. "Every Monday. All sorts of other things too – bikes, tools, lawnmowers, furniture. But I've got some news," he grinned again. "I'm joining the army."

They were surprised. And then not surprised. North Norfolk was a paradise for Lawrence and Eve – but not for a young man. There was hardly any proper work. But there was more to it than that. They had learned you had to get away from a place before you could appreciate it. You had to see the world and then come home to England. Then you'd know something about the value of England. Meantime there was nothing for him here. Better to get out, even if it meant taking the Queen's shilling. But he mustn't die in exile. So many did and filled a corner of some unworthy foreign field. The churches had enough record of that.

"Well, Tom did it," Lawrence admitted. "Even though to the navy."

"Like Nelson, then," Eve reminded them both. "He came from round here and look where he ended up – a Hero!"

"Yes, but he was always seasick, lost an eye, then an arm, then got shot dead," said Lawrence. "He'd have died in bed of old age up at his dad's vicarage if he'd stayed at home."

"More like died of boredom," said young Mark. "But anyway, none of that's going to happen to me."

Nothing to be said about that. Lawrence bought him a pint. They drank and chatted together like the friends they had become.

"My Dad's thinking of making a change, too," Mark told them.

"Derek? I thought he loved fishing." Eve was surprised.

"No! Can't stand it! Can't even swim, either. He's looking around for something to do. Says he wants a change at his age."

"What? He's about as old as us," exclaimed Lawrence.

"That's what I mean. Reckon that's why you two came up here."

Soon the door blew open. In came Jimmy Blake with a wet bag over his shoulder and dribbling all the way to the bar. Lawrence put his hand in his pocket.

"Don't bother with that, Lawrence," said Jimmy. "I've given you about four pounds weight there, so make it a pint with a shot of whisky."

And he did. Even if they hadn't yet got something to exchange they were halfway there. They talked again with Mark about the army. Jimmy was against it. He was one of the old school. He had learned to make a trade in North Norfolk and was suspicious of authority. A real Norfolk man.

"They'll order you around something chronic, Mark," he told him, shaking his head. Mark grinned.

"Well, I'll see about that. Anyway I want to see the world."

He promised he'd call in to say good-bye. And in due course the couple took their slow way home along the winding coastal road.

*     *     *

By now they had long got into the habit of leaving their front door unlocked when they went out, something that everyone in the village seemed to do. In fact they only locked it when they both went to London. And that was only once so far. So they felt it would almost be rude if they were the only ones to lock their door. For example, one day they had been to visit Prospero. He had been out but the door had not just been unlocked. It had been ajar. And so they had walked into the house. And it had been like the Mary Celeste. The radio was on – some Italian station – and his computer was humming. He wasn't at all upset when they told him. As he said, "Yes, for you know we all know each other here! Of whom, living here, do we need feel fear?"

But what they remembered about that visit was not how Prospero's house had been left unlocked and his computer still on. Lawrence had ventured upstairs and in one room had discovered a long brass telescope mounted on a tripod. Prospero's house was on a hill that overlooked most of the village. And the telescope was at a window. And of course Lawrence couldn't resist looking through it although he could hear Eve downstairs telling him to hurry up and not to be so rude by going upstairs. And he saw that the telescope was trained on a side window of the Pottery in the Village Marxist's set of rooms – a window that wasn't visible from the street. The curtains were pulled back and the room was empty. Somehow he couldn't stop looking. After nearly a minute he saw Justine rush into the room as clear as crystal and as close as if he could reach out and touch her and then the Village Marxist came in after her. While Lawrence watched them he cupped her face with his hands and drew her to him. At first she resisted, but suddenly she threw her arms round him and kissed him passionately. They stayed locked together for several seconds. Then suddenly she pulled away and put her face in her hands. Her shoulders began to shake and she got up and ran out of the room.

Lawrence left the telescope and came downstairs. He decided not to tell Eve what he had seen. She was bad enough as it was. And this would just make her worse.

*       *       *

That evening they had an idea. It was after seven o'clock and night had fallen when they put on their warmest clothes, found themselves balaclavas, filled a thermos with hot soup, packed a loaf of bread, two legs of chicken, a bottle of wine and a couple of strong glasses, picked up a couple of cushions and drove to the beach. They parked by the beach café and walked along the shingle. After a few hundred yards they came across what they needed – a boat pulled well up from the sea and broadside on. There they sat, backs against it and protected from the southwest wind. They tore off pieces of bread and poured each other some soup. Soon they began on the chicken and opened the bottle of wine. Silent now, they toasted each other, listened to the crash of the waves, saw the surf flash by the light of the full moon as it rose above the beach – and were in paradise.

They had needed a couple of chairs for their kitchen, something simple – but made from old pine. And Lawrence was looking for a vice for a little workshop he was building behind the kitchen. Mark had told them of Norfolk's auctions and by now they were becoming adventurous. True, they hadn't actually got as far as Norwich. Unless you counted passing through to London on unsavoury estate agent business. But this time they decided to travel all of ten miles inland to the market at Aylsham. It was a definitive English country town and another example of how North Norfolk's clock seems to have stopped sometime around 1935. In fact parts of it were more like 1835. The road into Aylsham seemed to set the spell for the whole area. A mile or two before reaching it they passed Blickling Hall. It was a breathtaking jewel of a Jacobean mansion, built at the far end of a wide approach. Its three grand gables spread out like scalloped necklaces, each on a pair of elegant shoulders – a Norfolk stately home through and through. Blickling Hall was as different from Holkham Hall as a spider and its delicate web was from a toad. Its gables matched the filigree patterns of the branches of Norfolk's trees in winter. And their curved fronts of burnt sienna bricks and Norfolk flint looked much as they had looked over four hundred years ago. Their own Gibraltar House was a proud member of the same family.

Soon ivy-covered flint walls, rose bushes and well-cut lawns began to line the road into Aylsham. The Regency villas they enclosed spelled class, security and leisure. Wasn't that the pluck of a racquet? Maybe soon it could be time for a glass of Pimms. Lawrence glanced furtively at his watch. At the side of the next house stood an old conservatory and a well-tended rose garden. Down gravelled entrance drives appeared pillared front doors, porticos, bow windows and carved lattices. They were still the homes of the English professional classes – and had been for the last three or four hundred years. Here had been raised the officers and the gentlemen, the soldiers and the sailors who had guarded the British Empire – especially its routes to India. Here spinster sisters might have peeped anxiously out through the lace curtains, hoping that the carriage turning into the drive signalled the homecoming of that dashing captain, their brother. Here, too, officers had languished on half pay while the Admiralty decided what to do with them.

News had always travelled slowly to Norfolk. The Indian Mutiny had come and gone long before Aylsham had even got to hear of it. But nobody seemed to bother. The Corn Exchange must have been built round about then. The square's hardware store next to it was nearly as old. Inside, almost everything hung from hooks in the ceiling. When you bought something they put it into a little paper bag. The bags were all threaded through with string and the string hung from a hook at the end of an oak counter. And sunk into the counter's edge was a three-foot brass measuring rule. Yes, Imperial ruled here – there's nothing metric. Oh no! After all, in 1935 we still had India. The attendant wore brown overalls and was, of course, polite and elderly – not to mention English.

At the newsagent's next door they had to wait for ten minutes in the gossip queue to buy a newspaper. He picked one up but by the time he had reached the counter Lawrence had read the main pages. With some effort he resisted the temptation to put it back. So he paid for it, which left the sports pages unread, which he didn't want – so he threw the whole paper away in a bin by the counter. Result – nothing for 60p except honesty. And in the nearby pub you definitely could not buy food. It was a genuine drinking shed. If you got a bag of crisps you felt lucky – even surprised. Next door a chemist's shop breathed out pot-pourri fragrances. Yard-high tapering jars sat in the windows – as at Wells. They were filled with soft-hued violet and purple liquids, through which billowed the noontime sunlight. There was even a grimy old post office. It crouched motionless in a corner of the square, unkempt, stained and trembling like a blind and abandoned pet.

Beyond the square the round-towered flint church grazed in long grass behind its herd of tombstones. A short prayer away, on the door of a Queen Anne town house, a worn brass plaque said: "Walpole and Son, family solicitors." Down a side street they came across a printing works built like a zoo's enclosure – but enclosing only one animal. Lawrence squinted through the window and saw it standing in the centre of the empty room – a huge oil-stained machine with cogs and handles and racks and flat slabs that slid in and out of the heart of it with huge black rollers crashing down on them and the whole thing the size of a combine harvester and shaking and throbbing desperately away like a whale stranded on a beach and gasping for breath but still fighting. Every so often sheets of paper six foot wide were fed into one end by its keeper, a young man in overalls with a shaven head and three ear-rings who sometimes seemed to appear, covered in ink, at the other end.

"A-pun-a-pun-a-pun-a-pun," went the call at the auction rooms. The auctioneer stood on a revolving platform operated by a thin lad with no eyebrows and a leather apron. He had pink eyes and a long pink nose, and from the latter swayed a drip that was perpetually threatening to part company with its owner. Pigs at 8.30am – rabbits, too. Flowers and shrubs? 9am sharp. You want a hundredweight of spuds? Same time. Don't drop the sack on the roses. It's not often you can smell both at once. Furniture? Next door – and crammed into a huge shed, 10.30am, not so sharp. Everybody squeezing past each other and wandering around between the piles of furniture. The cast? Two or three hundred heavily dressed dealers, buyers or onlookers. Their faces were weathered and burnt the colour of the bricks at Gibraltar House. Their hair grew like neglected busbies and was streaked by oil and adversity. Their bodies were wrapped (not just dressed) in various layers with hats of various colours jammed on their heads. They were vast and overflowing and sleepy – or gaunt and tall with eyes looking everywhere at once. One woman was almost invisible inside an ancient fur coat. Once or twice Lawrence had to ask Eve which were men and which were women (she invariably knew). And at last he realised that most of them were dealers and that he and Eve must have stood out like two sore thumbs.

And the dealers bid nonchalantly, hardly ever looking at the auctioneer, sometimes chatting with their neighbour during the bidding then in mid-sentence waving a newspaper over their shoulders without looking at him. But most people never bid at all. Perhaps they had put something into the sale and wanted to know who bought it. But they weren't telling. And just about everything was there, coffee tables, kitchen tables, dining tables, wardrobes, chests, grates, old chesterfields, chairs of every possible style and material, mock-Tudor, Georgian, Victorian, modern, mahogany and pine and oak and walnut and ebony and horsehair and ivory, miniature paintings six inches wide – often of a giant lugubrious pig, antique desks, an engraving of Norwich Skating Rink (1935) and a large moth-eaten portrait of a sheep. As each lot was being sold an assistant in overalls tapped it with a billiard cue as if it were a wand and he could change a crudely painted china frog into a gilt-framed portrait of a Renaissance prince.

Eve turned to Lawrence, a movement requiring concentrated effort since she was jammed between a stuffed salmon in a glass case and an overweight dealer.

"Where does it all come from?"

Lawrence, jammed too, would have shrugged his shoulders if he could have released them.

"I was thinking that, too," he said. "There must be so many old and undeveloped houses in Norfolk. It's one of the things I love about the county – it's old England. And this stuff looks as if it's all been in the same families for generations. Well worn."

"Not the same families. Similar ones, but different. For example, look at this roll-top escritoire desk." She was sitting on it at the time and slipped off for a better view. "It was made, what, maybe mid-eighteenth century, d'you think?"

"Perhaps. It's quite battered, anyway."

"Well, it can't have stayed in the same family since then. Look at us! You had to sell your grandfather's partners' desk, didn't you? Yes, darling, I know." She touched his arm gently. "Well, it's the same here, almost a tradition, even. That escritoire might have belonged to a captain in the Navy. Maybe his wife's parents bought it for them as a wedding present when he was a midshipman or maybe a landlubber at Chatham dockyard on half pay and waiting for a ship. And when he went to sea and one day became an officer and then a captain and the Admiralty posted him to a West Indies station to fight the French, she must have sat at it to write to him. Look, there's a lot of ink on it, this desk isn't just a decoration. Then, about ten or fifteen years later, it would have been, he was drowned in that battle with Napoleon at Alexandria."

Lawrence looked at her.

"Napoleon wasn't even there. He'd sailed back to France. Anyway you're getting a bit bloodthirsty, aren't you?"

"Well, plenty did get killed, didn't they? And it was sometimes the women, too," she replied. "The Empire didn't grow on trees. Look at those horrible massacres in India – all those babies sliced in two or thrown down a well."

She abruptly stopped speaking and shut her eyes for a moment. Then she took a deep breath and continued.

"Anyway, anyway, his wife wouldn't have been able to live on the pension the Navy gave her, not in that big house any more. Don't forget, she still had to bring up her children. She probably had eight or nine of them, there was no proper contraception in those days, it all wore her out, so she had to move to a smaller place and sell the furniture, maybe to another officer's family, maybe not."

"Well, you've got it all worked out," commented Lawrence. "So someone else bought it, perhaps a Norfolk farmer grown rich on, what was it, the Corn Laws in the early 1800's? He wanted to move up in the world. Then cheaper corn from America caused him problems, he might even have been made bankrupt. It happened."

"No, it wouldn't have been him," she said. "That was later, wasn't it, at least the 1850's? I remember; I did that bit at school. It was his son who had thought it was easy. He was the one who was spoiled and couldn't adapt and was made bankrupt by the cheaper corn. Rags to rags in three generations, wasn't that it?"

"So it was his turn to sell the escritoire?" Lawrence took up the baton again. "Perhaps to someone in Bradford, maybe a Jewish refugee from Germany with a name like ... something like Rothenstein, maybe ... who was coming up in the world and wanted to assimilate into the English way of life. Maybe he was a wool trader and he did well and so he sold it after a few years for something bigger. So who bought it?" Lawrence looked at his wife. She didn't hesitate.

"R. B. Bloomfield, Harrow, 1875," she said.

"Now you're being ridiculous. There's no point in being as precise as that. You're making it up."

"I'm not," she laughed. "Look!"

And she showed him the name carved on the top panel. "R. B. Bloomfield, Harrow, 1875. So there!"

"Oh!" He laughed. Then he bent down and looked closely at the wood.

"See those little holes?" he said, "that's white ant. He's been in Africa, this R. B. Bloomfield has," said Lawrence.

"How d'you know?"

"I've lived there and I know white ant holes when I see them." He nodded to himself and his voice became dreamy. "The scramble for Africa was about then, or a bit later. It must have been shortly after that anyway or it may have been his son ... or his grandson. He'd have been at Harrow, too. All of them would have. Yes, maybe he was the District Commissioner at somewhere like ... like maybe Archer's Post in British East Africa up towards the frontier with Somaliland. That's Samburu country – plenty of white ant, you know. They make themselves little castles – hundreds of them, all over the bush. And it's only about forty miles from the Equator."

He looked at his wife.

"My car broke down near there once. I managed to patch it up more or less but it took me four days to get back to Nairobi. I was losing water and I had to sleep in the car and I heard lion every night. But him ... he'd have been young, only about twenty-three or four, straight out from Harrow and then Cambridge with a useless degree like Greek to oversee a few hundred thousand naked natives in an area the size of Wales – "

"Africans," she corrected him primly.

"OK, OK, not then though, but anyway they were lucky they got us and not the Italians or the Germans. Oh, yes! Anyway he'd have been like a king there, the bwana mkubwa, the only white man around, if you don't count the missionaries, who were usually more trouble than they were worth, what with them trying to stop local customs like circumcision and causing unrest."

Eve quickly changed the subject.

"Did he have a wife?" she asked.

"Not likely, not at that age." Lawrence paused and looked at her again. "And, in case you're thinking of it ... no black girls either. Don't forget we're British, him too. Anyway the life he led wouldn't have been comfortable for a wife. Not that that would have worried him by himself. After all he'd been to Harrow. That was what the public schools were for. They educated the boys to run the Empire and get used to hard conditions."

"He might have married on leave back home," she insisted, "and taken her back with him."

"Ok, yes, very likely. A man can't last by himself for ever. But by the time they came home for good they must have done thirty or forty years service in the bush. School room most days, which meant early morning lessons, very early, two or three dozen children squatting around him – "

" – her."

" – before the sun got too high in the sky, it was blazing, you know, not much shadow, it's the equator – and them on the ground in front of him, her, sitting at this escritoire of his – "

" – theirs."

" – beneath a baobab tree. Then every month he'd go on circuit, a week-long safari handing down judgements on complaints and criminal cases, often witchcraft, too. He must have had a caravan of about fifty bearers and two of them would have carried this writing desk. He would have sat at it all day long, a sort of mobile throne giving him status, a bit of magic, too, like a tabernacle, its roll top down to create a bit of mystery and all the pigeon holes would have been full of notes of all the tribal leaders and their prisoners, probably a Webley service revolver too. Couldn't be too careful up there, you know. The relations of someone he'd sentenced might not have liked his justice and might have had their own ideas. Witchcraft was in their blood and wasn't fussy about the Raj, let alone the D.C. Anyway, he would have written up his judgements sitting at this thing. By the end of his tour – what, thirty or forty years – they must have got very homesick. They wanted to retire to a decent sized Georgian house in England (did you say Norfolk?) with some stabling and grazing land for maybe a couple of horses after all those years of living at Archer's Post."

"Yes," now Eve's voice had a dreamy tone, "you know there were people in Africa, Englishmen, they'd been born in Africa and they called England Home even though some of them had never been to England."

"Yes," said Lawrence. "And this D.C., he'd been sitting in that hot and dusty country all his life thinking of those few acres. He must have drawn pictures of the sort of house he wanted. I did when I was living in Africa, you know."

"Yes, I do know, darling. You told me – several times."

"Ok, ok. Well, duty kept him there and he loved it too. You know what they say?" he paused.

"Can't think!" replied his wife, smiling at him.

"All right, I know I might have told you. Well, once you've lived in Africa you can't get it out from under your skin." He shrugged, "but anyway while he was there he must have pined for his own people, for soft rain and lush green grass, for muddy tracks and elms and oaks and rooks circling around their top branches, not for fishing in Lake Victoria, not even for Mount Kilimanjaro. He'd got tired of shooting lion when the natives asked him – "

"Africans."

" – and now he wanted to shoot pheasants instead. He didn't want the souk in Mombasa, full of noisy Mohammedans and carpets, however colourful. He wanted a reasonable Wilton, nothing flashy, from a haberdasher's in an ordinary English market town like this one, like Aylsham – really English, the heart of England. You know? Yes – you do, we both do. And although he'd have been like a king in East Africa and at Home he'd have been nobody he wouldn't have cared. He wanted to be able to chat now and then with the vicar and have a pint of warm beer in the pub but most of all he wanted to be buried in the churchyard here – at Home."

"You'll be telling me they wanted a walled garden like ours next," Eve smiled at him.

"Well, they did, darling," he replied, and then he paused. "And the rain on their faces, too. We did. And we're English, like them. And we've got it."

"D'you think...?" She paused and looked at him.

"What?"

"Well, I was just thinking ... they could have come back and bought our house. What d'you think, darling?"

"Not a hope. We've not got enough land. Not after Africa."

"Oh, well. Just an idea." She smiled at him again.

"So they came Home, as we all do," said Lawrence. "As we all do. And he became what he always had been – an English country gentleman."

He paused.

"Well, your turn. What happened next?" he asked her. "How did it get here?"

"Well, that was the trouble," said Eve. "The thing was, it had stayed in his family for over sixty years and then suddenly, it wasn't too long ago actually and anyway you've forgotten that his wife had been pregnant and had died of malaria in Mombasa and she's buried in the cathedral churchyard there with their still-born child." Eve paused for breath. "It was a little girl and had been premature and there weren't any mid-wives but when he came Home he had married again to a lonely widow in Aylsham whose husband had died early in the Great War but they were both murdered, yes, by an unhinged deserter from the trenches in France, poor man, who'd been suffering from shell-shock – "

Lawrence looked at her.

"You made all that up," he said accusingly. But at that moment a bidder next to them wearing a combat jacket and a woollen hat turned to them and said that if they wanted to go on blathering away like that why didn't they go and stand outside because he couldn't hear the bids. So they did. By that time they were both exhausted. They realised they had got carried away imagining who had owned those sticks of furniture and what had happened to them.

Furniture of any age had a story of human achievement or misfortune. They were all different yet all the same too. The odd thing was that although they had often been to auctions in London they had never thought about the people who had owned the lots. The furniture just went under the hammer, bang, bang – less than a minute for each one. But somehow, deep in North Norfolk, they had felt the need to think of the history behind those sticks and why they were being sold.

Alongside a bicycle stand outside was a long steel table laid out with dozens of nuts and bolts and knives and taps and spanners and trowels and fifty-year-old hand drills and set squares and broken car jacks and a brand-new welding kit. He found himself playing the old-fashioned childhood game where you have 30 seconds to memorise things brought in on a tray. No difference – except that this tray was 50-ft long.

Then hundreds more 'things' were laid out on the ground next to this long table. They were the 'big' items – half a dozen wheelbarrows, two ship's rudders of different sizes, four old Flymo lawnmowers, lengths and lengths of wood of all dimensions stacked about wherever they could lie and taking up a lot of space, two carpets hanging on a rail (one with a hole in it and an odd-looking stain), a dozen pairs of shears (mostly rusted together), piles of floorboards, sheets of corrugated iron, several doors, two large boxes full of car headlamps, piles of plasterboard panels, a six-foot high ship's anchor with 10 feet of chain shackled to it (rusted again, of course, not that anyone seemed to mind) and fourteen lavatories in assorted colours, some broken.

As Lawrence paused to watch the bidding the Flymos came up. A small green one had a dent in its cover and looked very ropey. In fact they all seemed a bit rusty and only one of them found a buyer – at £45. Pretty cheap, he thought, and put his hand up when the next one started at the same price but Eve pulled it down and told him not to be so silly because they already had one.

Beyond the rows of Flymos, lavatories and rusted anchors was a smart group of auction rooms where real antiques were sold – not accumulated junk from Norfolk's attics or scrap yards. At that time they hadn't realised they were at the de luxe end of Norfolk's auctions. They found that out later.

Meantime they were exhausted by all this non-bidding. Eve hadn't found any chairs she liked and Lawrence hadn't seen a vice for his workshop. So obviously they needed lunch. They took a gentle drive north out of Aylsham, wound past an old mill and followed a row of willow trees on the banks of a shallow stream. Three cows standing in it watched the car cross the stream at a hump-backed bridge. A hundred yards further on the stream bordered the lawns of a flint-walled Georgian house. Ivy was growing everywhere and behind the house was a tennis court next to an old well with a little roof. Soon they

passed a thatched church, resting place for the last few centuries of Sir Thomas Erpingham of Agincourt. Dipping down to a tiny valley, they drove through woodland and crossed the stream again – this time at a ford. They blew through a farmyard, missed a couple of dozen squawking chickens and turned left past a sign that said "No Through Road." And so, after running this heraldic gauntlet of an English landscape, they came at last to the Saracen's Head, that delicious pub planted in the midst of North Norfolk's wide and empty fields. Today it was empty. After all, it was Monday and only just past noon. The only sounds were a few muffled curses from someone out of sight and a newly lit fire crackling away in each bar.

Lawrence and Eve looked at each other. They thought of all those poor people slaving away in London offices. Oh dear! They shook their heads sorrowfully. They called for two glasses of chilled Chadonnay, subsided before one of the fires, opened the Eastern Daily Press, closed it again and picked up their glasses.

On the blackboard, which passed here for a menu, their host Reggie had written: "A bottle of wine keeps reality at bay."

"Only one?" Eve asked her husband, and smiled. "Or is that one each?"

"For you, lovely creature, the world," said Reggie, as he walked in preceded by his stomach, which was covered by an egg-stained jumper dating from boarding school days. Below it – matching purple corduroys; above it – a cloth cap.

He sat down with them and confided: "I have something special for you today."

He was in the habit of advertising lunch by announcing: "Lost in North Norfolk – the £4.45 lunch."

"Delicious beef rissoles! What about that?" He leaned back and beamed at them.

"You mean they're the leftovers from yesterday's roast beef?" asked Eve. He looked pained.

"I defy you to know where it came from," he protested. "But our motto is 'The customer is always right,' unless it's the Inland Revenue, of course," he added caustically. "Did I tell you of the time that one of those worms visited me here during luncheon and he actually ..."

"Yes, you did," Lawrence said quickly. "Last week." He was feeling hungry and his wine was getting warm. To start with they ordered some stockpot soup, a piece of boned game, rabbit or pheasant – or both, with a bit of pork in some soup with fried onions, and some stone-ground brown bread, a meal all by itself.

Outside it began to rain – just a drizzle at first. But the drizzle turned into a downpour and the windows were soon streaked. But all that was outside. Lawrence watched it pour down and thought of all those plasterboard panels and the Flymo lawnmowers laid out on the ground, not to mention the fourteen lavatories (in assorted colours) and the tins of nuts and bolts, all of them getting a new layer of rust.

But Eve and Lawrence were having lunch in the middle of nowhere amidst the fields of North Norfolk. Lawrence threw another log on Reggie's fire with the nonchalance of a prosperous landowner. Eve lay back on the cushions. He topped up their drinks and they tilted their glasses to each other and smiled happily. They couldn't have wished to be anywhere else.

Reggie reappeared with a tray of lunch.

"How's that fellow Jan – you know, the owner of the Albatross?" he asked. "He seems to be with Justine now. She lives in your village, doesn't she?"

"Yes, it's true – " began Lawrence.

"So far as we know she is," cut in Eve. "But there's someone else too."

"Darling," Reggie told her. "I'm sure there is but if there wasn't you'd make one up."

Eve blushed and they both laughed.

"Anyway, Jan's sailing out of Wells nowadays, I'm told," he went on. "He was here with Justine last week. But that ship ... it's really North Norfolk, you know. I think it sort of represents the – "

Then the telephone rang, he became involved in a discussion about a horse and never told them what he thought it did represent.

But he was right about the beef rissoles. They were delicious. It's a resourceful cook who can concoct something out of leftovers. And Reggie could – worth more than £4.45, too.

It was amongst the clientele of the Saracen's Head that they some-times noted more symptoms of the English disease – county, not country. The disease is highly contagious, even infectious. Those afflicted were often the couples at the bar drinking lager and lime. Early symptoms exhibited by carriers include uniforms of cavalry twill trousers or twin sets, depending on gender (which, to give them credit, was at least unmistakable), and braying (a little too loudly) in voices remarkably similar to those of the beasts upon which they had the habit of travelling (at least when chasing foxes). Another early symptom was the dropping of well-known names like poor fieldsmen at cricket. Give yourself a name like Gurney, Walpole or Coke, let alone Bowes Lyon, and they'd be lying on their backs in no time. Preventative measures could be taken – perhaps with a strong vaccination of rabid communism. The problem was that a cure like that gave the sufferer an even worse disease. For of course its symptoms were just as severe as those of the original malaise – if that could be imagined. Indeed Prospero had once suggested to Lawrence that the Village Marxist might have been given such a vaccination in his youth. This, he told Lawrence, would have produced his current unhappy condition.

The disease is so virulent that people within sight or even hearing of those already infected usually exhibit symptoms at once. The medical paradox is that it infects the new host to a stronger degree than in the carrier. Later, when the disease had controlled the senses, other symptoms became manifest. These included assuming everyone was deaf, or invisible if from a different background (like being foreigners), killing animals for sport, speech deformation with high volume and minimal consonant usage (the glottal stop), idiosyncratic clothing (scarves and cloth caps), insular group habits and often slovenly table manners (throwing buns). Such characteristics all showed what they had in common with what they no doubt described with a certain amount of affectionate contempt as the lower classes. But the social ladder is a one-way street and the disease is usually incurable. Its symptoms grow more severe further west towards its source at Sandringham, the home of its terminal cases. These have been weakened by centuries of inbreeding, producing a receding chin, a harelip, a blood disease or penuria cerebrum. They are often shown to the public on ritual occasions where, as a formal warning, they are exhibited as examples of extreme forms of the disease. Such presentations also have value as professional medical demonstrations. Naturally police barriers and uniformed attendants are always present to protect the public from contact with the sufferers. However, such is the nature of the disease that these measures are not always enough to prevent some of the public from attempting to make physical contact, invariably resulting in transmission of the disease.

Lawrence sometimes wondered what Harry's reaction would be if he stood next to them. Virtual incomprehensibility, no doubt – on each side, too. But that was the nice thing about North Norfolk. It's no coincidence that Thomas Payne came from these parts, for they breed independence. No one gives a damn.

*　　*　　*

Before they left the Saracen's Head Eve had noticed that Reggie was wearing red socks.

"Never wear anything else, darling," he told her. She had been looking for more socks for Lawrence. These looked inviting. It seemed they were made from angora goat's wool by a friend of his on a nearby farm. They decided to visit it.

"My friend's called Larna," said Reggie. "And tell her I need four dozen eggs for tomorrow. And not to forget the two brace of pheasants I ordered for tonight."

A pair of red angora wool socks, two brace of pheasants and four dozen eggs. All in a North Norfolk day's work.

The farm was a few miles away beyond the church at Erpingham. When they found it the rain had stopped but the air was still damp. Thin strands of a late autumnal mist were streaming over the empty fields. At the farm's entrance two or three rooks were perched at the top of an elm tree. Lawrence drove along a muddy lane past a group of barns. Some were falling down. Some were still standing but were leaning over as if about to slump at any moment. Inside a hay barn several dozen sheep were grouped uncertainly together. They looked as if they were waiting for something but had forgotten what. A few newborn lambs staggered on trembling legs from parent to parent. In the next barn a group of cows sat dozing, heads up but half reclining – like Roman senators at a feast. Three horses gazed with benign wisdom out of their stable doors. Lawrence parked the car and two South American lamas cantered up to greet them. In a summer house a couple of goats with wispy beards sat together like Chinese monks – the sock factory, no doubt. And there were chickens, dogs and cats everywhere. It was Noah's ark, but mud not water. They squelched through it to the house, an ancient Queen Anne pile facing south over a rough-cut lawn. A decrepit conservatory was propped up, as if exhausted, by the west wall. The house had been weathered to the same burnt sienna of Gibraltar House. It had a neglected and ageing beauty that you would never find in the Home Counties. If the house had been within Jaguar range of Dorking Station it would have been repainted every year. But here it looked untouched since before the war. But which war? Lawrence wasn't sure. There had been so many since the house was built. The paint was peeling off anyway. There was no gravel drive for chauffeurs to crunch along in expensive limousines.

Just a weed-invaded track of earth that led to a battered Landrover. Together with a trailer spilling with hay, it was parked by the front door. In Surrey there might have been a horse in the paddock but as for goats – dear me, no. In Dorking its front door would have gleamed gloss black and been fitted with well-polished brass knockers and double security bolts – not to mention a security eyehole. Here in North Norfolk a splodge of manure smeared two panels and the door was jammed open by a dog basket containing an old blanket and someone's half-eaten slipper. Next to the door two brace of pheasants were hanging from a hook into the wall. They smelled just about ready to eat. Lawrence could tell that from five yards.

Eve peered round the doorway and made out four or five shotguns stacked in a corner of the hall. On a dresser a pile of cartridges spilled out of a soup tureen. A narrow staircase was lined with portraits of black-and-white silhouettes wearing frock coats and top hats – all family, it went without saying. A large and elderly Alsatian was snoring gently on the landing. His head lolled down over the top stair. Filling the dining room was an enormous mahogany table beneath a dusty chandelier that lacked four of its eight candlelight bulbs. On a mahogany sideboard stood two cut-glass decanters (both empty) and three silver dishes (one full of bird-seed). Next to them were an empty birdcage and an old brass microscope. Victorian dining chairs filled the rest of the space in the room. Some of them had seats. Some didn't.

"Can't you imagine George Eliot living here?" laughed Eve, looking at the microscope. "Not the place for an intellectual Victorian lady. She'd be standing in this mahogany gloom every wet afternoon, gazing at the rain pouring down outside and growing more and more desperate."

"Well, it was even wetter in Venice – as she found out," said Lawrence. "Or, rather, her husband did when he jumped into a canal on their honeymoon."

Suddenly a door burst open behind the stairs and a determined looking woman in maroon riding breeches and an emerald silk shirt with a Dior scarf around her shoulders emerged backwards pulling a large cardboard box behind her. Was this Larna? But given the background, she seemed another contrast in North Norfolk.

She straightened up and shook her hair free, a shock of silver curls like the waves crashing on their beach.

"You wouldn't mind giving me a hand, would you? You can't believe how heavy they are. I've got some people coming to take one of these little creatures this evening."

Lawrence and Eve each grabbed a corner – and heaved.

"Did you just come from Reggie? He rang." She smelled of dog and Dior. Eve felt that smelling of dog was better than smelling of sheep, goat, chicken, horse, cat or lama, let alone cow. But her scent wasn't surprising because at the bottom of the cardboard box four Border Terrier pups were rolling and wriggling around all over each other.

"I'll take the eggs over in half an hour. He said you wanted some socks, is that right?"

"Yes, maybe three pairs. Do you make them on the farm?"

"Well, my husband shears the wool from the goats and we get it spun. Then we knit them ourselves," she said, pulling open a drawer. She looked at him and grinned. "It's better than watching telly."

He chose three pairs. They were red, thick and soft. And they didn't smell of goat. He turned to show them to Eve but she was gazing mesmerised into the cardboard box.

"We've just got to have one." She was looking at the puppies with the sort of glassy-eyed drool that women sometimes have with babies. He peered over.

"Well," he admitted. "They certainly seem rather fetching."

She reached in with both hands as if scooping a bran tub, pulled out a puppy and hugged it.

"You could take it for walkies," she said, turning its head towards Lawrence. It had brown eyes and floppy ears. Then she kissed it. That wasn't difficult. It was licking her all over already, even though she didn't smell of Dior.

"Quite impossible," he said firmly. "I'd have to get up early in the morning."

"It'll do you good," she said.

"And what about the cat?"

"He's smaller," she said.

"And training!"

"Only little bits and only for a few days," she said.

"Ha! Well, who's going to clear it up until then?"

"We'll take turns," she said.

"What about travelling?"

"We live here. We're not going anywhere," she said.

"What about when we're older?"

"He'll be company for us," she said. She took hold of a paw and waved it at him. "Hullo, Dadda!"

"You look as if you could do with some exercise, anyway," Larna told him as she unwound her Dior scarf, wiped her hands with it, winked at Eve and walked off to collect the eggs from the undergrowth beneath the trees.

Lawrence groaned. What could a man do?

So it was settled. Larna slung the pheasants into the Landrover with the eggs.

"Four dozen eggs get us a meal at Reggie's," she said. "And the two brace of pheasants pay for the wine. Mind you, a bottle of wine is usually only one brace around here but his wine's so expensive."

Lawrence and Eve drove home with the puppy. She held it close throughout the journey.

"Well," she explained, "he'll cry at leaving his brothers and sisters so he needs to be comforted."

And on the way, Lawrence realised that after all a dog was the anchor helping them create the extra continuity that they needed for them to belong in a new home, especially in the country. For a moment he felt it as a replacement for his sons, and tried to avoid thinking of the advantages. He looked suspiciously at Eve. In Holt they bought a dog basket and placed it by the Aga at home. Later that night they put their dog in the kitchen, closed the door and went to bed. That was the signal for a wailing of unutterable misery. It filled the house, penetrating two thick doors in the process. Eve gave in after a couple of minutes. He was so happy to see her that his tail wagged hard enough to fall off. He had obviously forgiven them immediately. And after that he always slept at the end of their bed – when he was not actually trying to sleep in it.

By lunchtime next day Lawrence and Eve had become so passionately fond of their puppy and his total affection for them, his constantly wagging tail, his humour (teasing the cat, who spent the first two days on top of the wardrobe before she landed a few sideswipes with her claws, producing a squeal) and his mischief (fighting a slipper to the death) that they were already beginning to wonder how they had ever managed without a dog. They took him round to the pub to be introduced to Ronald who shook paws, lifted him onto the bar and offered him some warm beer in a small saucer. He tilted his head and looked quizzically up at him with dark eyes. And one of his ears flopped inside out.

"What a charmer," groaned Ronald.

In the afternoon they took him for a walk on the marshes. Just a short one – after all, he was only a puppy. They had often seen walkers and their dogs far off on the sea bank. Both had been silhouetted against the clear light, the man walking steadily and the dog running ahead but staying near. Now they had joined the club. And their puppy bounded about around them.

Soon they came home to crumpets for tea. And their dog lay asleep by the fire.

\*     \*     \*

There hadn't been much low-flying recently. No doubt that was due to the late autumn weather rather than to Lawrence's offensive against the Ministry of Defence. But that weekend he read some interesting details in his Sunday newspaper. So he waited the statutory fortnight and then told the Ministry all about a European alternative to the US SLAM-ER ground-to-ground missile. It would shortly come into trial production. That Sunday paper was really very well informed. The Ministry must have learned a lot. His reward was a telephone call from the boss of his faceless civil servant correspondent. His last letter must clearly have got them worried for they invited him to discuss the problem at Marham Airfield near Swaffam. Apparently that was where all those jets came from – the ones that flew over Gibraltar House. It was a military runway and civilians were not allowed near it. Eve was worried. She didn't put it past them to poison his coffee, dump his body over the North Sea and call it suicide. Lawrence laughed.

"Not even the Ministry of Defence," he pointed out, "would be quite that stupid."

But then he remembered something in the papers about suicide. And he wasn't sure.

\*     \*     \*

Even without the risk of being thrown out of a plane, the prospect of the meeting was somewhat tense. He knew it was his last chance to stop the flying. If he failed to persuade them, there would be nothing more he could do. The night before, Eve suggested a visit to a concert in a nearby church.

"It's not just the food of love," she pointed out. "It calms the savage breast as well."

As usual she had seen the notice nailed to a tree. The church was in the next village and only a mile away across the water meadows. They filled a casserole with a brace of pheasant and a couple of bottles of red wine, left it on top of the Aga for supper later and decided to walk there. But it was a long walkies for a little dog. So they left him with Ronald.

"I'll put a bit of warm beer in his water," he said, and laid down a bowl for him. "He'll like the hops."

"Only this once," Eve told him. "We don't want him to become a dypso dog, you know. He's only small."

But it was distraction enough to let them escape without being noticed. Eve was relieved. She knew she could never have resisted the agony of his despairing wail of abandon.

And so the couple came alone to Wiveton's simple thatched-roof country church across the valley from their own church. Like theirs, it overlooked its village green and pub. Behind it the grass in its cemetery almost hid the tombstones. And behind the cemetery an embankment had been the village's port. This, with the port at their own church, had flourished in the days before the river silted up. Most people had made their living from the sea or the land. There had been noisy markets and busy shipyards. Sailing boats like the Albatross had unloaded fish or taken on grain and wool. But now few clues remain from those times – merely a levelled bank and a few rusted rings. Tonight the only signs of life near their own dimmed church were pale lights from the windows of the Three Swallows, a few seagulls and a wandering dog.

But Lawrence and Eve were at Wiveton Church across the valley and its tall windows glowed with light and they walked to the door along a path lined with candles and inside they found candlelight and shadows wavering on rows of people sitting in the pews all whispering together and rustling programmes and waiting for the concert to begin. The candlelight made long shadows on the flag-stoned floors and flickered on the walls lined with regimental flags and plaques. The shadows reached higher to the hammer-beam roof. From it a great hook supported a cast iron candelabrum and seven thick candles.

Everyone was still settling in and the air was full of creakings and whisperings. It was an exotic prelude, soon to metamorphose into sounds and sweet airs. Anticipation was already creating delight, as if the very church itself, like some colossal unblinking black whale, was stirring into life.

Suddenly a bat flashed past Lawrence's nose. At least he thought it was a bat. It was alive anyway, a fleet flash of flight that flitted from the shadows and back as if trying, like the soul of the devil, to escape damnation.

By now there was only standing room at the font near the back of the church. Behind them stood a table of wine bottles and glasses. Casually Lawrence filled two glasses for him and Eve – and put one to his lips. At once came the taste of the pheasants lying at this moment in their casserole dish on the Aga at home. Before they left for the church he had tried a spoonful. The casserole had been beginning to bubble just a little, only the merest burp now and again. The pheasants would be ready when they returned. They smiled to each other over the rims of their glasses and gently clinked them.

The performance began with Bach's "Jesu, Joy of Man's desiring." He found himself holding his breath to the tune as it danced in triplets round and about and up and down and all through the church like a joyous spring-clean and over everyone in it too. He ran out of breath halfway through, but it still went on – a bit like Ravel's Bolero but with Jesus for added value. The church was shadowy dark but little noises rustled everywhere and he felt it was alive. That wouldn't have happened in St Paul's Cathedral but that was how it was this night in this little English country church. Then two pieces by English composers and finally an aria by Purcell – "Genius of England." Perfection untroubled by continental discord and meddling.

In the darkness by the font Lawrence turned and topped up their glasses with a little more red wine. As the musicians played he and his wife silently raised their glasses to them and to Purcell. But most of all to England.

During the final applause they left the church. They walked the corridor of candles towards the lych-gate and crossed the silent turf of the darkened green to its brightly lit pub. Spiritual to secular in thirty seconds flat. Ah – North Norfolk, the land of contrasts! Thank heaven they had seen that notice nailed to the tree. Lawrence ordered two glasses of Coonawarra red at the pub. As they toasted each other again, they realised that for weeks they hadn't given a single thought to that albatross, their mortgage.

Late that night they were woken by a telephone call.

"Oh, darlings, are you alright?" cried Eve. "Thank goodness. But you know the time? ... well, you know, we were asleep ... oh never mind! I'm glad you're having a good time, but ... you've what? ... you've got some what? ... and you can see Mount Everest? ... and what? ... there's a dragon dancing on its peak? ..."

She looked at the telephone. "Are you all right?"

There was a click.

"They seem really funny," she told Lawrence who was half asleep. "They were talking about a dragon. I don't get it. Anyway guess where they are?"

"Khatmandu," said Lawrence with his eyes shut. She looked at him.

"How did you know?" she asked suspiciously.

"Everest – but it's probably K2. And they've got hold of some LSD."

The following evening Zeus and Leda had invited Lawrence and Eve to supper at their cottage. They lived on the far side of Matlaske, a clutch of pretty houses in the empty fields between Holt and Aylsham. And the invitation capped their happy mood. For that morning they had at last received another offer for the London house. It was low, but they remembered what had happened last time when that buyer had backed out after the survey. They were lucky to get another offer anyway and of course the new buyer must have been aware of that. They accepted. So now there was hope. As they drove they gazed contentedly at the passing landscape. It was early November and the fields were looking definitely bare. And they felt more at home than ever. Their relief gave them the light-hearted air of being on a Sunday outing. They sailed gaily through an empty village or two, dipped into a wooded dell and gazed through trees at a moated flint mansion. Was it fifteenth century? Lawrence wouldn't have been surprised if nobody outside North Norfolk had ever heard of it. A few miles further on the hedge gave way to an old gate with a broken hinge. On its other side stretched a long avenue of fresh uncut grass. It was lined by rows of massive old oak trees. Perhaps five or six hundred yards away and only just visible through the early winter air they could just make out an ancient mansion. It was a trembling image of three tall Dutch gables – as delicate and as priceless as an antique jewel.

"What a glorious place," exclaimed Lawrence – then paused, thinking for a moment. "But those oaks in this avenue, you know, just as much as that house at the end, however wonderful it is ... they're England's heart, its oaken heart," he smiled. "We know they were planted for a purpose, probably before Nelson, too – nowadays it's called forward planning or something – to make ships' timbers to beat off the Europeans, the Germans, French, Danes, Spanish, the Dutch, let alone that lot with the hare-lips, who were they?" He looked at Eve. "Well, you tell me. Anyway we've had at them all at one time or another." He paused and thought for a moment. "Well, not counting the Italians, I suppose. Oh yes, we fought them in the last war. But they changed sides halfway through. They don't count anyway, not in a war. But anyway a lot of England's history is Europe's history, it had to be to keep the sea open, to keep us fed and free – even though we've kept out of it. I mean, they've been fighting each other for hundreds of years. Well, that suited us, of course."

"You mean, even though we've kept them out of England," Eve smiled at him. "The last one who got here was William the Conqueror."

"Apart from the ones who got shot down in the last war."

"But there's something else," said Eve. "Quite apart from the oaks, something else that makes that place here so English. It's because it's discrete. No showing off. It doesn't have to. It's English – quiet confidence," she spread her hands. "Who's ever heard of it? But those gables, so beautiful, so full of quality, but they don't even bother to mend that gate! Not showy."

Leda's home – and Zeus's too for some time now – was not far off down a track. Two cottages had been knocked into one and were hidden in a copse with a stream flowing somewhere beyond. Inside they discovered a haven of love and artistic chaos. Paintings and reliefs were on every wall. Any available space held Leda's late husband's sculptures. He had carved from wood and fibreglass, as well as stone. And there were paintings in every space – small, gigantic or moderate. Lawrence found he couldn't walk down a dimly lit corridor without brushing against a plaster head or a pair of wooden nipples on well-modelled wooden breasts. Candles in alcoves lit the kitchen. Wall sconces and shells were dominated by an old Aga shuddering in a recess like a slowly awakening mammoth. The plates piled on top of it were all painted in different patterns. A painted casserole dish was gently bubbling away full of rabbit and mustard and coriander and wine and garlic and brandy. Its smell bewitched everyone. Next to the plates a black cat lay asleep on a turban of tea towels. Their puppy caught sight of it and caused a noisy diversion before he was dragged off and made to sit on Eve's lap.

Zeus sat at the head of the old pine table. Five buttons of his shirt were unbuttoned and curly black hair cascaded everywhere as if released from a painful confinement. Those five undone buttons were a sure sign of his five-star status here, thought Lawrence. As everyone gossiped together in the candlelight Leda moved to and from the Aga with the sort of serene and all-embracing smile that dated from the time before time.

"You know, I keep my ex-husband's work here but that's just because I don't want him to be forgotten. It's not a mausoleum, you know. Life goes on. I'm still young." She smiled.

Eve saw Zeus look at her out of the corner of his eye. Did he blush? Did they both blush? Eve looked sideways at Lawrence and creased the corner of one eyelid ever so slightly.

It was another magical evening, full of affection and warmth. At last they stood up, stretched and woke their dog. He had been asleep since the episode of the cat, now and then contributing merely a dreaming whimper to the conversation. Before they left they were led out to meet a young artist whom Leda was lodging in a caravan by the stream. He was painting a vast mural but there was some difficulty in deciding what it represented. This led to a discussion on modern art. There was a good deal of derision about formaldehyde sheep. The artistic demi-monde of North Norfolk was at work. Lawrence and Eve were pleased to be among it. They saw again how it produced such creative independence. Finally they found their car among some trees by the stream. And slowly home they drove.

A slice of moon balanced above their heads like a swing that had swung back and was about to dive down – like one of Pippa's paintings. It gave just enough light for them to glimpse a Georgian farmhouse sleeping by a black pond. The lane crept quietly round it. For a moment or two their headlights silhouetted a coven of witches caught in some weird dance on the hill's ridge and masquerading as a group of winter oaks. Despite the pretty flint cottages and the thatched and homely churches, the North Norfolk countryside was as savage and primitive as any symbol of fertility.

*     *     *

It was three days after their visit to the auction at Aylsham. And they still needed a couple of chairs. Next auction? Today at Fakenham, of course. Another town stuck in 1935. The smell of the place? Very agricultural. Plenty of mud, or worse – the city slicker's enemies. The auction was a little more down market than Aylsham, thought Lawrence. Cardboard boxes full of comics or broken bits of kitchen equipment weren't what they had come for. Strangely enough he saw three rusty old Flymo lawnmowers that he could have sworn were the ones that didn't get sold at the Aylsham auction. As the bidding went on, he noticed that only one of them found a buyer. For only £35 too – £10 cheaper than before. But in spite of the cardboard boxes there were a few choice items. For example Eve saw two chairs that looked Regency, although part of their backs had been cut away. But they looked good to her and she got them for £10 the pair. When they left the auction rooms Lawrence found a £10 parking ticket stuck under the car's windscreen wiper. A parking ticket in North Norfolk? Horror, horror, they said to each other! Ah well, no matter – that's the North Norfolk premium. And the chairs were still cheap at £10 each.

They were out of Fakenham early, before the sale ended and the pubs filled with farmers. They took a diversion home past Great Snoring Church and remembered that summer concert and Mozart's Requiem sung by the Fakenham Choir. A few miles further through the fields they stopped for lunch at the Three Horseshoes at Wareham. The pub was empty. There was gas lighting and the floors were worn stone flags. The heavy old pine tables were as pitted as the surface of the moon. They were so large that separate groups could sit at them and not get in each other's hair. Old posters and clay pipes were on the walls (last decorated in 1935, it seemed) and the coals in the grate glowed like a kitchen fire. Lawrence and Eve stood at the wide hatch and chose their beer from the names chalked on the barrels behind – warm, too, of course.

Nothing smart or foreign about the menu here – no fancy food as Nelson once said. Just Mrs Beeton's best English ... Smokie Hotpot, Iron Age Fort Game Pie, Potted cheese and Port or a Steak and Beer Pie. If that's not enough there's always Spotted Dick for a top-up.

But the magical thing happened after Lawrence had started on his second pint. Jimmy Blake arrived, dressed in sou'westers and thigh boots. A sack of mussels was on his shoulder. With him was Horace Nelson, the Jack Tar they'd wanted to buy a scooter from and who lived by the church. He had a round of Stilton under his arm and a couple of loaves of bread in one hand. Neither of them was surprised to see Eve and Lawrence.

"Philip gave me this," grinned Horace. "Did some weeding round a few tombstones. Told me the sheep look nice but they refuse to eat thistles."

At the hatch Jimmy called for a saucepan and tipped the mussels into it, a sudden avalanche of short and blue-black nuggets tumbling noisily into the pan.

"They'll do well with a couple of chopped-up onions and some garlic," he said to the barman, obviously an old friend. "But strain 'em and don't forget some cider and a bit of parsley at the last minute. And got any cream?"

Lawrence bought them each a pint of beer and soon they all sat down together with bowls of mussels and chunks of Stilton on a big slab of bread. Their dog sat beneath the table, nose twitching – alert.

And with their arrival – and of the mussels too – came a feeling that although Eve and Lawrence still didn't quite understand the magic of North Norfolk they knew they were getting closer and closer to it. Yes, it was simple pleasure – the deepest pleasure of all – but it was something else, too. And whatever that was, it was something they had never experienced in London.

Next morning they found a couple of pigeons in the garden. They were plump and healthy, not like the ones on Trafalgar Square that sometimes were so poorly that they had often lost one foot. And both of these pigeons had a band around one leg. Carrier pigeons, he thought – and wished them well.

Not so their cat. Two days later she appeared to have something wrong with her eye. It was swollen. And the pigeons had gone.

"It's inflamed," said Eve, in a worried tone. "I think I'd better ring the vet. I don't want her to lose an eye." She bustled off for the telephone directory.

Lawrence had a look at it. Then he understood.

"Don't worry," he said. "She'll recover. She got more than she bargained for this time, that's all."

"What d'you mean?"

"She had a go at one of the pigeons and it gave her one in the eye with its beak, that's all."

Eve put back the telephone directory and picked up the Sphinx.

"Goodjie, woodjie, poor little pussy," she went. "Were you attacked by that nasty pigeon, then?"

And she completely ignored Lawrence when he pointed out that the cat had tried to kill the pigeon, not to mention eat it beforehand.

*　　　*　　　*

He still hadn't found a vice for his workshop. But he discovered from Tom that there was an auction every Friday at North Walsham beyond the Saracen's Head near the east coast. And Friday was tomorrow. So he persuaded Eve that they should be there.

It wasn't totally up to the class of Fakenham's auction, let alone the one at Aylsham. The shed was full of dirty washing machines and bulky furniture like decrepit wardrobes. Outside was a collection of nondescript items ranging from old anchors to rusting hinges. He was surprised to recognise amongst them the two Flymo lawnmowers that hadn't got sold the day before at Fakenham.

"And weren't they left over from the sale at Aylsham?" asked Eve.

She was right. A streak of suspicion began to form in his mind, no bigger than a bidder's finger but growing every sale day. One of the lawnmowers went for £25, leaving just the dirty green one with a dent in its cover. Every time he didn't buy one he saved £10, in fact. But even he couldn't claim that he was making money by not bidding. By now it was obvious that although there was a class hierarchy amongst the auctions in North Norfolk, there wasn't a class barrier. Lawn mowers seemed to pass through them like radio waves through a wall. He suddenly had an idea and his eyes lit up.

"If I can find out where the last one goes up for sale I might get a bargain," he told Eve. She looked at him and rolled her eyes.

"You know very well that we've got a lawnmower," she said. "I've told you – several times."

"Yes, but it'd be such a bargain," he protested.

Meanwhile there didn't seem much chance of finding anything unexpected in North Walsham, like in Fakenham. But in a box of assorted ironmongery (a saw, four dozen nuts and bolts, a few adjustable spanners, an electric drill and a plane) he found the bench vice he had been looking for. And in the box was also a club hammer. Ah! That was always bound to be useful in North Norfolk, he thought, even if only for breaking flints.

At first everyone ignored the box, so the auctioneer picked a starting bid of £20 off a passing cloud. But the crowd at the auction were Norfolk dealers, an oily-haired and beady-eyed group of cynics who could have doubled for Fagin any day. They just stared blankly at the auctioneer as if he was stupid or they were deaf – or both. But he was used to them. He abandoned his starting bid and ran the price down like a stone in water until he reached £1. At that figure a man in greasy overalls and a cloth cap over his eyes pointed a pipe at him and nodded. And this, as if he had 'come out' and been the first to admit to some revolting perversion, released a trickle of bids that raised the price, like a dead fish in the same water, slowly but inevitably up to £20. Lawrence wondered why they had bothered. He felt in his pocket and found he had £21. So he bid £21 – and someone else bid £22. Then his finger somehow took on a life of its own and he went on bidding and after a few moments he was left with the box at £36, a pound higher than the bid of a man standing in front of him, a burly fellow with a forest of hair that seemed familiar. But he didn't have £36. He only had £21.

"Hey," said Lawrence and tapped him on the shoulder. He was in a bit of a panic. The auctioneer was coming up for the money and he didn't have it. "I only want the vice and the hammer. You can have the drill and the rest for £25."

The man turned round. It was Horace Nelson, last seen in the Three Horseshoes with a round of Stilton under his arm, this time wearing a pair of enormous navy dungarees with about eight pockets – all of them stuffed with some sort of engineering tool.

Horace recognised him and winked. He paused dramatically and said, in a bloody-minded Norfolk way, "Oh, it's you, Lawrence. OK, but £24."

Lawrence laughed. They shook hands and he took the vice and the hammer out of the box and gave Horace £12.

"That'll make £36 if you give him the £24 you'd have paid me. OK,

Horace?"

And at that moment the auctioneer arrived with his hand out, into which he put £12 and Horace put £24. Result: happiness, as Mr Micawber once said. Something had turned up – and Lawrence smiled to himself as he and Eve drove for lunch to the Saracen's Head a few miles away. He had £9 – and two lunches there cost £8.90. Result: happiness twice in one day plus 10p, two full stomachs and contentment. Lawrence even began to feel optimistic that this latest purchaser of their house might actually buy it.

\*　　　\*　　　\*

The next day he drove to RAF Marham's Airfield where he met the group captain in charge and discovered that the reason why the planes kept on flying over them was because the village and its windmill was in direct line with Marham's airstrip – North 44deg 30 East, to be precise. And so the village was on their flight path before they turned left to go over the North Sea. So he asked him to tell his lads to turn left a bit earlier instead and fly over someone else's back yard for a change. After an hour's discussion he agreed. But Lawrence knew that the technique was to give the troublemaker a drink and some blarney and no doubt it usually worked. He also knew that low flying tended to stop in autumn and winter – just when it got difficult, as he told them. He was going to have to wait until the good weather returned next year to find if they were really going to co-operate. But for now the serpent was banned from paradise.

Lawrence could see they had been puzzled. Was he some sort of secret adviser? But if so he wouldn't have drawn attention to himself and what was he doing in North Norfolk anyway? There must be something behind it. For example how did he know all about the latest ground-to-ground missiles, Uninhabited Combat Air Vehicles and the Future Offensive Air System programme? And what more did he know? But Lawrence didn't see much point in telling them. After all, in a couple of days that Sunday newspaper would be out again and it might print something useful to attack the ministry with again.

The following morning's post brought bad news. Their bank had sent them a final notice:

"Court proceedings for eviction will take place without further notice unless the advance is repaid within 21 days of date of postmark."

Lawrence suddenly went cold. The house would be repossessed, bailiffs would evict them and they would have to leave North Norfolk. But where could they go? Not home to London. The tenant had three months notice and they daren't give him notice anyway, even if they managed to fend off the bank, in case the agent couldn't find another tenant. Anyway they might not be able to get him out at all and he could sit there not paying rent for another six months or more if he felt like it. The law was loaded against landlords – as they had discovered.

Lawrence's panic was so great that even before he had finished reading the letter he had a mental picture of the caravan that he and Eve would be forced to live in while they waited for a buyer. It was in a caravan park crammed with a hundred others on the cliffs outside Cromer. Dirty white it was with wheels on blocks and grass growing round them, hardboard walls, no heating, a cramped bed, a blocked sink and a stinking lavatory. When it rained the roof leaked and the site was five yards from the communal ablutions where unemployed skinheads hung out, snorted crack, got drunk and brawled every night. He became white-faced in half a second.

His wife put an arm round him.

"Courage, darling!" she said. "Ring our solicitor."

So he did. Could our solicitor do anything? He said he might be able to get a stay in proceedings until their buyer had a chance to put his money down to exchange contracts. He said he would contact the bank and the buyer's solicitor as well. Lawrence felt relieved. Lawyer was to speak unto lawyer.

After a couple of days he rang back and said he'd arranged it. Lawyer had indeed spoken unto lawyer. And lawyer who represented buyer had told lawyer who represented vendor (Lawrence and Eve) that buyer was bona fide and lawyer who represented buyer had telephoned vendor's bank. The bank had heard it all before. But it agreed to stop eviction procedures for three months. For some reason they called it "staying." But Lawrence wasn't fussy. The caravan from hell faded from his mind. For some time now they had lived from day to day – or from buyer to buyer.

"But this is the only time we'll be able to do this," warned his solicitor. "The bank won't wear it again. Just make sure that your buyer isn't a flake like the last one."

They prayed for his soul. In fact they prayed for the soul of everyone they could think of, even for the bank manager's soul, if he had one – which, thought Lawrence, remained a matter of unrealistic conjecture.

The snake in paradise had been repulsed the day before. And today Lawrence and Eve had repulsed the devil – at least for a time. So they felt they deserved a treat and they knew where to go, for they had discovered that every now and again the Saracen's Head held Feasts in an upstairs room. The table seated twenty on each side and each Feast had some sort of "theme" – Mediterranean Night (bouillabaise and osso-bucco) or Norfolk Night (mussels, pheasant and hare). Tonight it was Empire Night (roast beef).

St George's flag was flying and Reggie's camel-park was crowded with cars when they arrived. They had to park in a field across the road.

"What about our boy?" Even suddenly asked. Their dog, now named Wagga on account of his incessant tail movement, was in the back of the car. "Will Reggie let him in?"

"Do I allow dogs?" said Reggie. "Only in the kitchen. And they come out cooked."

So Eve felt it safest that Wagga stayed in the car. She kissed him a dozen times – for which she got her face thoroughly licked – and told him they wouldn't be long. Wagga believed her.

The table had forty seats and every seat was taken. Lawrence sat next to a lady dressed as Good Queen Bess. It was clear that the British Empire still lived – in North Norfolk, at least. She talked like the Queen but owned a caravan park near Cromer. Well, that was definitely useful and he couldn't believe it. Was this fate? He made a point of taking her name – they might need her. Eve sat next to her husband. He seemed to be wearing the Union Jack. On Lawrence's right was a girl scarcely out of her teens from trendy Norwich. He had the feeling that she had so little in common with him that he could have come from Mars. She probably drove an open red Ford Escort, had a jacuzzi at home and was into telesales.

Reggie excelled himself. He appeared dressed as Mr Pickwick with a monocle, side-whiskers and a top hat. He cracked a coaching whip wildly a few times before making a few artistic flourishes with a large carving knife. Then he wheeled in a huge carcase of roast beef and began to carve. He caught Lawrence's eye and raised an eyebrow.

"Got to give the punters what they want, dear boy."

Lawrence noticed that the roast potatoes were very crisp.

"How did you manage to get them like that?" he asked.

Reggie arrested his carving knife in mid-swoop, looked at him as if he was an imbecile and rolled his eyes up to the ceiling.

"My dear boy," he sighed. "I haven't got time to explain. Look at all these people waiting for my attention."

"I know." Eve told him. "You bash them around in a saucepan when they're half cooked."

He looked pained. "Good gracious, dear lady. It's much more complicated than that."

He shook his head and sighed again. Reggie was caricaturing himself – better each time, too. The evening looked promising.

And the promise was fulfilled. Lawrence surprised himself by his curiosity about caravans to the left of him and jacuzzis to the right. He was never lost for a polite question, especially after a bottle of rich Australian Shiraz. In fact he began to feel delighted that his fund of knowledge on these subjects had been so amply, indeed so extraordinarily, enriched. Later Eve pointed out they wouldn't have room for the jacuzzi described by the girl on his right if they were forced to live in the caravan provided by Good Queen Bess on his left.

"How about a final cognac, dear one?" Reggie suggested to Eve before they left. "We'd better not give one to your husband. He might have to spend the night in a police cell."

And that was enough to start him off.

"What a law that is! Everyone knows that you drive better with a bottle inside you," he said, pouring out two cognacs. "Mind you, I'm on the wagon. The police picked me up once after I'd spent an hour in the pub with an orange juice. I was stone cold sober. Well, OK, the wife was smashed but she wasn't driving. They followed me for three miles. Then they asked me when I'd last had a drink and went mad when I told them "fifteen years ago." You'd think it was a crime the way they went on about it. They breathalysed me of course. And when they couldn't get me for that they got really annoyed – as if I'd ruined their evening! They spent hours walking all round the car, shining their torch on the tax disc and the tyres, frantic to find something they could do me for. They even looked up the exhaust pipe. I ask you! This fellow took his helmet off and lay on the ground and squinted up it. I told him not to be obscene. But I admit it didn't help when the wife threw up out of the window just when they were snooping around her side. Fairly got spattered. Well, it was enough to make a cat sick they way they were going on. In the end I told them they were causing a traffic obstruction."

He poured them another glass each. "What a bunch of fascists!"

"I see you've got the St George's flag up," said Lawrence.

"I certainly have," he agreed. "I'm not having those council fellows tell me what to do. I got a solicitor to write to them to tell them that it was on my property and I could do what I liked in it. That shut them up. Mind you, I'm half surprised they didn't get some Scotch lawyer to reply to him."

"Why not an English one?"

"Well, you know we've got Scotch and Welsh politicians at Westminster and no English ones in the Welsh and Scotch parliaments? It's ridiculous. They can both tell us what to do but we can't do the same to them. We might as well be a colony. Here's your bill."

Lawrence glanced at it.

"But you've put the cognac on it," he protested. "I thought that was on the house."

"On the house? My dear fellow, you do have some odd ideas." He turned to Eve.

"Are you sure he's feeling all right, my angel? Tell you what, you can have a room upstairs at a special discount. Ten quid instead of forty. Save you thirty quid. How about that? And it's only because you're so beautiful. Actually I don't know what you see in your husband." He sighed and slapped Lawrence on the back.

By the time they staggered up the stairs to bed they had spent most of that thirty quid on cognac.

*     *     *

It was when they were on their way home from a trip to Norwich in mid-November that Lawrence discovered what had happened to the last Flymo lawnmower – the one that hadn't get sold at any of the auctions.

They were in Norwich to treat themselves to lunch. The new buyer had accepted a survey report on the house. And his solicitor had confirmed his offer. So Lawrence reckoned that if Paris was worth a Mass, the report was worth a good lunch. He would even have bought the surveyor lunch, too – in advance, of course; and perhaps accompanied by an undefined promise of future delights. All this last year they had been so absorbed by their bell jar of North Norfolk that they had neglected Norwich. Next year, they promised themselves, they would explore. First, the Norman cathedral. It commanded the Close and the cricket ground, as one expected in England. Then there was the nearby castle built on a huge mound by one of King William's earls. The River Wensum embraced them both before leaching itself through the suburbs eastwards towards the sea. And what about that ultra-modern shopping centre beneath the castle? And the covered market nearby? And, look, there's even a cinema. All this and North Norfolk too!

After getting caught down a few one-way streets they had found themselves in a medieval warren called Tombland opposite a cathedral gateway built by Sir Thomas Erpingham. Rows of half-timbered houses hung over the cobbled lanes. One of them was an almost empty restaurant. They began ordering and the owner drifted over and, in response to a few queries, explained its origins.

"All the houses around here have had dozens of functions. Our first owner was a priest but he had backed the wrong side at the Wars of the Roses. Got his skull split open and they hacked his limbs off him at Bosworth Field," he explained cheerfully. Eve began to feel queasy. "So the Tudors made a drinking shed of it and then a lupenar."

"What's that? A lupenar?" asked Eve.

"Oh, that's what they called brothels in those days, dear." She jumped.

"What – in this room?"

"Wouldn't have been surprised."

She blushed.

"Don't worry, though – the Council made us give it a good scrubbing. Well, I mean a clean-up."

"Well, I think I'll just order lunch for the moment," she forced a smile and frowned at the menu. They ordered Cromer crab, a dish of venison and a bottle of Coonawarra red. The owner wandered back.

"After Henry VIII died they kicked the girls out and it became a refuge for prods being hunted by Queen Mary."

"Well, that's better than a lupenary ... or whatever it was called," Eve was relieved.

"Yes, well, when Elizabethan became queen the tables had been turned and Walsingham – you know, her chief spy-catcher? – he'd turned it into a nunnery to eavesdrop on the customers."

"Customers at a nunnery?" Eve didn't get it.

"Ah, yes, but it meant something else then. Hamlet was playing at the time in London. Remember what he told Ophelia?"

"Ah, yes," Lawrence butted in. " 'Get thee to a nunnery', wasn't it? And didn't it mean a brothel?"

"Not again?" Eve was disbelieving. "Didn't they do anything else in this house?"

Just then the crab arrived and the owner retired. But later he brought them the venison himself.

"Don't worry, dear," he told Eve. "After that things got quite tame. I mean, an illegal mint, debtors' jail, highwayman's lodgings – run-of-the-mill stuff, you know. Ah, yes, well there was a bagnio once."

"What's that?" asked Eve. "Oh! I can guess, don't tell me!"

"Well, there was a massage parlour before us, though."

She groaned.

Later they took the slow lanes home and, in the way one does after a good lunch, detoured far off their route. They found themselves trailing north east of Norwich towards the Broads. This lost country of wetlands was a world of disregarded woods, swamps and rotting trees. Sometimes a track petered out at a creek and they saw open water stretching away for a few hundred yards. Once they passed a flint church at a quay near a couple of mooring posts. Between the trees they saw a row of cottages sinking into the ground. And they passed miles of reeds where a few herons flapped their way through the grainy air to the empty waterlands beyond and out of sight. Frost bleached the reeds that the sun had not reached.

Passing the ragged village of Stalham on the edge of one of Norfolk's sailing broads they saw the sign: 'AUCTION THIS WAY'. Baling twine tied it to a telephone pole. In a field nearby a rat-faced city slicker was gabbling out sales slush to a few listless punters. Lines of rusting hardware were spread out on the grass like a cat's vomit. And there Lawrence saw the last remaining Flymo lawnmower, the little green one with a dent on its metal cover. He had seen it not once but several times – at each auction, in fact. They didn't really need another lawnmower anyway, as Eve had often pointed out. But he couldn't pass it by. He had become obsessed by them all, by the way they had appeared every time, like a family of zombies haunting him, their motors fused, their blades broken and their petrol tanks choked with rust. They had been desperate for Lawrence to buy them and put them out of their misery, not with a stake through their hearts, perhaps, but at least by driving a steamroller over them so that they could die in peace and no longer face weekly rejection at North Norfolk's lawn-mower slave markets. And now there was only this one left, the one that everybody had ignored and it was his responsibility because he'd seen it so often, the runt of the litter, the weakling, lame and silent, dented, dirty and neglected.

He shook himself out of his absurd reverie, the latest of the fantasies with which North Norfolk seemed to possess him, stuck his finger up before his wife noticed and got it for £15. So he had saved £30 by not buying when he first saw it. It might even work.

"Well, you don't know that," said his wife scornfully.

"OK, But if it doesn't, I'll knock out the bump, paint it a different colour and put it back into the Aylsham auction next Monday."

\*     \*     \*

It was nearly mid-day a few days later when the telephone rang. Eve and Lawrence were still in bed. True, they had woken up two or three hours before and got themselves a cup of tea but one look outside had made them plunge back into bed at once. North Norfolk in November was living up to its reputation – wet and windy – grey too. And they didn't need to get up and go out into the garden to prove that it was also cold. Somehow they felt they could take that for granted, even though there had been brilliant pale blue skies the day before and they had walked all the way to the beach and back – with their dog, too. He could not only manage the distance already but had probably covered twice the distance what with all his running around.

"Lawrence? Zeus here," said the voice on the line. "It's so miserable in the forge now, I mean it's so wet outside and cold and bloody miserable and there's no one in here buying anything, so I thought Leda and I'd shut up shop and bring something to eat over to you two and we'd have lunch together. What d'you think?"

Lawrence couldn't have thought of anything better. He put his hand over the phone and explained to Eve. And nor could she.

"Of course, my dear fellow! And for you we'll actually get out of bed," he told Zeus. "What? Well, we didn't see much point in getting up, really. One look out of the window was quite enough ... half an hour? Good – don't bother to bring wine, we've got a couple of bottles. What? Oh, well, I won't refuse. Ours? Well, of course they're red ... what else in this weather?"

Eve jumped out of bed.

"I've got to make some soup at least. We can't have them bringing all the food. I'll do some onion soup."

And that the prophecy would be fulfilled they soon heard a crunching down the gravel of their drive and in walked Zeus and Leda – without knocking of course. By now no one seemed to bother with ringing the bell. Zeus was wearing his fleece and carrying paté, a bag of olives, cooked sausages, a pork pie and some ham. Leda was in an old overcoat and wearing oven gloves and holding a large dish. She put it down on the hall table and they threw their coats and scarves onto a settle.

"Meals on wheels!" laughed Leda. "Well, four legs anyway. I've got baked vegetables in here, Eve darling. All hot. I hope you like garlic? I thought so – just as well, really, considering. Plenty of olive oil, too. We've got peppers, carrots, parsnips, spuds – what else, Z?" she called to Zeus in the kitchen where he had gone to help Lawrence taste some wine and undo a button or two on his shirt. "What else did we put in the oven for the roast veg?"

"Can't remember, darling. Something edible, I'm sure." He ran his hands through his hair. "Oh yes! I threw in a few onions and grated some Stilton over the spuds. But we'd better put it all in the Aga for a few minutes just to get the cheese a bit crisper before we sit down. And I suppose it wouldn't do any harm to give the sausages a blast under the grill, too. It'll keep 'em honest!" Zeus laughed. "John Hurlingham made them for me. God knows what he put in them but there's hardly any bread. I think they're venison. Got any mustard, Lawrence? Have a drink, darling." And he handed a full glass of wine to Leda.

And then he had noticed that Eve's eyes were red.

"Are you OK, Eve?" he asked her. He became embarrassed. "Have we come at a wrong time? Is anything the matter?" He put his arm round her.

"No, silly," she said, laughing – and leaned up to kiss him. "It's just the onions. I always cry when I do them. Thanks, though, Z darling!"

Before they arrived Lawrence had lifted a few papers, two books and the cat off the kitchen table and laid it with knives and forks and spoons and soup plates and glasses, put out some English and Provencal mustard, ratcheted the Aga's temperature up by a few degrees and set near it a couple of opened bottles of Coonawarra red – the least he could do, he thought, since their friends had brought the food. And after their dog had enthusiastically welcomed Zeus and Leda – a jumping display of berserk joy as usual – and had been persuaded to calm down and hang around under the table waiting for something to fall from it, they all sat down together. Eve had toasted a few slices of wholemeal bread for the paté.

"It's just a country paté I made last night," said Zeus. "Nothing special. A rillette, I suppose."

"Just the thing for weather like today. Not a time for foie gras."

"Anyway, the ham is Bayonne, and here's the vegetables and sausages and pie and ... and ... and – " he undid another shirt button, scratched his chest and wrinkled his forehead ... "oh yes, we've got some chocolate cake that Leda made for pudding."

And so they sat and began with the onion soup and talked and drank and drank and talked, huddling together in front of the radiant Aga, now and then tearing bits of bread off the loaf rather than wait for it to be toasted. And, as usual, during the soup, the paté, the sausages and the chocolate cake, the main dish was gossip.

Was Justine now really with Jan on the Albatross? "More soup?"

What did Prospero really do? "Or paté instead?"

Was Ronald really going for a dry-out? "Anyone for sausages yet?"

Was Brian the painter really having a show in London? "Will you help me drink it if I open another bottle?"

And was Millicent really standing for the European Parliament? "Chocolate cake, anyone?"

Nearly three hours and another two bottles later Zeus suddenly slapped his forehead.

"Ahhh ... I said I'd be back at the forge at three o'clock. Someone's coming round to sell me some spices. Can I use your phone? I've got to rush."

Groans all round – and lunch broke up. As Lawrence said later, "it was either that or opening another bottle."

Zeus and Leda hunched themselves into their wet weather coats.

"It was really lovely you had the idea," Eve told them. "I'll bring the oven dish round tomorrow."

\*     \*     \*

There always had been something about North Norfolk that made it different from anywhere else. As soon as Lawrence and Eve had arrived they had sensed some sort of secret quality. They could nearly feel it, for it had a mesmeric impact on them. It almost made them catch their breath. And that was before Lawrence had even begun to work out exactly what it was. But that time of working it out ... that apprenticeship ... that itself was part of the secret too.

And when it came to Lawrence, it came with a rush like the tiny birds that swooped down after the midges at twilight over the gable at Gibraltar House.

Meanwhile he had discovered over the year that it had nearly as many parts to it as there were birds in that flock – like a patchwork quilt. There was the rural life, the climate, the seasons, the food, the people, their natural independence and the edge! They combined to make everything even richer.

Take the seasons – everyone dresses to suit them. They eat what the seasons give them and pay court to their moods like suitors. But despite this attention the seasons still buffet everyone around. They freeze them, drench them and sunburn them with no consideration at all. And, as one might expect, this sort of treatment makes everyone keener than ever. It sharpens the deep satisfaction that comes only with living close to the land. So everyone is eager for more. More snow on the fields and in their hair. More winter outside and rain on their faces. By early March winter will have almost exhausted them. They are about to give up when spring dances in, raises her skirt a fraction and teases everyone into new hope. But the hemline goes down and up a few times before summer comes. Now there's more sun in the sky and in their eyes. So, aroused by this show and sure of the promise of new life, everyone submits again to the stimulus of the seasons. They accept them and this is part of the secret too.

And then where else than Norfolk does England offer this mix of seafood and game? In the midlands or even the north? Plenty of game there but not so much fish as off Norfolk. And was there as much game in the south west – or fish, for that matter? Eve and Lawrence were reasonably convinced now that only Norfolk's larder offered so much game and seafood – and all fresh, too, that great secret!

As for industry – there's nothing heavy in North Norfolk. Just a few one-man businesses making things like picture frames, pig troughs or garden sheds. But tourism? In North Norfolk they haven't killed the thing they love – no theme parks, monuments or sports centres. Nothing spectacular. People come here to live for a time the way every-one here lives all of the time. And for that they travel hundreds of miles. There's enough tourism to generate an income but not enough to ruin the place – essential basis for the secret!

But they had realised North Norfolk seemed cocooned in a time warp. And, fancifully, they had felt it preserved in 1935. Even now the sweet barrier of distance keeps the force of North Norfolk's magnet at arm's length from the rest of England. There's no through traffic at the terminus of Norwich Station – no one is on the way to anywhere else. Of those who visit, few leave without returning. Some never leave at all – as if they were in a Black Hole where the force of attraction is greater than the impulse to leave. It seems as if everyone in this valley of the two mills lives in almost medieval style, hardly moving far from home. They live with all their needs around them – including friends. And that's part of the secret. Those who live here are those who have discovered it. They were not born here, they didn't have it thrust upon them, but they have all achieved it. The entry fee? You have to want it enough! And the price? Ambition!

So: their lives now? They're rich, free of stress, everyone working for themselves, full of friendly intrigue and wit. Once, someone in London asked Lawrence: "why shouldn't friends all live in the same place?" Impossible, he had thought at the time. But here it's true and it's part of the secret – that those who come to live in North Norfolk came because they wanted to. And so the shared motive links them all together.

Any place can be bearable if you live among friends. It's the most important thing of all. But North Norfolk's magnet and its isolation lures odd people – independent ones, too. They employ their talents along this coast. They are the mavericks who threw up their careers to pursue something more arcane. They laugh at the fools' gold of vaulting ambition. Architects graduated to artists, former naval person now crab fisherman, banker become birdman, entrepreneurs to writers, soldiers now a different sort of persuader, businessmen to philosophers ... and the commune turned potters. They have all fought their battles around the world and returned wiser, stretched and knowing their abilities. Those who live in North Norfolk are themselves the keys to the coastal paradise. But they are those keys only because they know they are. And this is also the starting point to achieve the intensity of awareness of which that Anatolian mystic Gurdjieff had spoken and which Lawrence had from time to time experienced – through feeling the richness of their life up here.

He had discussed this with Prospero late one night in early December when again they were sitting by his great fire. The flames were crackling and the rain lashed the windows behind the burgundy curtains. Prospero explained.

"There was a time, when I lived in the south, I interpreted a dream I once had."

He said that the dream was about an idea to create a harmonious society – something every philosopher contemplates. Yes, he smiled patiently, perhaps a contradiction in terms. But he told Lawrence that his dream had given him the idea to form the commune. This led later to the larger and more ambitious group that became the Pottery. It was more practical too. After all, it earned money. He explained that this led him to expand the idea. He had of course recognised that British society had deteriorated over the last thirty or forty years. And that had led him to come home and apply the idea in an area where the old English qualities still had a chance to flourish. That area had to be in a part of the country with a particular beauty – not just prettiness. And it had to involve the sea, expressing danger, the edge between life and the wild – and something more. It had to have an atmosphere that attracted a certain type of people. And the area he had found with that beauty – the sea, the climate, the food, the people, and that other secret mystery – was the area from the North Norfolk coast inland to the road between Cromer and Fakenham, and as far west as Wells. He smiled.

"And it is centred in our village here. And binding us together in this work, 'no kind of traffic would I then admit.' "

He pointed out that the people who had come to live here were all dedicated to 'closeness, neglecting worldly ends'.

" 'Rough magic' fills this bell jar where we live. My idea's now no more a wishful dream."

Philosophers have long known the merits of what they called 'the mean', he added. They were the merits of the middle state between obscurity and excessive power. Moral systems developed on such moderation made men more likely to be happy – and to make others happy. So those who live in North Norfolk could say with the great Voltaire:

*"What's to be done about it all? Work your land, and your vines, walk under the trees you've planted, be well housed, eat very well, read good books, live with decent people from one day to the next, think neither about death nor about the malice of the living. Fools work for kings; wise men take pleasure in sweet retirement."*

"But that's why we came up here!" smiled Eve. "We just wanted to cultivate our garden ... to try and live with decent people, as he says, in a community."

"Well, that is my aim – and with the help of all who live up here with England's history as their mothers' milk."

Lawrence and Eve fell silent and thought to themselves of the history around them in North Norfolk. It was a lonely but dedicated history, like the once self-sufficient monastic community of bleak Binham Priory, wind-thrashed across the fields for nine hundred years;

religious echoes like Walsingham's Catholic settlement of abbey, churches and chapel inspired by a slippery vision; tumble-down history like half-ruined Baconsthorpe Castle, once a vilified lawyer's fortified home; intimate history like Mannington Hall, a medieval family's moated jewel; elegant history like thrice-gabled Blickling Hall; and well-lined political history like Walpole's swag of grand residences.

But the most important history of all came centuries after all those other histories. It was a time when no one kept company with England – when she fought alone. And when to give in would have meant death or slavery. The evidence of that fighting is still here. Not much, though – and none of it has beauty. In fact it looks the least impressive of any of those centuries-old ruins. But it helps explain why everyone in North Norfolk is still here – why everyone in England is still here, for that matter. Among them are a few odd buildings, like that big dome at Langham, a much smaller steel eggshell on the coast path near Blakeney and the concrete circle on the marshes between Stiffkey and Wells.

And every few miles anybody might come across a small six-sided brick building – not so wide as a barn door, nor so high as a man – but ready to serve. There'll be a doorway in one wall and horizontal slits in each of the others. You'll find them on the high ground, at crossroads or overlooking the sea. Nowadays they are ignored, their insides strewn with garbage, their bricks crumbling and their openings choked by undergrowth. None of them had had to prove their worth but those

inside them had been ready to do their best, for they were ready, willing and desperate. And during that time any one of them was more important than the Tower of London.

But there are other relics too and those were the ones that had a job to do and did it – day after day and year after year. All you can see of them now are mostly bits of concrete roadways. Nowadays, of course, they are cracked and weedy. And anyway after a few yards they usually disappear under heaps of sugar beet or peter out into a ploughed field. Sometimes bits of these roadways run in a curve. Added together, a strip under a hedge, another strip each side of a new house, and you might be able to see how, for some almost forgotten reason, they would have formed an uneven perimeter enclosing flat land a mile or so across. You might even see small bits of other concrete roadways that would have crossed this perimeter and all heading north east, for some reason. And near the concrete areas there are still one or two nondescript little buildings, prefabs really. They are only two storeys high anyway, if that, and most of them have some wire posts sticking out of their roofs. They are derelict now, of course – their windows broken, their wire posts bent, rubbish blown into corners and their doors swinging in the wind. Then you might find one or two high buildings – all usually empty shells, a hundred foot long and with wide roller doors. Nearby there might be some corrugated iron huts. Nowadays they are all rusted and often full of burst sandbags and old farm machinery, all decayed and ignored. But they did their job when they had to. They helped to keep England independent. And if you had to find one word for North Norfolk, it's independent.

And around all this is the landscape. Everyone here lives in an empty landscape that isn't pretty but is almost unbearably beautiful. It sprawls head down, flattened, naked and drowned at the bottom of the rimless bowl of sky. There is nothing claustrophobic, no dramatic mountains, no mysterious forests – and no conspicuously pretty land-scapes or unstable glamour. Every landscape in North Norfolk shows the same understated yet confident stability of the English character. And there are no dividing and divisive arterial barriers. That's part of this secret, too. You can lie on the flat Scolt Head sands to the west, empty for miles they are, and cry out a groaning shriek of pleasure that nobody could hear – but a shriek that can carry on all day. Wide, open, empty ... that's getting close to the secret.

Everyone in North Norfolk lives on the wild flat edge of the coast, flat like the edge of the world. And beyond it lies the sea.

And the sea, this tells the secret. It's freedom, of course, that other ingredient! For the sea offers freedom undiluted – however wild and dangerous it can be – and has symbolised it throughout history. No one is compelled to go on the sea. It's enough just to know that it is there. And that is part of the freedom, too. We have the choice. And it enhances everyone's feelings even just to think of it. You can stand by Gibraltar House and the windmill, gaze on the little river that has flowed down from the mill at the head of the valley to this mill at its foot, watch as the outgoing tide pushes it past the reeds and round the corner and widening all the time and moving on towards the sea and you think to yourself: "I could take a boat on this water to Cape Horn or to Australia without passing any frontiers, without anyone trying to stop me."

So the flat, barrier-free landscape under the open skies, the isola-tion, the self-reliance and independence, the food and the rich and natural life, the lack of stress, the seasons, the community of friends on the edge of the world who all know their fortune – all these are linked together by the secret of freedom carried by the sea.

That spirit of freedom is England's real gift to the world. And the sea was not just a symbol of freedom. It was the wall that many times protected England. It made England a crucible, allowing its society to develop peacefully and transform tyranny into freedom under the democratic law, so easily destroyed by human nature. Nowadays the sea would never ward off Europe's infection. The suspect amalgam of European unity would see to that. But tolerance and the right to freedom have long now been the mainstay of the English way of life.

Prospero had calculated well when he chose North Norfolk to

found his renaissance. Its sense of freedom lies quiet but strong – a sense everyone here feels every day. And it carries the kernel of how England once was – and can be again.

And until then that landfall's spirit takes shape with that old schooner, the Albatross. She carries the secret of North Norfolk whenever she rigs her yards for sea, hoists her sails, catches 'the gentle breath of wind', casts her ropes off at Wells harbour to crab her bows away from the quay and nose along the channel to face 'the calm seas or the auspicious gale', but either way to 'go down to the sea again, to the lonely seas and the sky ... to the call that must not be denied.'

And Lawrence watches her and he thinks: "... is it to the ends of the earth that she's sailing?"

Lawrence first began to suspect the secret soon after Justine rang and said that the Albatross was homeward bound from Rotterdam with a full cargo. Jan had rung her from the ship by mobile phone. He was going to bring the ship close inshore to the village for everyone to watch her sail past. Would he and Eve like to join her, asked Justine? Of course! Then she asked to speak to Eve.

"Yes, hello? Justine? Hi!" said Eve. "What? Oh! You've made your choice?" she cried – and glanced sideways at Lawrence. "Well, who...?" She listened as Justine explained how Prospero had interpreted her dream.

"He said he'd told you about it but he wouldn't tell me what it meant for ages, but anyway he said that I felt safe on the sailing ship but longed to feel deep emotions – and that's what those big waves meant. You know? And jumping into the sea meant I wanted to feel these emotions but when I was experiencing them, you know, in the sea, I was afraid that Jan – well, he was the ship apparently – was drifting away, well, he could handle the emotions, the ship – Jan I mean, could, it was sailing on them, using them as he wants, the ship's master – the master of the emotions, something like that, experiencing them but using them for everyone's benefit, for the future, what our community needs, Prospero said, well anyway Karl was on land and far away getting further and anyway he had no contact with emotions, he's never taken any risks anyway, Prospero got that right all right and he pointed out that I saw Karl only when I was afraid or in trouble – well, all right, maybe that's quite often – and Karl always reacts personally, well he's good with his hands, I mean, well, no, you know what I mean, but otherwise a bit negative, it's never his fault, you know, and that's not always good in a village like ours... well, so swimming about like that meant apparently that I can't make up my mind – well he knew that all right – so I was in trouble, well that's right too. Anyway in the end he said that it's obvious that Jan was the right choice for me, you know, because apparently my feelings are for him, the feelings, the emotions, that's the water, they are with him, also that I didn't see him in the dream meant that he wasn't going to boss me around, well he didn't put it like that, something about not being authoritarian, can't remember, but anyway he doesn't need to be around to be with me. And I like that. I really do."

She ended, out of breath.

"Well! How wonderful!" said Eve.

She put the telephone down, looked at her husband and smiled happily.

"Well, who's the lucky man?" he asked her.

"Ah!" she told him, still smiling. "You'll find out soon."

They had known that the Albatross had recently left Wells to pick up another cargo in Rotterdam. At the pub a fortnight before Justine had told them that her daughter and a friend had gone along for the ride. Apparently Zeus had taken his two boys to see her cast off. He had told Lawrence how the three of them had run hand in hand down the channel, keeping up with the ship and waving wildly to the passengers as they stood at the bows waving back and laughing as the schooner stood towards the open sea on the tide with all sails set and her three jibs on that long upward-stretched bowsprit billowing high as they caught the wind.

"What an adventure!" Zeus had cried to his boys, eyes shining and shirt flapping.

And now they were nearly home. So everyone in the village went to the beach and saw her pounding past them a hundred yards offshore at a good seven of eight knots under a full fore-and-aft rig of those jibs, main and mizzen and all sails close-hauled into the wind that pitched her bows into 'the merciful sea' and sent a spray back over decks and hatches clapped tight over a hundred tons of cargo. On shore every-one waved – and laughed with relief too with the young ones now safely home, seeing them holding on to the mizzen-mast by the wheel and waving to everyone with their free hands. Lawrence thought how it had been for them. How they had left busy Rotterdam, noisy and full of ships everywhere, and sailed out of sight of land for a long night and a long day or two with nothing to see but grey waves and a few seagulls, and then to see land but only its low lines, seeing it come closer, then

Jan sailing really close so that they could see hills behind the shore, and sailing closer and closer so that the dots on the beach grew bigger and then slowly recognising everyone from the village and they were waving and waving. What an adventure!

And so it had been then, as she swept past, that Lawrence had finally sensed the secret of their lives in their community in North Norfolk, that sense of freedom! Yes, it had come to him with a rush, the way those tiny birds had swooped across their gable. And by then he knew that the Albatross symbolised not only their sense of freedom but the freedom that was represented by England itself.

And suddenly he became aware of Prospero near them, although he had not heard him arrive. He was standing there, his coat loose over his shoulders as usual, and gazing intently at the ship.

"The gentle breath of mine your sails must fill," he was saying to himself, "Or else my project fails. Art to enchant, spirits to enforce..."

He smiled benevolently at them, turned and disappeared inland.

And as Justine stood on the beach, Lawrence knew that she, the free spirit, was the link between that ship and the land. Prospero had liberated her from the group at the Pottery, recognising her need to leave and be independent – for she was a loner. Tall and slim, with a straight back and long flying hair, deep-set eyes, high cheekbones and a Roman nose, she had the profile of a tea-clipper's figurehead poised above the creaming waves. The freedom in her spirit matched that of the sea and of the Albatross.

And if there was to be someone for her it must be that other loner Jan, the tall and quiet skipper of North Norfolk's royal good and gallant schooner sailing towards her at that very moment.

Lawrence and Eve never realised how long it could take to post a letter in their village until the end of that first year. For by December they knew so many people here that they couldn't walk down the street without having to run the gauntlet of various friends on the way. A three-hundred-yard journey to the post office often took them half an hour. And now that they were pulled along by their dog Wagga he often made it worse because of an irresistible need to examine every puddle or dubious stain, or to leap up and lick the face of any friend that might appear en route.

Naturally the first hazard was Ronald at the pub, although they often managed to pass him without going in – well, before mid-day, anyway. But if it was near lunchtime they often stopped for a pint and a sandwich, maybe some of Tom's fresh crab, maybe egg mayonnaise, maybe fresh chicken and coleslaw ... not something you can get in every pub in England.

Then they often got caught in the Pottery. Maybe they bought something. Maybe they just wandered around. In any case they gossiped with the Rhine Maiden and the Guardian, that incomparable couple fitting together like a jigsaw; she with her serene smile (with whom Eve discusses some gossip about Millicent's last parish council meeting), and the Guardian always with a lugubrious twinkle (with whom Lawrence talked politics). Or the Village Marxist too, full of caustic comment about the government – about any government, in fact. Perhaps they knocked on Justine's door across the road to ask her when Jan and the Albatross would be back from Rotterdam. Then – what about an impulse buy at the Smoke House? Well, who could resist rows of newly smoked kippers, let alone the potted shrimps? And then there was the Bookshop. Lawrence could never pass a second-hand bookshop, anyway, and they could always rely on Jekyll 'n' Hyde for some barbed comment about his customers.

But the difficult one to walk past was the Deli. In fact they didn't – they couldn't. Lawrence wouldn't have been surprised if scientific evidence showed that it radiated irresistible gravitational forces dragging people into it. It was a siren's trap, a Circe, a Scylla and Charybdis. So they always gave up and went in, even if only to kiss Leda, talk about women with Zeus, share smiles with the attractive girls he always has serving behind the cheese counter and wander about in the wine department. Sometimes they meet their ample friend Victor at the bellows.

"The bar is open!" they all agree as they try some local North Elmham white or some new Chardonnay from one of Australia's boutique wineries.

"It's only to give me an appetite for lunch," protests Victor to Lawrence but still holds his glass out to Zeus who appears with a twinkle and a newly opened bottle.

"Anyway," Victor always adds. "I'm only here because Pat's in the queue. She's buying some vegetables. And it's cheaper than the pub."

This time Zeus fills Victor's glass, thinks for a moment, scratches his chest, tells him to hang on a moment and reaches into the cheese counter. He lifts up a huge round of Roquefort and hands it to Victor. He sees Lawrence watching.

"Business has been rather good this year. Victor gave me some brilliant investment advice last week," he explains.

"Barter is an ideal system for a small community," points out Victor. Without looking round he passes the cheese behind him to his wife, who is already grappling with four bags of groceries. "The important thing you need to make it work is that anything anybody wants can be provided by someone here. And that's likely if everyone has some exchange. So no-one has to go outside for what they want and have to use money. Good for the community, too. And in the village we do have everything we need, of course."

He looked back to his wife.

"Did you get some more champagne, darling?"

"Yes I did, Victor," she replied somewhat abruptly, while still trying to get a grip on the round of Roquefort as well as all the bags she was carrying.

He turned back to Lawrence.

"See what I mean, young man? You'll have some exchange one day, too."

"But you're only getting two glasses tonight," she says. "Look what happened last night."

"Oh yes. That was rather annoying," he explained to Lawrence. "We ran out of champagne and I had to drink some odd Spanish bubbles instead." He grimaced. "Gave me indigestion."

Zeus grins at them and refills Lawrence's glass as a sort of consolation prize for having no exchange. It's not surprising that by the time they cross the coast road to reach the post office they miss the post.

*     *     *

It was a chill Saturday towards mid-December when Eve put down the telephone and turned to Lawrence with a broad smile.

"The Rhine Maiden and her Guardian are getting married!" she smiled. "Isn't that nice! They're having a wedding feast tomorrow. We're invited."

Actually Lawrence had thought they were married anyway. Somehow it didn't seem to matter up in North Norfolk. It was an area that seemed outside society – as well as being almost physically apart from the rest of the country. But even though they'd been together for years it was clear that the Rhine Maiden and the Guardian thought differently.

The wedding feast was in the village hall at Wiveton. They walked there over the valley river's hump-backed bridge. It was the bridge they had crossed with the bridal couple when returning from dinner with Pippa, so many months ago. They had brought their dog – he seemed keen to meet the neighbours. In fact, whatever Lawrence and Eve did, he joined in full of enthusiasm. He reflected any emotion they felt. They laughed? He jumped up, almost uncontrollable. They were quiet? He lay in a corner, head down, ears flopped, watching them. If they praised him he wagged his tail swiftly. If they were angry he would slink forlorn to his basket and look up at them in total misery, showing the whites of his eyes – instant guilt. And, of course, they too felt guilty at once. They had made him unhappy. But they knew he meant well.

As they walked he trotted confidently ahead and his tail waved happily from side to side. They almost felt that he'd only been waiting for them to come along, so full was his love and trust for them.

In the village hall they found most of the people they had met at the Guardian's birthday party in the spring. It seemed so long ago, before they were part of it all. Lawrence waved to Millicent, that authoritative and impassive figure – in charge of food as usual, this time behind the long trestle table, the one that she also used for cricket teas in the summer. But now it held none of the dainty cucumber sandwiches, orange juice or buns essential to the English cricket tea. And certainly not hot sweet tea. Today the wedding guests were offered serious food. There was a pyramid of lamb curry. There was a mountain of glistening saffron rice. There were some of Zeus' dark and juicy game pies with crisp pastry. There were layers of smoked salmon from Moses at the Smoke House. There were rounds of cheese and plenty of bottles of wine and beer – also from Zeus. There was a business-like leg of pork from one of Hector's pigs, which had presumably not been consulted (its skin now transformed into criss-crossed golden crackling – he hadn't forgotten the marmalade). And everything was served on dishes from the Pottery.

Wagga skulked under the table, eyes watching, alert for something to fall. Lawrence caught Millicent's eye.

"Those aircraft seem to have stopped flying over us," she called out to him.

"Must have been those vol-a-vents you served to that nice flight sergeant," he told her.

"Oh, that's very kind! I did think they were rather good, though I shouldn't say so."

"They were delicious. Effective too, I should say!" he added. They both smiled.

"You're too kind," she told him.

Bride and groom were at the door. Now legally as well as socially English, the bride was embarrassed but pleased and, yes, radiant and slightly dewy-eyed in the tradition – even though they had been living together for years. She wore a pink satin dress and her pearly hair was held back above her ears by a pink ribbon. Eve and Lawrence kissed her and shook hands man-to-man with the Guardian. Today he had trimmed his beard and side-whiskers, abandoned his patched jacket and sported a new Irish thorn-proof tweed suit. He pulled out his note-book, quickly noted something and looked up at them.

"Yes, here's a goodly sight!" he said. "Our revels now have just begun. Got that?" He winked at Lawrence and waved his arm around the room, now packed with guests. Then he raised an eyebrow and scratched his head. He brought out his notebook again.

"Excuse me a moment," he said apologetically. "That reminds me of something again. I must have a word with J 'n' H. He's meant to be making a speech."

Her sleek black hair swaying, Pippa beckoned to them to sit with her at one of the little tables spread around the room. This time Lawrence and Eve knew all the people she spoke to. They hugged Brian and Marilyn, strolling together like an old married couple, who invited them to a house-warming party the following week in Sheringham, where he had just found a new studio. He told them it had been a kindergarten hall and didn't yet have a bathroom so every morning before he started painting he went to a municipal pool nearby.

"It's a pound a day. At that rate it would take me at least thirty years to pay for a bathroom," he grinned. "But this way I've got one at once – plus the exercise!"

"One day your studio will be on the tourist route." Eve told him. "The English Tourist Board in Tokyo will have it on their list of artistic things to see."

Apparently he was hiring a heavy metal band for his party. "My God!" said Lawrence. "We'll need ear plugs! But we'll be there."

Freddy Blake was here – in a wheel chair now. They had heard he was very poorly nowadays and had had a stroke, too. But he seemed very cheerful. On his lap was a tray with a plate of mutton and a bottle of stout – and he had a big grin for everyone.

"A change from cricket, eh, Lawrence?" he called as he caught sight of them. "But the food'll still be OK. Millicent's in charge!"

They didn't know it then, no one did of course, but this was his last public appearance. As always, though, he was cheerful. Soon Zeus and Leda arrived arm in arm. His two sons were carrying his drums and helped him set them up in a corner. He undid a couple of buttons and liberated some hair. He folded his sleeves up and soon his sticks rattled out the first notes of a jazz session. Marilyn came over at once to dance a step or two and after that it wasn't long before everyone merged together into a walking, talking country scene. Glasses in hand, groups of couples moved around calling to each other, dancing erratically, changing partners, drinking and laughing together with the back-ground of Zeus' drumming. His two boys began a mild fight over a hamburger. Wagga climbed over them both, trying to grab it or at least to lick their faces.

Eve and Lawrence pushed their chairs back and moved around, too. In a corner the Village Marxist was explaining something to the young girl with huge eyes and a mass of curls they had seen with Prospero at the Guardian's birthday party. Judging by the attention she was paying him she had clearly decided to become a Marxist herself. Lawrence heard him making some reference to 'dialectic materialism.' She nodded sagely – clearly she thought of little else. The subject was all so complicated that he had to reach out and stroke her cheek during his explanation.

"The VM's obviously a hands-on teacher," whispered Eve as they passed him. "But at least he seems to have got over Justine pretty quickly."

Prospero arrived a few moments later, coat over his shoulders as usual. He left his hunch-backed assistant sitting by the door, rubbing his nose and holding on to the golden retriever which, after looking round to seek a nod of permission from Prospero, had developed an urgent need to inspect the rear end of Wagga. He was not at all averse to such an interest but was distracted by the hamburger belonging to Zeus' boys. His nose kept on twitching back and forth between the hamburger and the retriever. The sequence ended only when one of the boys ate the hamburger. This led seamlessly to a final pas de deux as the two dogs pirouetted around each other's rears.

Prospero shook hands with the happy couple and the Guardian smiled generously and patted him on the back. That wouldn't have happened months ago. Marriage was clearly a wonderful thing. The Rhine Maiden and Prospero held each other's eyes for a long moment. Hector had appeared in his army greatcoat. It seemed to have been in the wars again for a tattered hem trailed unnoticed behind him. He was waving half a pork chop at Wagga in an effort to distract him from the retriever. It worked at once. He dangled a jam-jar of pond water in his other hand. It contained two newts and he tried to inter-est the boys in it. Moses was standing silently in a corner. His arms were folded and his eyes gleamed benevolently. Hands entwined, Justine and Jan sat engrossed with each other in another corner – she with her Roman nose and her hair tumbling down her straight back and he with his bushy beard and penetrating eyes. Justine had a faint and secret smile, almost as if smiling to herself, in the knowledge that she'd "picked up the pilot and made landfall" – and the flying Dutchman was anchored at last. For one brief moment she and the Village Marxist exchanged a glance across the crowded room. Both smiled quickly but fondly. And that was that.

Soon the Log Lady appeared with her own small sons. They imme-diately made a dart for Hector's jam-jar of newts, which made Zeus's boys forget their quarrel and try to push them away. She went over to Eve and gave her a hug.

"Oh, dear!" she said to Eve, embarrassed. "They're not usually like this."

"Never mind, Karina," laughed Eve. "Boys will be boys. Mine were!"

They had become friends ever since they had met at the time of the flood, when Lawrence had missed her – being out at the pub.

"Men, too, sometimes," said the Log Lady, grinning at Lawrence.

"You can take him into the Wild Wood any time you like," Eve told her. "Make sure you get a good price for him, as well as for the logs. And he'll need to be dried out, if not cured."

Jekyll 'n' Hyde had been approached by the Guardian and although at that first party he had shown a low opinion of Norfolk's reading habits he now treated everyone to a professional speech extolling marriage.

"I've found a quotation from somewhere very suitable – but I'm not telling you where – you'll have to guess!" He cleared his throat.

"Quiet, you lot! Now for some donation freely to estate on these blessed lovers," he announced and continued:

*"Honour riches, marriage blessing,*
*Juno sings her blessings on you.*
*Long continuous and increasing*
*Hourly joys be still upon you!"*

After which he somewhat spoiled his speech with St Paul's conclusion: " 'Tis better to marry than burn." It seemed that everyone agreed. And the Rhine Maiden came forward with a few words.

"Well, living with someone before you get married might be jumping the gun, but it's safer than taking pot luck. I mean it's not a pig in a poke. Well, life's a lottery and you only live once so you've got to grasp the nettle and take the bull by the horns. Anyway, better the devil you know ..." She stopped and blushed.

"Well, that was definitely not a true word spoken in jest."

She gave her new husband a kiss. He managed to disentangle himself for a moment and waved to everyone, saying dryly:

"Well, at least she's not marrying me with a bun in the oven."

Everyone laughed to raise the roof and Zeus crashed out a crescendo on his drums. Prospero leaned over him.

"Twanging instruments are no match for drums," he smiled.

"Well, you should know," grinned Zeus, undoing another button.

Eve had buttonholed the Guardian.

"We saw a beautiful table lamp in the Pottery window yesterday," she was telling him. "We want it but we're going to have to save up for it. Could you keep it for us until we can afford it?"

The Guardian smiled.

"Well, it's my wedding day. I might offer easy payment terms," he smiled – and made a dramatic gesture. Then he paused in mid-flight.

"I've got a better idea, though. You know we're having the local elections soon? Well, I'm standing and I'm responsible for our political manifesto, but because I'm standing I don't have enough time for it. Do you think you could string some slogans together for me? We could do a deal with the lamp."

Lawrence looked at Eve and they both smiled. They could offer something! It had taken a bit of time but at last they were now in the system.

"By the way," asked the Guardian. "What's your persuasion?"

They both laughed.

"Don't bother us with the details," Lawrence told him. "Left or Right, we'll do it."

The Guardian smiled, stood aside to make a note in his booklet and nodded to Pippa, who pulled out a sheet of paper.

"And now, something I have written for the occasion." She looked up, her eyes gleaming – and giggled. "Well, you could consider me the valley poet, if you wanted." She gave a big sniff and began: "I'll only read a bit of it. But it's just right for a wedding –

> *"My man was strong.*
> *He made me feel like a marshmallow*
> *Sugary and sweet and good to bite into.*
>
> *My man was fiery.*
> *He made me feel like a marshmallow*
> *Crisply cooked on his toasting prong."*

She stopped reading, waved the paper at everybody, wobbled slightly and giggled.

"Well, there's lots more. I'll read the rest at the next wedding so long as I catch the bouquet at this one!"

Everyone laughed and clapped. Then the door burst open. A late comer had arrived – Mark the one-time gardener, barman and odd-job-lad and now a strong and virile soldier wearing a trim uniform, shining black boots, cap under his arm, hair sheared for action and the biggest of grins.

"Back home from Aldershot. I've got a 48-hour pass," he grinned to everyone. "Not much, but I couldn't miss this party. I'm off to Belfast tomorrow on active duty!"

He turned to the Rhine Maiden.

"Congratulations!" he cried. And gave her a big kiss.

"None of that, young man," interrupted The Guardian. "That's a married woman. I know you army types. Rape and pillage all over Europe. I'll have you confined to barracks."

As Lawrence and his wife left the party Zeus and Leda came up to them, smiling broadly and obviously bursting with a secret.

"We don't want to take attention from their day," he said. "But we're getting married, too. I've just proposed and Leda's accepted!"

Eve bust into tears and she and Lawrence hugged them both. Then Lawrence thought for a moment. He had remembered being told that a few years back someone had opened an arts centre in Wells. It had soon collapsed – lack of interest. Now he thought he knew why. In North Norfolk people somehow didn't need "art" added to their lives – or at least organised art. They lived the most important function of art, the one connected with people. The rest? That was just decoration.

When they reached home they found three messages on their answering machine. The first was that, as had been agreed a day or two before, Victor and Pat would pick Eve up in a couple of hours for midnight mass. The second was that the buyer for their house had exchanged contracts with their solicitor and paid the ten-per-cent deposit. They had sold it! And even if he didn't complete the sale they could keep that ten-per-cent. It would at least be something to throw to those wolves of bank managers. And the third was from the boys. Apparently they'd reached Down Under and had met up with a couple of sheilas and they were all lying on a beach somewhere in Queensland.

"It ain't half hot, mum," was the message. "I don't know if you can hear me. My mobile sounds funny. I got sand in it and tried to wash it out with Fosters but it's still a bit damp and ..." The line began to crackle and then went dead.

Lawrence shook his head.

"It's a hard life."

And he poured them both a glass of Coonawarra red.

Later that evening their friends' car stopped at the end of their drive, where they were waiting under that arch which said "Gibraltar House". Pat made room for Eve.

"By the way," she said." We're having a party next week. Can you come – Saturday night? About eight?"

What a question! Eve and Lawrence smiled to each other.

Victor leaned over to Lawrence. "And I'll take the opportunity to pray for you tonight, young man."

"Ah ..." Lawrence was put off balance for a moment. Then: "well, I suppose it can't do any harm," he told Victor – and added: "but make it a double."

*     *     *

They were so pleased to have sold London that they gave their dog a special treat the next afternoon – a long walk high above the coast road to a heath. They were late and darkness was beginning to threaten the daylight when at last they reached it. They made their way through the scrub, the thorns and the briars to its edge where the hillside sloped down to the meadows below them. Beyond lay the marshes and the sea. Wagga was tiring a little now but still ran ahead, darting left and right, smelling everything, full of life. Far off a dark rain cloud bulged over the sea like a sodden blanket.

A track wound towards them from the coast road. From its foot it made its way up the body of the hill in a deep scar between a pair of long paddocks and a couple of grassy mounds and, after a slight crease, cut its way through the hairy scrub on the heath's widening back to pass them at the shoulder's edge and join another track at the head of the hill a few hundred yards behind them.

"Those tracks have been there for hundreds of years," said Lawrence. "See that one? Curling uphill in that deep fold between the paddocks?"

At that moment a horseman appeared far below. He rounded a hedge by the marshes, crossed the coast road and began to ride up the track towards them. The heavy sea clouds were moving inland and the light was failing and at first he wasn't much more than a dark speck but they could see he was moving at full gallop and standing on the stirrups with his head down over the horse's neck and freely using his crop. Quickly the pounding of the hooves came louder to them and the thwack of the crop sharpened as the horse galloped up the track. Suddenly Lawrence realised it was unstoppable and cried out – "Get Wagga safe!" Eve held their dog and they watched without breathing as the rider beat at the dark horse with his crop, eyes intent on the track and not seeing them but racing up towards them and they heard the horse's furious breathing and the hooves pounding on the hard earth getting louder and rising in pitch as they stood rigid there and it had crashed past them with a thunderous rumble, the sound dropping and wasting away behind them in the twilight as the horse joined the other track with a brief and already faint clatter of hooves as it vanished out of sight.

"Well!" said Lawrence after a deep breath. "That's not 1935. It's 1735. And did you see who it was? It was Jill – Jill at the shop!" He turned towards Eve but she was gazing after the horse, not hearing him, tense and whispering -

> *"I am a horse: who knows man,*
> *"I am a hill: where poets walk,*
> *I am a hawk: above the cliff,*
> *I am a stag: of seven tines,*
> *I am a lure: from paradise."*

She stopped, turned towards him and buried her head inside his coat. "Paradise! It's true! It really is true," she murmured.

\*     \*     \*

The year was coming to an end, the days were at their shortest and the weather had become chill and unwelcoming. When they walked to the sea, they went at mid-day. It didn't do to be caught on the marshes in the dark in mid-December. Often rain came at them in gusts like sprays of machine-gun fire. Sometimes the sun shone through it and sometimes it didn't.

It was just before Christmas and the afternoon of Victor and Pat's party. Lawrence had taken Wagga for a walk to the beach. This was the shortest day of the year and he told Eve he wasn't going to be long. So she was merely curious when Wagga came home alone half an hour later.

And even then she only became worried when he didn't appear too and it suddenly occurred to her that something serious might have happened. And then she got frantic. Had he tried to go after Wagga and fallen into one of those dykes? Was he even now lying with a broken ankle in some sodden ditch in the marsh? Was he gritting his teeth as he desperately tried to drag his useless leg after him? Were his

clothes saturated with water and his body trembling with cold? Was he almost fainting with pain? Was he already anxious of how much longer he would be able to crawl, increasingly weak and already too exhausted to cry for help in that unfriendly dark, before giving up his struggle to the freezing and inhuman swamp? She became convinced of it all in two or three seconds.

In a panic she rushed round the few yards to the house of Victor and Pat. Victor swung into action as soon as she explained.

"I'll ring a friend and get him to check out the pubs."

"Pubs!" cried Eve. "He hasn't gone there!" The very idea – when he might have known she would be worried! Victor turned to her, telephone in one hand and the tide tables in another.

"Well, you never know. In any case, it's ringing now so I'll leave my message and then we'll drive to the beach. He might have fallen and knocked himself out. And if he's done that at the edge of the sea he could be in trouble." Victor glanced at the tide tables. "Yes, look – we're just after low tide now so it's rising. In an hour the water will have risen enough to cover him. And if he's unconscious ... that makes a bit of a problem."

He kept his eyes on the tide tables and didn't actually say "he could be drowned" but Eve got the message and began to tremble.

"Yes, yes. Quick OK let's go please PLEASE!"

They scrambled into Victor's huge black Mercedes and rushed off to the beach. It was shortly after dark.

It had been still daylight when Lawrence had reached the beach. Once there Wagga had rushed off at once on dog business. When he didn't come back Lawrence began calling and went on calling – but no dog appeared. Then the light began to fail. After that he reckoned there was not much point in going on calling in the dark and took the path home. While he walked he watched the sun sinking behind Blakeney Hill. Soon it had grown to the size of a huge molten cauldron. It was spilling everywhere and eating away so strongly at the hill's trees near the church that their black trunks became thin stalks but the earth had had enough of all that and rolled it away and out of sight behind the hill and left everything to black night. Just before the sun vanished a small V-formation of geese swept very low over Lawrence's head – maybe only ten feet or so, so neat and gentle they were, necks stretched straight out and honking amiably together like a group of old friends as they flew west towards the hill. They kept good formation although one young one wavered behind a bit. Soon they all grew smaller and smaller and their honking was lost as they became dots and then they too vanished into the blackness.

Lawrence was so riveted by this latest episode of how North Norfolk's landscape hypnotised him that it was only out of the corner of his eye that he glimpsed a big black car driving past him to the beach. Who on earth was this who wanted to go there at this time of day – dark, cold and wet? He shrugged and walked on. Obviously a tourist with more money than sense. Ten minutes later he was off the marshes. He reached home almost at once, found a note from Eve saying: "we've gone out to look for you," deduced that 'we' meant her and Wagga, assumed she'd be back soon, found a bottle of wine and began to open it – when he heard someone stomping down the drive. It was Victor, his car now at the end of the drive.

"Ha, Victor!" he said. "Trust you to turn up when I'm just opening a bottle. Feel like a glass?" Only to be reprimanded.

"Eve's very worried. She's being comforted by Pat. We thought you'd been drowned. We've had people out everywhere. I've just been to the beach to see if you'd been knocked out. We all nearly froze looking for you. I'll go back and reassure her – no, you must ring now. And you'd better get changed and come over. The party's starting soon, anyway."

And so it was. He thanked Victor and rang and thanked Pat and reassured Eve in the next few seconds. Soon he was changed and over at their house where Wagga, innocent that he had been the cause of great worry, leaped up and down and licked his face all over – several times – as if to say "sorry, Dad!" Present were some of the more well-established members of the village. Lawrence's near escape was the talk of the evening.

"Now you've learned that it's dangerous to be out late on the marshes, young man," commented Millicent magisterially. "You must have been quite, quite perturbed."

"Well, I wasn't actually in any danger ..." he began.

"But," she continued without a pause, "of course Victor's so good in an emergency – considering ..." she added.

'Considering' what, Lawrence wasn't quite sure of, but he smiled dutifully and gratefully accepted a glass of red wine. She then button-holed Philip and told him how well Horace Nelson had been looking after the flowers by the church door.

"But he still won't come to our luncheons," she said, puzzled.

"I'm not really surprised. Would you if you were him?" smiled Philip. "Mind you," he added politely, "perhaps he doesn't realise he's missing your rather good cooking!"

Victor handed a glass of champagne to Lawrence, who suddenly remembered that he'd promised to pray for his soul at midnight mass the other day.

"Well!" he told him. "You certainly came to my aid today. But, you know, it must have been around half-past-twelve that night I did have this warm glow coming over me. It was before you had brought Eve home from church."

Victor looked narrowly at him. He seemed suspicious.

"That would have been around the time," he said guardedly.

"Well," went on Lawrence. "I thought – 'well, he's done it! A miracle!'"

"Well, there you are!" replied Victor smugly. "Even you are not beyond redemption."

"And then I realised it was the cognac I had put in my Horlicks."

Victor groaned.

"Oh, well. I might have known that saving your soul wasn't going to be as easy as all that," he admitted sorrowfully. "Well, I haven't got any Horlicks, but I'll find some good cognac for you. Come into my study but don't tell anybody else. They'll all want some, too, and I've only got six bottles left."

And they went off together to his study where Victor opened one of those remaining six bottles of Remy Martin and filled two balloon glasses, the contents of which made them both feel warmer after their harrowing experiences on the marshes.

Ronald had made a rare appearance away from the pub and was wandering around looking for some beer.

"I want some for Wagga," he said to Pat. "He must have been frightened coming home alone."

He found a bottle and poured some into a saucer, which Wagga sniffed at suspiciously, licked at for a moment and then lost interest.

"Perhaps it's too warm for him," grinned Lawrence.

Hector appeared from Hector Hall, shrouded as usual in great-great-grandpapa's greatcoat. Behind him walked his wife, slim now but with their baby son blissfully asleep in her arms and with a bubble of milk around his lips. Hector pulled a brace of pheasants out of a canvas bag.

"These are for you two, Eve. I gather Lawrence has had a narrow escape," He pushed his spectacles back onto his nose and gave her a kiss. "You both need some good North Norfolk nourishment after that bit of worry. I remember being home on holiday during the flood of '53 and that was tough enough without getting lost, too. Nearly as bad as school, in fact. The beds were so hard at Eton. Eve, you know, grandpapa was out shooting duck when those floods began and he ignored it. Thought it would make good cover for him. Nearly left it too late to get home though and he had to abandon the punt. We found it after the flood – smashed to pieces at Salthouse and halfway up to the church.

He bumped into Victor and they began an earnest discussion about the age of their respective houses. As Lawrence listened he had the feeling that it was a subject they discussed every time they met. He saw Hector take Victor by the arm.

"You remember, Victor, of course, that Hector Hall has early fourteenth century foundations beneath the kitchens?"

"My dear fellow, I had heard something of that, yes," replied Victor. "Your house must be very old, then. I didn't know they had kitchens in those days. Of course, you've modernised it since then. I mean, we had a fine dinner last time we visited you – considering." He smiled innocently at Hector and pressed a glass of Bollinger champagne into his outstretched hand.

"Incidentally," he went on. "Is your place in Pevsner? You know of course that book Dr Pevsner wrote describing all the houses in Norfolk? Well, of course, "he added blandly, "all the important houses in Norfolk, that is. He wrote nearly half a page about my house, you know" – he saw out of the corner of his eye that Hector was about to say something and quickened his pace – "well, at least half a page probably more actually I should think a page really – is yours in it? If you'd care to come over to the fireplace here, I can show you a few bricks that Pevsner said were definitely thirteenth century."

He refilled their glasses with champagne and, the bottle swinging from his hand, led Hector towards the fireplace.

So a good time was had by all. Especially by Eve and Lawrence who both felt secretly proud that their neighbours and friends had made such an effort to look for him.

*     *     *

Next morning the call came through that they had been awaiting. They had both been worried but neither had mentioned it to the other. They knew they were on the very last step and were secretly holding their breath. They knew that very few purchasers backed out after signing the contract because they would lose their deposit. But still they were worried. They'd been worried so long that logic no longer came into it. By now they were sure Murphy's Law was how things operated. And they both felt that, now that winter was coming, it would be too much to have to undergo all that anxiety again. Lawrence was almost becoming convinced that the ten percent hadn't been paid after all – a clerical error or something – and that the buyer had vanished. It sometimes happened, he thought: oh yes! And he didn't dare tell Eve. She might think it was true. Well, it might even be. But the news was good. As they had promised, the tenants had left the house two days before. Yesterday the buyer had checked that it was empty. For some reason he didn't want tenants. And he had paid the money. His solicitor had just rung their solicitor and told him that a bank draft was on its way. When Lawrence asked: "Are you sure?" their solicitor drew himself up to his full height (as far as he could judge over the telephone) and said: "I beg your pardon?" It was clearly lawyer-to-lawyer stuff. Lawrence and Eve laughed and hugged each other. It was enough to make a cat laugh – theirs, definitely. No hitches – and their mortgage was paid off. Just like that!

An immense burden was lifted from their shoulders and they immediately forgot their troubles. So since it was nearly lunchtime they clearly had to go out and celebrate – but where? By now they had so many friends who owned restaurants in North Norfolk that it was difficult to choose. After a discussion lasting ten seconds (they had suddenly become hungry) they decided on The Moorings in Wells, promised themselves more celebrations everywhere else in the New Year and were soon heading west past Blakeney. They could see the chill sea mist rolling in over the marshes. From the road it looked like a loose gauze curtain but it soon became dense. As they rounded the water meadows and climbed up to Stiffkey it had become a fog and was billowing over the road. The rear tyres began to break away on the corners and Lawrence had to hold the car steady. It was only just after mid-day but he switched on the headlights.

Wells looked empty as they rolled down through the town to the harbour. The amusement arcades were shuttered. The candyfloss stall was locked and the ships' chandlery boarded up. The fishing boats' spars rattled. Fog hid the sandbanks and rolled over the empty quay. At its far end lay the Albatross. It seemed as lifeless as a corpse. A canvas hood shrouded most of its deckhouse. Its masts and booms were bare. The deck was abandoned and every hatch was battened down. Steel hawsers ran from bow and stern to bollards on the quay.

But a light shone in a round porthole in the deckhouse. Eve turned for a moment to Lawrence in query – then skipped up the gangplank and tapped on the thick glass. After a few moments Justine opened the door, her hair rippling down her back and her figure silhouetted by the cabin light behind her. She gave a broad smile, beckoned them in and called below. In a moment Jan appeared, saw them, dipped back down a ladder and reappeared with a bottle of acquavit.

"As you can see we're laid up here for the winter," he told them as they all sat down and he filled four tiny glasses. "But I've still a few bottles of this from the last time I was inward bound from Copenhagen. Enough to last until next spring. You know it's called the water of life?" he told them. "Skol!"

They raised their glasses to one other.

"And 'skol' to freedom and the Albatross, the symbol of our coast, wherever it leads us!" contributed Justine, her eyes shining and her arm on Jan's shoulder.

Some time later the couple left them and quickly headed for the restaurant. They were the only customers but again not the only diners. Jocelyn and Gerald joined them. Luckily this restaurant had no prohibitions about dogs. Wagga took up sentry duty beneath the table and spent a happy fifteen seconds eating a chicken leg.

Their first bottle was opened and drunk while hardly being noticed so Gerald opened a second one and everyone set to with a menu of gossip. The hors d'oeuvre – a sort of mixture of crudités. What had they been doing? What of their friends? What of their hosts' friends? What of friends of friends? Then the main course: selling their house in London, naturally, a rich casserole of partridge (the house) with baked vegetables to go with it (carrots were the worry, peppers the lawyers, parsnips the tenants and – of course – sauerkraut for the bank). To follow – the enticing ginger pudding, which prompted the only appropriate topic: 'was the Rhine Maiden/Leda/Justine pregnant yet? Or all of them, for that matter?' And over the coffee they chose various cheeses, each representing slices of gossip about various people they had heard of and linked them together with a cognac – then another cognac just, as Lawrence put it, to be sure.

Later that afternoon, as they passed the now darkened Albatross on the way to their car, Eve gave it a pat on the hull and smiled happily.

"Our albatross is dead, long live the Albatross!" she said.

\*     \*     \*

In twilight now they rolled easily through Stiffkey. Near the low bridge on the winding road and before it rises to the Morston straight, they came across a track that led north towards the marshes. They had explored a few of these tracks during the summer. Lawrence was always excited about finding a new route through to the sea. Escape routes, he called them. It had been a good lunch and they were still on top of the world, floating in relief and happiness after selling their house. So they, or at least Lawrence, felt like making an extravagant gesture – and he decided to explore this track. He swung the car off the road. But the track quickly turned into a stretch of mud. Ah, well; post-lunch euphoria began to deflate like a cold soufflé. He stopped and turned the car towards the road but it got stuck. The wheels turned and sprayed mud everywhere but didn't move the car. He turned the engine off, which revealed the only noise in North Norfolk to be the pattering of a steady drizzle on the car's roof.

"Oh, no!" cried Eve, looking out. "And it's raining. You've done it now. What d'you have to start exploring for at the end of December?"

"Because we've sold London!" he told her. "That's why. But don't worry. Something will turn up. I'll find a tractor."

"You've said that before. Too often."

"Well, I've never said it about a tractor before."

"Very funny. Anyway, you really will be lucky if you find one. Not just before Christmas. And at this time of day? It must be nearly five o'clock. Well, you'd better get on with it. I don't want to spend the night in the car."

She went "hrumph" and sank back into her seat.

He trudged up the track to the road, their dog leaping about and running ahead. Wagga was clearly happy – and so was he. That cognac was still warming the pit of his stomach. But he needed a tractor to pull them out and it was getting dark. If he didn't find one Eve would never let him forget it.

In North Norfolk tractors are not uncommon. But perhaps not before Christmas. But it really was Christmas. For a few hundred yards away on the other side of the coast road he found not one but five of them in a big shed where several farm workers were standing around a vast mound of cabbages. They were all wearing jackets and ties. Two or them wore hats and one of those wore a waistcoat and was holding a clip-board as well. His hands were clean, too – so Lawrence reckoned he must be the boss and explained that he needed help.

"Not half, you do," said the foremen. He took out a tin of tobacco, slowly rolled himself a cigarette, folded his arms and leaned against the shed door with a box of matches.

"Having a bit of a winter holiday, then, are you?" He carefully lit his cigarette and slowly tossed the match away. The others went back to the pile of cabbages.

"Oh, no. We were coming back from Wells. We live only a few miles away, beyond Blakeney," explained Lawrence.

"Oh, ah?" He seemed surprised, yanked himself off the door and stamped on his cigarette. "Come on lads. We don't want to have to pull car out in dark."

They all left the cabbages, crammed into one of the tractors and rumbled down the track towards the car. Eve was staring at the tractor in amazed disbelief. Lawrence grinned at her.

"This is a tractor," he called out to her – slapping its side as it clanked to a halt. "Seen one before? Four more back there if you don't like this one."

She could hardly believe her eyes – but secretly began to believe in Lawrence's luck herself. After all, they'd just sold London. But she didn't tell him. He was bad enough as it was. And this would just make him worse.

Lawrence gave them £10. They didn't want to take it. Well, not at first anyway.

"We've only been here five minutes," they protested.

"It's the least I can do," said Lawrence. "I could have been here until tomorrow morning."

And it was true. Anyway, £10 wouldn't get them much more than a pint each at the pub in Stiffkey.

As they turned into the main road they drew into a passing place to let a pale blue Morris Minor go past. The driver waved his thanks in the conventional ritual. Lawrence raised a finger briefly, a polite thanks for having been thanked. And the driver of the Morris Minor waved again.

"How polite he is, that driver," he told his wife.

"Yes, but that was Philip," said Eve. "Our rector. Wearing his dog collar."

Yes, all was well in the valley of the two mills and the five churches.

On the way home they stopped for petrol at the garage in Blakeney. It's the garage staff who fill your tank here and you can't use the pump yourself. So while he fills your tank you can rest your elbows on the roof as if you were leaning on a horse. And you can exchange news about your families and tell each other what you both think of that new fellow who moved in near the church and is building a hideous modern bungalow next door. Then you can both have a go at the government. Like the counter in Tom's shop, the queue at the post office, the Deli's wine bellows display, the dry cleaners in Holt and the bar in both pubs, they were all a never-failing source of the latest news and opinions. You can even spread a bit of gossip yourself, even if it wasn't true. And Lawrence had sometimes seen the garage man reprove a holidaymaker who had tried to serve himself – and snatch the pump away from him. What's the point of talking to them? They'll be gone next week, you could hear him thinking. Lawrence mentioned that they had just got stuck in the mud on the marshes outside Stiffkey.

"Ah, yes, they're tricky this time of year," he replied. "Here, I've got the kettle on. You fill yourself up, it was a full tank, wasn't it? Make a note of the cost and drop into the shop when you've finished. I'll have a cup for you both – milk no sugar? OK."

So they did. Should they tell him they'd paid off the mortgage? But anyway it was clear that they were accepted – as much as any incomer could be, of course. And they rolled happily home.

\*     \*     \*

Paying off the mortgage had not just meant that a great anxiety had been lifted off their minds. It also meant that their roots in London had at last been pulled out. And their new roots were nourished by all their friends in North Norfolk. There were so many of them that they had recently bought another address book.

"It's been a good start for us, this year," said Eve thoughtfully as they left the garage, Wagga half asleep on her lap. "I've never tasted better vegetables than those in my little patch – safer, too. None of those pesticides and preservatives that you get in the supermarkets. And the herbs, our herb garden with that church clock face! We'd never have had space for that in Notting Hill ... and then all our new friends to those lunches in the summer under our apple tree."

Lawrence nodded. But he was thinking of those night trips down the river with Prospero, and that midnight summer barbecue with him on the beach. And then the country auctions and bidding at them, especially those Flymos.

"Actually the dining room is my real dream, " he said. "It always was, ever since I first saw it. That fire, roasting woodcock on string over it ... or just dozing in front of it late at night, you know, when you can hear your heart beat in the silence. Remember when I staggered out into the garden at about two in the morning and heard the sea – thought it was the Russians?"

They both laughed. Wagga opened his eyes for a brief moment and slowly closed them again.

"Oh, but my favourite is the sitting room, you know," she replied. "With the conservatory opening off it. It's so elegant and so summery – the way you can slip into the conservatory or just walk into the garden through the French windows."

She paused – and looked across at him.

"But what's best are the people," she went on. "You know, the Pottery group and Victor and Pat and that crazy Hector with his wonderful pork, not to mention Zeus, can't forget him. What a wonderful day that was with him and Leda at his beach hut at Wells ... and then when they invited themselves round for lunch last month when it was so wet. Oh, so many people. And where would we be without Jocelyn at The Moorings and Reggie at the Saracen's Head – what a place! And then everyone at the Guardian's and the Rhine Maiden's wedding feast. But don't forget poor Iris's funeral. It was such a privilege, you know, to have been expected to have gone to it, to share everyone's sadness."

She fell quiet for a moment and began wrinkling their dog's ears. She was thinking of the evenings of music in Norfolk's churches, the outdoor performance of that Shakespeare play at Felbrigg Hall and carrying their sofa to the Restoration comedy at the Hall in their village. And then she remembered Pippa's private view and smiled at him.

"Isn't she so warm-hearted! She gave us that picture, just because you praised it!"

He turned his head sideways and nodded to her while watching the road as they turned left at the Deli for home.

"Is it all due to Prospero's spell, his plan? Well whatever it is it's all true anyway. And it's working. But could Prospero be responsible for the food? Well, maybe part of his reason for choosing North Norfolk. And not just the game, the pheasants and the partridge, or even the woodcock. Remember that time we were at the Three Horseshoes? And Jimmy Blake and Horace coming in and his mussels cascading onto our plates and the warm beer and the Stilton? Somehow it helped me realise the sense we have of freedom here, although I didn't realise it until much later. And then the wine tastings and that summer picnic above Salthouse Church and mushrooming in the marshes at dawn."

"Not you, usually," she interrupted him. "Mostly I went alone and you stayed in bed, remember?"

"Oh, all right," he grinned. "But anyway, it's the atmosphere almost as much as the food, I mean. But don't forget that stone-ground brown bread with kippers for breakfast, mackerel for lunch, potted shrimps for tea and ... and listening to Pippa's poetry after supper, perhaps a rabbit or a brace of partridges."

He paused.

"That seems so long ago now. But it's not, not really."

They smiled together at the trust of the people in the shops who said "send us a cheque later," the hedgehog holding up the traffic after cricket on the sands at Cromer, the witty paintings of Brian, those hairy ferrets at the church fête, real cricket – on the green by the church and the pub, finding their dog at that crumbling Queen Ann farmhouse and above all living in the bell-jar of 1935 in that heraldic valley of the two mills.

"But together with the silent pubs hidden in the countryside," said Lawrence, "I really mean really buried and the flint everywhere and the sea and the flood and the rain rattling at the windows and the seasons ... the most important thing of all, it's our sense of freedom up here. Well, we know that now. But what helped us, if we needed it, you know, was the Albatross. It's the symbol. You can just look at it and know we have it. When it sails past the coastline we feel we can almost jump onto it any time we want to. And it's not as if it's giving us the chance to get away – why should we want to? No, it's as if it's part of us and showing us what we have here."

"But you've forgotten something, darling," she told him.

"What, then?"

"We took the risk! We took the risk to come and live up here when it all looked so difficult!"

"Yes, of course! Well, I'm so used to it, I suppose." Then he remembered. "But wasn't there someone who had to be persuaded? No? Well, it could have gone either way once or twice, I admit. But actually, I suppose we took our attitude from Tom's outfit. You know, what is it – 'Who dares wins!' – something like that, isn't it?"

\*     \*     \*

Now it was Christmas Eve and time for the village carol service in that huge church behind the Three Swallows. The previous evening the boys had arrived home, bringing with them the two Australian girls they had met on that Queensland beach. They were on a high, as they put it – and this time it wasn't LSD. They were just happy they had managed to get home in time for Christmas – as the English do, come rain or shine. But there were changes.

"Carol singing, Mum?" they protested. "We're not into church any more. We're Buddhists now."

"OK," said Dad. "Well, that'll save me a bit. Buddhists don't drink champagne, do they?"

"Dad!" they both cried out. "Yes we do, Dad – that's Muslims!"

"OK, well, I'd better get another couple of bottles up from the cellar, now we've got company."

"Thanks, Dad. Just as well, actually. We went round to the pub but it was closed. Can't understand it on Christmas Eve. I mean, we wanted to chill out. They're like losing business."

"Oh," said Dad, "that's Ronald for you."

Eve smiled at the girls.

"You'll have to keep them both in order while we're out," she told them – and turned to her sons. "Darlings, might you like to decorate the tree while we're at the carol singing? We weren't going to have a tree if it had been just us, but we got this one and some special decorations when we knew you were coming home."

And so it was agreed.

Eve and Lawrence pushed open the church's oaken door and saw that candles at every pew had set shadows swaying high up to the beamed roof. Empty bookshelves and a pile or two of chairs were stacked in dark corners. There the dust lay as thick as in the attic of an old country house. It was early yet and a hint of chill cooled the air. Footsteps of the first arrivals echoed from side to side of the empty church. Someone's voice reached the lofty clerestory windows. And their echoes seemed to summon centuries of palpable faith to invest the church and cast a spell upon it. The Victorian military brass plaques seemed slowly to tarnish, the silver elegance of Georgian England to shimmer and then vanish, the piracy and palace poetry of the brilliant Elizabethans to fade into echoes and the brasses of the blood-streaked royal dukes in the Wars of the Roses to dissolve, one by one, to reveal the cold and silent stone beneath. And before then, before the Frenchy accents of William's Doomsday men had replaced the broad vowels of their Anglo Saxon predecessors, England had long been abandoned by the Romans to scrape a leaderless existence in dense forest and rotting swamp. In a land empty, forlorn and neglected, disuse had soon cracked apart the imperial roads. The officials' villas had soon lost their roofs, ivy had assaulted their walls and wild cats had given birth in their crumbling rooms. Scandinavian invaders swarmed over what the Romans had abandoned. But at last Alfred's mixture of genius and luck had stemmed them all and unified the country. England was ready for the role of sea-walled crucible that enabled the migrant Christian faith to take shape in peace. Christianity had meshed like chain mail with the newly stable Anglo Saxon rule. And so developed the secure and moderate society that underpinned the success of William's arrival. Like the fleeting caress of a bird's wing against the peak of a mountain, those English feet since ancient times have been gently wearing away the church's flagstones, first wrapped in animal skins, then in sandals, clogs, boots, elegant hose and patent leather to today's fleeting caress of the green wellies of the congregation that was this evening taking its place in the pews.

Now a couple of cheerful and rosy-cheeked ladies from the Women's Institute appeared and the spell was broken. They chattered away together and bustled around with carol sheets, cushions and flowers. The choir singers had already arrived, shielded from the cold

341

by overcoats and gloves, bright eyes smiling above thick scarves. Their quiet murmuring vanished as someone tapped a tuning fork and they discretely hummed a few notes in the still air. Millicent, tonight a churchwarden, a role which perhaps she loved above all others, gingerly clambered one step at a time up a creaking ladder to light the thick candles on the candelabrum. The vestry door opened and Philip appeared, beaming already, the kindly and affectionate emblem of the Church of England. He bustled forward to hold the stepladder for her – "Oh, how frightfully kind of you, Philip" – and everyone found their seats around the two of them.

The choir led the singing but found the congregation a little shy to start with. The first carol, "While shepherds watched their flocks by night," wavered as if playing hide and seek around the pillars. But all came right when the organ led everyone into "Once in Royal David's City" and "O come, all ye faithful," grand and stylish themes able to bridge the Catholic-Protestant divide if anything could. And with that gentlest of harmonies, "It came upon the midnight clear," they all now sang with tenderness, as if not wishing to awaken that little old lady who had fallen asleep in the third pew down on the right. After all this was the Church of England, not Rome, and if someone wanted to sleep through it, that was OK. And to make it quite understood that we were all on Henry VIII's side and no nonsense from foreigners, everybody launched with gusto into "Hark! the herald angels sing" and "Unto us is born a son." Finally everyone got to work on "God rest you merry, Gentlemen" with even greater enthusiasm, as if to point out that religion was all very well but this was England and Christmas and time for a good celebration. At that moment the little old lady awoke with a start, looked around her and beamed at everybody.

When the last chorus had died away the congregation made their way out of the pews, hearts quiet now but brimming with friendship and goodwill, to gather around the old candle-lit stone font and share in that loving English ritual of mince pies and mulled wine.

Baptisms, marriages and deaths, thanksgivings and community ceremonies like this carol service ... thousands of them had been played out down the centuries around that old font, its carved stations of the Cross chipped and defaced now but still powerful with ancient Christian magic. Perhaps the creed behind those rituals helped to explain how England's unwritten constitution upheld the paradox of its democratic monarchy. Reaffirming the faith over the centuries, its continuous threnody had linked the Plantagenets, the Tudors, the

Stuarts, the Georgians and the Victorians to take their turn to stiffen England in her battles for independence and freedom. And to keep her freedom England had fought with and against nearly every country in western Europe. For hundreds of years England had confronted the French at Agincourt, Crecy, Waterloo and a dozen other foreign fields. Then, with its growing navy, English sailors tackled the Dutch off the Norfolk and Kentish coasts. After Henry's snub to the pope, who wanted England back in his power, Drake chased the Spaniards in a running fight up the Channel. Two hundred years later, after Scotland and Wales had joined England, she built a great navy. When Napoleon arranged for half-a-dozen European states to blockade England our navy blockaded all their ports instead. That stopped them! Her Norfolk Hero triumphed against the Danes at Copenhagen, the French at Alexandria and the French and the Spanish at Trafalgar. On land the Duke of Wellington kicked Napoleon's soldiers out of Portugal and Spain and ran him to earth at Waterloo. Bismarck unified Germany – which made it Europe's biggest threat since Napoleon. So England changed her mind about the French and shared trenches with them against the Kaiser. Twenty years later Churchill stood for England, alone in the world after the humiliating collapse of the French. Of those battles against the Dutch, the Pope, Philip of Spain, Napoleon, Bismarck, the Kaiser, Mussolini and Hitler, England had won them all. Over all those centuries and alone in Europe England's borders had never changed.

But today, after those famous victories, the greatest threat comes not from a galleon or a Messerschmitt. Today it comes from unelected bureaucrats in Brussels who care little for England's interests. Will the European Union win where those countries failed – and without a shot being fired? The wounded lion has lost Scotland and Wales – and further dismemberment is planned. That meretricious Greenwich Dome, no match for this church's candle-lit font, stands as the apt unhappy symbol of England's slow decline.

"Soon we shall no longer be ruled from our Parliament but from abroad. Our rights will be restricted. Our economy will be ruled by others. We shall be told what we may produce, and what we may not. Step by step we shall be conducted further along our journey until we find that it is too late! And we can no longer turn back."

Winston Churchill spoke these words many years ago about another danger. Acceptance of that policy would have led to a destiny more brutal than that which is proposed for England today. But his words describe what has already happened. And this threatens the dissolution of the English character. It was also Churchill who told us that our proper role lay not with Europe but with his mother's country.

Lawrence had been unable to understand why it was claimed that Britain was a multi-cultural society when for centuries Britain had only one culture. Refugees had sought and embraced it. There had been nothing multi-cultural about any of it. The claim of being a multi-cultural society divides and so weakens the state. Was it Europe's idea? Certainly England now stands alone, undermined by social malaise and attacked by Europe.

As in all English churches this church held much evidence of British history – the flags, the plaques, the brass effigies and the medieval stone knights. In the graveyard stood the more recent tombstones. Their rank, their ages and the date tell the battle in which they died: Squadron leader, 22, 1940. Pilot, 20, 1940. Pilot, 18, 1940. Pilot, 18, 1940. That evidence of Britain's finest hour surrounded the congregation grouped in candlelight at the font. This village community was moulded by the tread of history through their generations and to them it had all happened only the other day. And if the need for vigilance was still present, as usual they wore it light. The people of England, the silent majority that never have spoken yet and who as always carry their nationhood unspoken, seem to be waiting in a complacent daze. North Norfolk's atmosphere, like that of 1935, was a bell jar protecting an isolated community in the valley of the two mills and the five churches. But did that bell jar obscure the danger of Europe's threat to its freedom? Perhaps Drake's drum, that ancient warning of danger to England, cannot be heard within the bell jar? Or, as so often, as in 1935 when all England except one man ignored Germany's re-arming, perhaps the English are playing bowls again and will awaken just in time. And the sweet irony of it all is that alone in Europe England has the strength to be its counter-balance against that central devouring power, that once cultured, mystical and family-loving country – Germany.

But enough! Churchwarden Millicent, now leading a supporting cast of smiling wives, began to serve everyone with mulled wine and mince pies. And Lawrence, Eve and Wagga (on a short lead) joined all their new friends. At the font everyone cupped their hands around their glasses and, heads together, exchanged words of good will in the old and understated English way: "What lovely singing" ... "I heard your boys are home for Christmas?" ... "So glad to see you here tonight" ... "Isn't it cold! It looks like snow!"

Zeus was wearing his fleece that with his wild black hair made him look bigger than everyone else. He grinned at Lawrence, clapped him on the back, undid a shirt button, looked round, saw Philip – and did it up again. Then he kissed Eve: "Philip has given me the concession for communion wine next year!" he grinned.

Jan twinkled, gave Eve a warm kiss, reached round behind her back and shook Lawrence's hand.

The Village Marxist's arm was in possession of the waist of the girl with huge eyes and the mass of curls he had been discussing Marx with at the Rhine Maiden's wedding.

"Prospero's done it again!" whispered Eve to her husband.

"What?" he asked her. "Done what?"

"You know," she added impatiently, "got the VM interested in someone else – remember we saw him talking to that girl at the Guardian's birthday party? Telling her how wonderful the VM thought her? Well, that's her there!"

Nearby, Justine was explaining to the Guardian how they managed to keep warm in the Albatross in this weather: "It's easier with two," she smiled. And the Rhine Maiden told them: "Well if it gets really brass-monkey weather you two can bunk up with us at the Pottery."

Meanwhile, Ronald was looking suspiciously at his glass of wine. Her black hair shining, Pippa bustled gaily around topping everyone up from a jug of mulled wine in one hand and a plate of mince pies in the other.

"Come along, Ronnie, drink up," she giggled, put the plate on the font, bit into a mince pie and filled his glass: "No beer tonight!"

Derek appeared from the shadows wearing a suit for a change: "I've swallowed my anchor, Lawrence," he grinned. "Started a taxi business! The tourists can keep the sea. Too wet and too much bloody hard work!"

Philip was deep in discussion with Pat and Victor: "Ah, Victor, the Lord says it's easier for a camel to pass through the eye of a needle than for a rich man to enter the kingdom of heaven, so I'll pray for you. We're all so very grateful for your generous gift last week. Do have some more wine!" He beamed mischievously as he carefully laid a wisp of white hair over the top of his head.

Nearby, coat draped over his shoulders, Prospero was standing between Tom and Millicent. He had his arm round Tom's shoulders and was gesturing to Millicent, who was smiling broadly. He clasped both their shoulders, smiled to them and put their hands together before turning away to his hunchbacked assistant in the shadows to pour him a glass of wine. His golden retriever sat behind him, eyes alert and watching him intently.

"And you're sure you've got a life-jacket to fit me, Tom?" Millicent laughed. "I don't want another drenching! But before we go out – it's Wells isn't it? – don't forget, New Year's Eve at 8pm, just us in the village. All very informal – no ball gowns, tell Jill!"

Prospero caught Lawrence's eye and murmured:

> "So many goodly creatures are there here!
> That spirit of our place; it comes on well!
> To this seedling group a mid-wife I was;
> Now I'm turned wet-nurse for their princely years.
> In this snug harbour our work will ferment
> To bring us England's reawakening."

Eve looked at him – then gasped.

"Now I know ..." she cried, "I've just realised! Aren't you ... ?"

"What? What is it you've realised, my wife?" her husband turned back to her as he held out his glass for Pippa to refill it.

She spread her arms wide over everyone: "O brave new world! Yes ... and all of us, we're all the people in it ... don't you see?" She put her hands to her head, tears came to her eyes and she began to laugh and cry happily. She reached out to put her hands on the font, looked at it nodding to herself, and took a deep breath, her eyes shining.

But Philip had caught sight of them both and broke off from his chat with Victor and Pat.

"Merry Christmas, my dear!" He kissed her on the cheek. "But oh, dear, I'm sorry to be the bearer of bad news ... but I have to tell you that Freddy Blake died this morning." He paused. "I know you were fond of him."

"I'm so sorry." The couple were shocked for a moment but Philip continued.

"It's not too sad," he told them. "He was in a lot of pain. Cancer is so merciless. But he was always cheerful and content, even at the end. Well, it was as if he was expecting a trusted friend to arrive at any moment. You know, he wasn't really an educated man. But somehow he didn't need to be. I sometimes felt he knew things not many of us know and that in a way he was teaching us."

He smiled at them and sighed. "Ah well! We're having the funeral on New Year's Day. I know you'll want to be there. Eve, can I count on your for the flowers? I know it's not your rota but your last effort was appreciated so much." He beamed at her. "Oh, and I nearly forgot, why not see if there are any aconites out already? They might be. He'd be overjoyed if you included some. And it's right, too. It's continuity." He repeated the word to himself. "Continuity ... Ah well!"

Then he brightened and smiled warmly.

"Oh, and did you know that Leda and Zeus are getting married? Yes? Well, they want it to be the day of Freddy's funeral, an hour or so later – won't that be wonderful! Zeus pointed out that if they were married the same day his spirit will still be around to enjoy everything. He told me he's going to drink a toast to Freddy – a glass of Guinness, I think he said. He might even make a libation – well I know that's Greek not Christian, but I think I'll make an exception. He is Zeus, after all! And it's continuity, you see!"

He beamed at them both, kissed Eve lightly, touched Lawrence on the elbow and turned away. As he did so his eyes met those of Prospero. For a moment they stood and bowed to each other. Then he left them all to have a word with the little old lady who had fallen asleep during the carol singing.

"Congregation Street is alive and well!" whispered Eve to Lawrence, smiling happily.

Finally, with choruses of "Merry Christmas" from everyone, Lawrence, Eve and Wagga prepared to leave for home.

Thump, went the church's oaken door behind them. Quietly, snowflakes floated down through the silent night. Gently, they settled on the tombstones. Warmly, the couple smiled to each other and buttoned their coats.

"Merry Christmas!"

\*     \*     \*

The man and the woman drive home from the church across the coast road and past Zeus and Leda's Deli, past Jekyll 'n' Hyde's Bookshop, past Moses' Smoke House, past that lovely Pottery of the Guardian, the Rhine Maiden and the Village Marxist, past Ronnie's pub, the George and Dragon – past some of the friends they have made during the year. But before they reach their drive the man stops the car and opens his door. The woman looks at him, puzzled.

"Ritual demarcation of territory," says the man. "What do they call it, sprainting?"

And he unzips and stands for a moment in the falling snow.

"You know – what lions do," he tells her over his shoulder.

And as the snowflakes swirl about him the man waters each gatepost at the end of the drive. The woman laughs.

"Not quite the lion of England, darling," she says.

"England expects," he says, as he bends over and zips up, "every man to turn his back on Europe. For England never was some corner of a European field."

He comes over to her and kisses her full on the lips.

"My love," he says. "We've found our roots and we know who we are. We have something to fight for and to keep."

They walk arm in arm to the green door in their wall and the magic happens again as it opens to reveal their garden. And the gravel crunches under their feet in that deeply satisfying way, the way they had loved from that first day a year ago.

"You know, darling, "she says. "About that gravel crunching and how it meant something I couldn't quite work out?" She looks up at him. "Well, I've realised during the year, it's so obvious really ... it's the satisfying feeling we get from living close to the earth. As Prospero said: 'it's where the magic starts.' And the sound of it makes it all the more real and satisfying."

"The music of the earth?" he asks her.

"Yes, why not? Remember the earth is alive – we've discovered that."

They fall silent for a moment.

Every light is on in the house and a steady rock beat is coming from inside. They smile at each other. Wagga runs ahead and stops at the front door. He looks back at them, wags his tail and waits.

"You know," says the man. "Wagga has done something to me. He's so welcoming, so happy, so eager to please. He licks our faces and immediately forgives us any punishment."

"It's true," the woman nods. "And he barks indignantly whenever there's a strange noise, even if it's the postman, sounding really outraged ... he knows it's his home too. He's not just a friend – he loves us."

"Well," he continues. "It sounds ridiculous, but when the time comes, I'll be content to die at peace in this house. I never thought it would be so easy. But I'm settled. And somehow this little dog has done it for me."

The woman smiles and pats his arm.

"Me too," she says. "And shall we tell him we've paid off the mortgage?"

The man looks pained.

"Well, he's only a dog!" she says.

"Only a dog! Oh, dear me!" The man frowns at her and shakes his head.

"You know something?" says the woman, serious now. "I never realised how the English countryside was so important to what it meant to be English until we moved here. I know we wanted to feel the rain on our faces and to live on the edge. But what was it you said? 'A rough track through an English wood and a few rooks circling overhead'? Well, that's a bit different. It's in the soul of the English character. You were right."

"I'm always right," he teases her.

"Oh, no you're not!" she cries. "We nearly sank!"

"Well, we didn't did we, my wife! All's well that ends well."

"Yes, darling." She took his hand. "Anyway I've realised that apart from nature, the thing that makes England is its history – that's what produced the freedom we have now; and love too, with the church today. Because I've also realised that the soul of England I just spoke of is in our little village group around that font. So long as we understand that our future lies in how we respond to our past, how we keep faith with it, that it's our security against oppression – even economic oppression against our English character – and so long as there are communities like ours – free, independent and on the edge – the English spirit will always prosper, even if we have to adapt to a few European habits."

"Maybe ..." he muses. "Oh dear! Well, if it gets that bad we can soften the blow and try to teach them cricket."

"Now you definitely are being too optimistic," the woman laughs. "As usual."

He winks at her and looks at his watch.

"Ten minutes to Christmas Day. I think we've just got time to open a bottle of champagne – if the boys have left any for us."

He opens the door, follows her inside and closes it behind them.

Tonight they will be sleeping soundly together, without the bedfellows of those disturbed and restless dreams that had become so familiar to them during the past year, with the gloomy prospect of awakening before dawn to lie anxiously together in the chill half light as it gradually opened into day.

Sound sleep is better than dreams. They no longer have need of such things, for now they are living their dream of England.

# The End